Automotive Fuels and Fuel Systems

AUTOMOTIVE FUELS AND FUEL SYSTEMS

Fuels, Tanks, Delivery, Metering, Mixing and Combustion and Environmental Considerations

Volume 1: Gasoline

T.K. Garrett
C.Eng, F.I.Mech.E, M.R.Ae.S

PENTECH PRESS
London

SOCIETY OF AUTOMOTIVE ENGINEERS, INC.
Warrendale, PA

First published 1991 by Pentech Press Limited
Graham Lodge, Graham Road, London NW4 3DG, England
and
Society of Automotive Engineers, Inc.,
400 Commonwealth Drive, Warrendale, PA15096-0001, USA

British Library Cataloguing in Publication Data
Garrett, T.K. (Thomas Kenneth)
  Automotive fuels and fuel systems
  Vol. 1. Gasoline
  1. Motor vehicles. Fuels
  I. Title
  629.253

  ISBN 0-7273-0114-4

Library of Congress Cataloging-in-Publication Data
Garrett, T.K.
  Automotive fuels and fuel systems: fuels, tanks, delivery, metering, mixing and combustion, and environmental considerations.
  T.K. Garrett
  v. 1
  Includes bibliographical references and index
  Contents: v. 1. Gasoline
  ISBN 1-56091-158-1
  . Automobiles – Fuel systems. 2. Motor fuels. I. Title.
  TL214.F8G37 1991   91-17980
  629.25.3-dc20   CIP

Printed in Great Britain by
Billing & Sons Ltd, Worcester and London

PREFACE

Following the phasing out of lead additives and the introduction of extremely strict controls over evaporative and exhaust emissions in both the USA and Europe, fuels and the design of fuel systems specifically for them have become subjects of major importance. This book, although intended primarily for automotive design engineers, should be of value equally to technologists in the petroleum industry and those, such as scientists, legislators and others involved in various capacities with our natural resources and the environment. In order to meet the requirements of students, however, the basics are explained in simple terms, others will, it is hoped, appreciate this approach, since most of us are well aware that gaps remain in our knowledge of the elements of our professions. These simple explanations, however, have been kept as short as practicable so that experienced readers will be able virtually to ignore them and immediately turn their attention to the more advanced concepts which constitute by far the greater proportion of the book.

The chapters on fuels are included primarily for the mechanical and electronics engineers engaged on automotive engine design and development and others who may be interested in petroleum technology. For engineers with the ambition to aim at eventually occupying leading positions in the industry, a knowledge of the nature and properties of fuels is desirable, since inevitably they will occasionally be involved in technical discussions and negotiations with oil company executives. An understanding of the latters' points of view will therefore be essential. In any case, designers of internal combustion engines need to understand the properties of the fuels on which they run, as well as those of any alternatives that might be open to them, and the implications as regards engine performance.

Whereas the principles of fuel and air metering, carburation and injection are widely understood, the design problems and technology associated with the fuel system from tank to metering unit are not. Furthermore, to obtain the latter information it has hitherto been necessary to wade through large numbers of technical papers and books. The aim, therefore, in condensing and collecting this information, in Chapters 4 and 5, has been to perform a service of benefit to even those who in most other respects are well informed on automotive design.

Combustion and emission control are fairly recently researched areas of science so, while many have had considerable experience in this field, there is still a majority of automotive engineers who have not. Consequently, the information in Chapters 12 and 13 should be of use to this majority, as well as to students. Another area in which information is hard to come by is that of gas carburation dealt with in Chapter 10. The Author hopes, therefore, that the book will serve to plug a number of gaps in the areas covered by the literature on automotive engineering.

Volume 1 covers gasoline and Volume 2, which will be published later, will deal with diesel systems. Since there is no point in duplicating in the second volume what has already been published, for example, on tanks, pipes etc, in the first, the latter inevitably will be the shorter. Most readers will need to refer to both to obtain the complete picture.

Kenneth Garrett.

Acknowledgements

Many UK and other manufacturers have very kindly supplied information and illustrations regarding individual items of equipment and complete systems that they produce. Indeed they are so numerous that it is impracticable to mention everyone here, but they have been named in the sections dealing with their products. The Author wishes to express his sincere gratitude to all.

Among the German manufacturers who have been particularly helpful is Robert Bosch GmbH, a leading pioneer of gasoline injection, as well as manufacturer of a wide range of injection equipment and its control and associated electronic systems. This company has provided information and given permission for the reproduction of many of the illustrations from its wide ranging series of books on its products. Volkswagenwerke AG, leaders in the art of fuel tank design, have been extremely helpful too.

Elsewhere, GM Rochester and AC-Delco, whose work on fuel systems in general, and on emission control in particular, has been truly outstanding, have been very co-operative. Weber and Marelli, especially renowned for carburettors and other equipment for high performance cars, have supplied information and illustrations of their carburettor, injection and associated electronic systems, and have very kindly given permission for the reproduction of illustrations from their excellent Carburettor Tuning Manual as well as from the publications on their individual carburettor and injection equipment. Finally, the Author is grateful also to Lucas Electrical Electronics and Systems Ltd, have been extremely helpful in supplying information and illustrations regarding their research and development on injectors, and to Ricardo, the world renowned consulting engineers, of Shoreham, for their considerable assistance in relation to emissions regulations and tests.

CONTENTS

Chapter 1

Conventional Liquid Hydrocarbon Fuels

The two conventional liquid hydrocarbon fuels for automotive use are, of course, gasoline and diesel oil. Despite the fact that the word petrol is still widely used in the UK, automotive engineers are beginning to replace it with the American expression gasoline. Consequently, we shall use the latter term throughout this book.

CRUDE OILS AND THEIR REFINING

The technical term for crude oil, which is a mixture of hydrocarbons and other mainly organic compounds found in natural underground reservoirs, is petroleum. Crude oil contains three main series of hydrocarbons: a group comprising alkanes and alkenes (sometimes called paraffins and olefins respectively), *cyclo*-alkanes (formerly called naphthenes), and the aromatics. All of course are compounds of hydrogen and carbon. Each series also contains isomers, some as many as 800 or more.

An isomer of a normal hydrocarbon is defined as one in which the atoms of hydrogen and carbon are arranged differently within its molecule. The basic, or normal, hydrocarbon is therefore prefixed *n*- and the isomers *iso*-, hence we have *n*-alkanes and *iso*-alkanes.

In the refinery, there are three operational stages: distillation, in which the individual constituents are separated out; refining, in which impurities such as sulphur is removed; and conversion, by cracking, reforming and other processes. The unsaturated alkanes termed *alkenes*, and the doubly unsaturated ones termed *alkynes*, also called *aliphatic hydrocarbons*, can be produced by cracking. The alkynes include ethyne, or acetylene ($CH \equiv CH$). Reforming can be used to produce the *iso*-alkanes from the *n*-alkanes and aromatics from the *cyclo*-alkanes. Also, the alkenes ($C_n H_{2n}$) can be produced by cracking, or splitting up the *n*-alkanes of higher boiling points into shorter chains of atoms, which are termed unsaturated because, as explained in Section 1.1, they have fewer hydrogen atoms. There are other processes such as the Shell Hysomer process, in which straight run (distilled) gasoline fractions are isomerised to increase their octane rating, and others in which alkylates are formed by coupling light *iso*-alkanes such as *iso*-butane with light alkenes such as butene from the catalytic cracker, to

1

Table 1.1 PERCENTAGE PRODUCTS BY WEIGHT IN CRUDE OIL FROM VARIOUS SOURCES

	N. Africa	N. Sea	Mid. East	N. America	S. America
Sulphur	0.1	0.3	2.5	1.0	5.5
Wax	3	9	6	7	2
Light gasoline					
0–70°C	8.9	5.8	4.7	2.4	0.1
Octane No.	73	76	72	75	70
Naphtha					
70–180°C	16.0	11.0	7.9	6.5	1.1
Kerosine					
180–250°C	26.3	18.6	16.4	15.6	4.4
Diesel oil					
250–350°C	18.2	19.1	15.3	19.6	9.6
Cetane No.	55	53	58	45	30
Residue					
350°C+	27.5	36.2	47.2	47.9	76.9

make high octane components. More details of the chemistry of all these processes are given in Sections 1.1 to 1.4.

Crude oil varies geographically as regards its content, those from America and the Middle East containing a high proportion of paraffins, from Russia cyclic hydrocarbons, and from West Africa naphthenes. An approximation of the proportions of products to be found in crude oils from various sources is given in Table 1.1. Substances found in the residue include sulphur, wax, vanadium and nickel, the metals in quantities ranging from zero to about 1500 ppm. Some of the sulphur compounds originally in the crude oil will have distilled off with the various fractions, ranging from about 0.1% from the North African to 7.5% from the South American crude.

CHEMISTRY AND CONSTITUENTS OF CRUDE OIL

1.1 Alkanes, olefins, alkenes and alkynes

The chemistry of the constituents is based on the carbon and hydrogen atoms, the former with four and the latter one valency arm. Methane, the simplest hydrocarbon atom, is arranged as follows:

$$H\!-\!\underset{\displaystyle H}{\overset{\displaystyle H}{\underset{|}{\overset{|}{C}}}}\!-\!H$$

This is the basis of the chain type molecules, which are the alkanes.

The next largest is ethane C_2H_6, the molecular pattern for which is:

$$H\!-\!\underset{\displaystyle H}{\overset{\displaystyle H}{\underset{|}{\overset{|}{C}}}}\!-\!\underset{\displaystyle H}{\overset{\displaystyle H}{\underset{|}{\overset{|}{C}}}}\!-\!H$$

Such molecules have no spare arms, and are termed saturated. An unsaturated molecule is one in which two or three of the arms of some of the carbon atoms are joined together as below, the generic names for those with two arms joined being olefins or alkenes, and with three, alkynes:

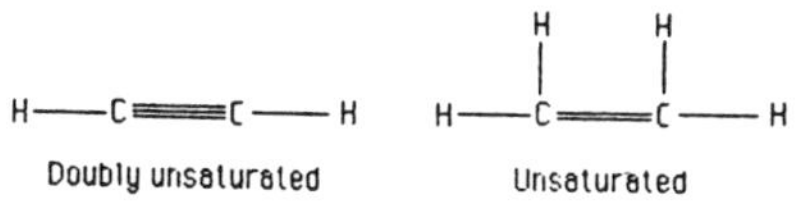

H——C≡≡≡C——H   H——C==C——H

Doubly unsaturated   Unsaturated

From the foregoing, it follows that the general formulae for alkanes, alkenes and alkynes are respectively C_nH_{2n+2}, C_nH_{2n} and C_nH_n, where n is the number of atoms of the element to which it refers in the molecule.

As can be deduced from the diagrams above, these particular unsaturated molecules are derived from ethane, and can be transformed back again simply by adding hydrogen atoms. The doubly unsaturated molecule illustrated is acetylene (C_2H_2), while the twin arm unsaturated one is ethylene (C_2H_4). Unsaturated hydrocarbons are rarely present naturally in crude oil but are the product of some of the refining processes, including thermal cracking.

In crude oil, up to 78 carbon atoms can be present in the chain. The longer it is, the heavier is the molecule and the higher the boiling point of the liquid. In contrast, at atmospheric temperatures and pressures methane and ethane are gases, boiling at -161.5 and $-84°C$ respectively.

1.2   Octane and heptane

A long chain alkane of particular significance is that known as *n*-octane, or simply octane, because its molecule has eight carbon atoms:

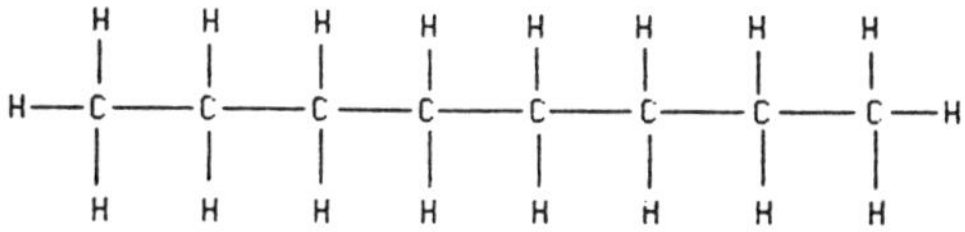

This significance arises because its isomer, *iso*-octane, has by definition, an octane number of 100. Moreover, mixed with *n*-heptane, which is defined as having an octane rating of zero, it is used as the datum for measuring the octane number of all fuels. Heptane, with 7 carbon atoms, has 9 isomers. The octane number of the fuel being tested is expressed as the percentage of *iso*-octane that must be mixed with *n*-heptane to give, under carefully controlled conditions, a tendency to knock, or detonate, at precisely the same compression ratio. An explanation of detonation is given in Section 2.2. The molecular arrangement of iso-octane is:

Where it can be taken for granted that everyone concerned understands that the subject under discussion is hydrocarbon chemistry, this diagram can be more compactly presented by omitting all the hydrogen atoms from it, so that it becomes:

iso-octane (C_8H_{18})

1.3 Cyclo-alkanes

The cyclo-alkanes comprise another series of hydrocarbons. These have ring-like arrangements of the carbon atoms instead of the long chains of the alkanes. Of those that exist in most crude oils, the overwhelmingly highest proportion comprises cyclo-pentane and cyclo-hexane, having respectively five and six carbon atoms arranged as follows:

These diagrams indicate that the general formula for the cyclo-alkane series is C_nH_{2n}. Abbreviating the diagrams, as before, to show only the carbon atoms, and adding some more hydrocarbon chain type molecules, of methane and ethane, we get the diagrams for methyl-cyclo-pentane and ethyl-cyclo-hexane, as follows, still having the same general formulae:

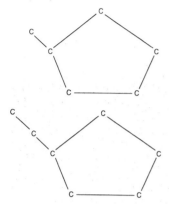

1.4 The aromatics

We now come to the aromatics series. These, again, have ring-like structures, but their general formula is C_nH_n. The arrangement is as follows:

This is benzene (C_6H_6). It can also be represented diagrammatically by omitting all the symbols H and C, leaving only the hexagon with three of its sides having double lines. By referring back to the diagram for cyclohexane, it can be seen that benzene is similar, but all the hydrogen atoms in the middle of the ring have been removed. This can be done by catalytic reforming of the cyclohexane, see Section 1.7.

Other products, termed the alkyl benzene series, can be formed from benzene by substituting a CH_3 alkane radical for, for example, the topmost hydrogen atom in the diagram to produce toluene, $C_6H_5.CH_3$, or an (H_2C—CH_3) radical to form ethyl benzene, $C_6H_5.C_2H_5$. Alternatively, substituting a second (CH$_3$) radical for the hydrogen atoms on the next, next-but-one, or next-but-two arms of a toluene molecule will produce respectively ortho-xylene, meta-xylene and para-xylene, all forms of dimethyl benzene of general formula C$_6$H$_4$(CH$_3$)$_2$.

THE PRODUCTS OF DISTILLATION OF CRUDE OIL

1.5   LPG, gasoline, kerosine, Derv, oils and waxes

As can be seen from Table 1.1, fractional distillation, Fig. 1.1, of petroleum yields, from the lightest to heaviest fractions, the following products: LPG, which is propane with smaller quantities of iso-butane and normal butane, all of which vaporize at temperatures below zero; light gasoline, boiling off at 0-70°C; light naphtha, which is the term given to the fractions boiling off at 70-140°C and known as petrol or gasoline; kerosine, boiling off at 180-250°C and, in the UK, known also as paraffin; diesel oil, 250-350°C, and sometimes known as gas oil or DERV, the latter standing for diesel engine road vehicle; and, finally, lubricating oil, up to 550°C; and paraffin wax.

Additional processing of the distilled products is necessary, however, for two main reasons. First, the constituents of the straight distilled product would be unsuitable for fuelling a motor vehicle. Secondly, the proportions

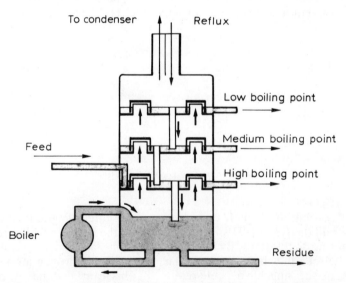

Fig. 1.1   Diagrammatic illustration of the principle of distillation. The feedstock enters the bottom tray at high temperature, the boiler below being for recycling that which has overflowed into the base of the still. In practice there are more evaporation trays, at perhaps about 0.6 m intervals, each drawing off different fractions as the temperature falls progressively from the base to the top of the still. The fractions leaving on the right, may be reprocessed in small side stills, to separate them further

of light and heavy products have to be modified in order to be able to meet the demands for them in the market. The processes that are used for producing light from the heavy hydrocarbons include, hydrocracking, catalytic cracking and thermal cracking, the last-mentioned having largely fallen out of use because of the low octane value of the fuels thus obtained from the naphtha. Incidentally, the term 'gas oil' originated from the use of this fraction in the early days for the production of carburetted water gas to enrich town gas made from coke. However, for that purpose, a slightly wider fraction was used, from 200 to 350°C.

Another incidental is that whereas, in the early days, gas turbines powering aircraft burned kerosine, in modern high speed aircraft the fuel may attain temperatures as high as 200°C even before it reaches the burners, so a special quality fuel, boiling range 150 to 250°C, is needed. This is called Avtur or ATK, short for aviation turbine kerosine. An alternative gas turbine fuel is Avtag or, in the USA JP.4, Avtag being short for aviation turbine gasoline. This has a wide boiling point range, 30 to 260°C, but the proportions of the heavy, and more especially the light, fractions that can be included in the final blend are, of course, strictly limited. The term Avtag must not be confused with Avgas, which is aviation gasoline.

PROCESSING THE DISTILLED PRODUCTS

1.6 Thermal, catalytic and hydro-cracking

Thermal cracking is a process for reducing the sizes of the molecules, thus producing lighter fractions having lower boiling points. It involves heating the hydrocarbons to temperatures from 450 to 550°C. The alkanes crack most easily, followed by the cyclo-alkanes, and finally the aromatics, which are extremely refractory. Thermal cracking of heavy distillates produces not only gasoline but also considerable quantities of gas oil and the heavier fuel oil for industrial use. However, a high proportion of molecules thus produced are olefins which, as explained in Section 1.1, have a lower ratio of hydrogen to carbon atoms than the alkanes. To render them suitable for gasoline or diesel fuel, therefore, they have to be hydrogenated.

As previously mentioned, the boiling points of hydrocarbons increase with the ratio of carbon to hydrogen atoms, as also does the octane number. For instance, methane (CH_4) has a ratio of 4:1 while pentane (C_5H_{12}) has a ratio of only 2.4:1. To reduce this ratio, hydrocracking may be employed. This entails the addition of hydrogen at pressures of about 150-170 bar and temperatures of approximately 450°C. The output is mainly olefins, both the boiling points and ratios of carbon to hydrogen atoms of which are lower than those of the alkenes. However, the output still contains mainly hydrocarbons of low octane rating but they are good feedstock for the catalytic reformer.

Catalytic cracking, Fig. 1.2, which is an alternative approach, is a process that gives a yield of high octane gasoline of considerably larger proportions

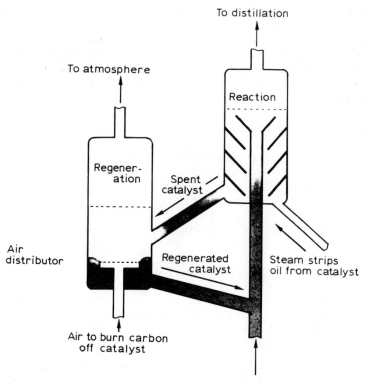

Fig. 1.2   Catalytic cracking by the fluidised bed process. Fullers earth can be used as the catalyst to produce gasoline of high octane No, which is then distilled to separate the fractions. Carbon formed on the catalyst has to be continuously burned off

than that produced by thermal cracking. It, too, produces olefins, but the excess carbon is deposited out on the catalyst, which therefore has to be continuously cleaned by burning off the carbon. Mixtures of silica and alumina are suitable as catalysts in this process. In contrast to catalytic cracking, hydrocracking calls for extremely robust, and therefore costly, equipment to withstand the temperatures and pressures, and considerable quantities of hydrogen must be supplied.

1.7 Catalytic reforming

For improving the octane number (from about 40 to between 95 and 100) of the naphthenes in the straight run distilled gasoline in the boiling range 70-190°C, a four-stage process called catalytic reforming is employed. Various catalysts are employed, including platinum and rhenium, on highly purified alumina. In the first three stages aromatics are formed, which characteristically have high octane numbers. The fourth eliminates the long chain alkanes, which have low octane numbers. A typical Shell Summer Grade gasoline for sale in the UK contains about 70% of reformate.

First the cyclo-alkanes are dehydrogenized, each molecule being stripped of one hydrogen atom, to form aromatics: since the ring type molecular structure is preserved, the conversion reduces the formulae to C_nH_n for the saturated and $C_nH_{n-1}.CH_3$ for the unsaturated naphthenes, hydrogen gas being released, as follows:

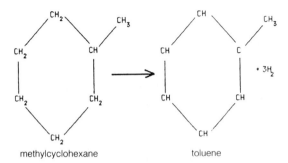

methylcyclohexane   toluene

Secondly, the alkanes are isomerized. For example, n-hexane becomes methylpentane. Then the naphthenes are isomerized, methylcyclopentane for example becoming cyclohexane, which is then dehydrogenated by the process described in the preceding paragraph, to form benzene (C_6H_6):

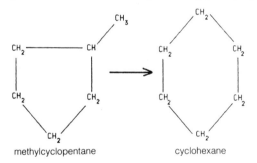

methylcyclopentane   cyclohexane

Thirdly, the remaining alkanes are dehydro-cyclized to form cyclo-alkanes. For example, n-heptane becomes methylcyclohexane $C_5H_{10}+H_2$. Then these too can be dehydrogenated, as before, to form aromatics.

Fourthly, the final process is hydrocracking. In this, the long chain alkanes are divided, to form lighter fractions. For example $C_{10}H_{22}+H_2$ produces $C_6H_{14}+C_4H_{10}$.

Chapter 2

Properties of the conventional gasoline and diesel fuels

Petrol was originally a trade name introduced in the early 1920s, by Carless, Capel and Leonard, a company that still exists. However, the American term gasoline is now widely used by engineers in the UK and even in countries in which the language is not English, especially those that have automotive manufacturing industries. This is because most of the companies producing this fuel are American owned, and they of course employ it in the technical literature they produce for both their internal use and for the information of motor manufacturers around the world. Other terms include motor spirit and petroleum spirit, the latter perhaps being technically the most suitable for a fuel that is produced by refinement of petroleum (the chemical name for crude oil).

2.1 Properties of gasoline

In its simplest form, gasoline is a complex distillate of crude oil, comprising fractions that boil off over a range from about 25°C (pentane) to 220°C for carburation, or ambient to 220°C for gasoline injection since such systems do not have float chambers from which the fuel can boil off when the engine is hot and perhaps flood the engine or cause vapour lock in the fuel system. Since evaporation from the surfaces of liquids occurs at temperatures far below their boiling points, these are useful as only a general indication of the relative volatilities of fuels or fractions: the fuel droplets and vapour entering the engine cylinder are mostly at a temperature lower than their boiling points. Fig. 2.1 shows how the different fractions affect various aspects of engine operation. By referring back to Table 1.1, Chapter 1, it will be seen that a gasoline fuel comprises a mixture of mainly light gasolines and naphtha but including a small quantity of the lighter kerosene fractions. The exact composition of the output from any one refinery depends upon the geographical source of the crude oil from which it was distilled, the additional processes through which it is passed in the refinery, and any blending that might have been done of crude oils or distillates from different sources.

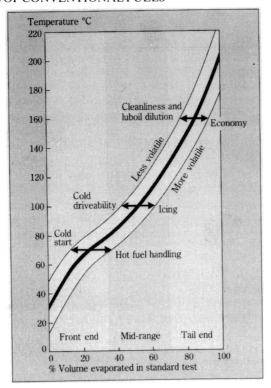

Fig. 2.1   Ability to start from cold depends on the percentage of fuel evaporating below 70°C, but too high a percentage can cause carburettor icing and impair hot running by inducing vapour lock. Too low a percentage, on the other hand impairs not only cold starting but also driveability, and leads to excessive use of the choke, thus increasing fuel consumption and dilution of the lubricating oil (diagram from Shell Science & Technology)

For use in motor vehicles, the gasoline must have certain chemical and physical properties, otherwise it will not pass satisfactorily up from the tank to the carburettor or injectors, form a suitable mixture with the air and burn efficiently in the cylinders to produce adequate power. These properties are:

(1) *Calorific value.* The greater the quantity of thermal energy a fuel contains per unit of volume and weight, the smaller is the quantity required to be carried in the tank in the vehicle to provide enough energy to transport a given load at a given speed over a given distance. High density fuels contain the most energy and they have the lowest volatility.

(2) *Latent heat of vaporisation.* A high latent heat of vaporisation causes the charge to be cooled, and therefore become more dense, as the fuel mixes with the air, so the charge passing into the cylinders of the engine will contain more energy than if that cooling had not taken

place . However, it can also cause freezing of atmospheric moisture in carburettors, which can severely interfere with the running of engines.

(3) *Boiling point.* The fuel must comprise a mixture of volatile liquids, called fractions, each having a different boiling point over the previously mentioned range of ambient to 200°C. This is so that, in the coldest winter conditions, the engine can start easily on the very volatile fractions yet, in very hot climatic conditions, it can still not only start, but also run satisfactorily on the heavier fractions at temperatures up to the maximum envisaged, without hindrance due to the formation of bubbles of vapour, within the fuel system, by the lighter in the heavier fractions. Good volatility in the middle range is desirable to help to reduce the length of time during which the choke must be used after start up from cold. Too little tail-end volatility (too high a proportion of heavy hydrocarbons) can lead to trouble: first, these heavy fractions could enter the cylinder in mainly liquid form, washing the lubricant from the cylinder walls and diluting it in the sump; secondly, they tend to form heavy carbon deposits. Fuels are blended appropriately for both seasonal and geographical variations in temperature.

(4) *Purity.* The presence of substances other than hydrocarbons in a fuel may cause it to deposit ash or corrosive substances when it is burned, or to corrode components in the fuel system.

(5) *Octane number.* A high octane number is perhaps the most important of all the properties required for a hydrocarbon fuel. With a low octane number, it will burn explosively instead of progressively in the engine cylinders, and this can cause overheating and severe damage to the parts that are in any case very hot and their strength therefore reduced.

PERFORMANCE CRITERIA

2.2   Pre-ignition, detonation and octane number

Pre-ignition is generally caused by incandescent particles of carbon or other products of combustion deposited on the walls of the combustion chamber. In a poorly designed engine, however, there may be small projections from components such as, for example, pistons or exhaust valves or their seats, which can become so hot as to incandesce and cause pre-ignition. The tendency of an engine to pre-ignition can be assessed in a manner similar to that for determining octane number, described at the end of this section, but one of the reference fuels is different: *iso*-octane, which is 2,2,4-trimethylpentane, is given the pre-ignition number of 100, but the fuel of zero value is represented by cumene $C_6H_5(CH_3)_2$, which is isopropyl (2 methylethyl)-benzene.

Detonation, on the other hand, is the spontaneous combustion of a proportion of the charge. In normal combustion, after the spark has ignited the combustible mixture, a flame front spreads progressively across the combustion chamber, heating and expanding the gases that it has consumed and compressing the as yet unburned gases in front of it. If the heat generated by both radiation to and compression of these unburned gases rises above that for spontaneous ignition, they explode before the flame front reaches them, and thus generate a shock wave. This is detonation, and it should not be confused with pre-ignition, which is ignition of the charge by incandescence before the spark has passed or a flame front reaches it.

In general, the lower the octane number of the fuel, the greater is its tendency to detonate. Detonation, sometimes alternatively termed pinking or knocking, can occur over the whole speed range, but its causes at low can differ from those at high speeds of rotation. At low speeds , knock can arise owing to rapid opening of the throttle. The consequent sudden increase in manifold pressure causes the aromatics, because they have high boiling points, to condense out on the walls of the induction system. These condensates are mostly the fractions that endow the fuels with their high octane numbers, so they leave only low octane number fractions to pass on into the cylinders: hence the tendency to detonate.

High speed knock, on the other hand, tends to arise when the engine is running with wide open throttle at a speed between that of maximum torque and maximum power, when therefore both the temperatures and pressures in the cylinders are higher than normal. It tends to be particularly insidious because, in most instances, both the combustion and mechanical noises in an engine in these conditions are at their highest and therefore may mask the knocking sound, which therefore tends to pass unnoticed before serious damage has resulted.

Other noises that can come from the engine include what are sometimes termed wild ping and crankshaft rumble. Wild ping is erratic or intermittent detonation caused by incandescence in the combustion chamber, acting in a manner analogous to that of a catalyst, encouraging detonation in conditions so marginal that it would not otherwise occur. Crankshaft rumble is usually caused by resonant vibration of the crankshaft in a bending mode, and it can be generated by either regular combustion forces or detonation. These forces may even alter the mode of rotation of the crankshaft in its bearings, for instance from coaxial to rolling around within them, and this can be another cause of the rumble.

Octane number is an indicator of the tendency of a fuel to detonate, as it burns in the cylinder. Detonation and the other terms sometimes used to describe it have come about because the shock wave striking the engine structure and mechanism generally causes a knocking or ringing (pinking) noise. This shock loading, together with the rapid rate of heat transfer from the burning gases to the components exposed to it, can cause catastrophic failures. Components especially likely to be damaged in this way include mainly piston crowns, piston rings and valves, but even in some instances main and connecting rod bearings and, in extreme cases, cracking of the cylinder head, or even cylinder liners or block castings. The higher the octane number of a fuel, the less is its tendency to detonate in an engine cylinder. Both *n*-alkanes and *cyclo*-alkanes have low octane numbers. The aromatics, forming only about 10% of crude oil, have high octane numbers.

Actually there are three different octane numbers. One is called the Research octane number (RON) because it is obtained in a single cylinder laboratory engine called the Co-operative Fuel Research Engine (CFR).

However, in practice, the knock resistance of a fuel in a multi-cylinder engine under normal running conditions is rarely as high as is indicated by the RON, so another method, called the Motor Method, was developed in which a more widely representative type of engine is used to determine the Motor octane number (MON). Typical automotive gasolines may have a RON of 98 and a MON of 88, the difference between these two numbers being known as the sensitivity of the fuel to changes in engine operating conditions. In the USA, the average of the RON and MON numbers is known as the Anti-knock Index (AKI) and is used as an alternative and slightly more realistic indication of detonation resistance.

Even the motor method is not entirely reliable, because engines of different sizes and layouts differ as regards their tendency to detonation with a fuel of a given MON. This is to a large extent due to inequalities of distribution of the fuel fractions between the cylinders by a carburation or single-point injection system, and its associated induction manifold: heavy fractions tend to be flung, owing to their inertia, to the cylinders most remote from the intake, leaving the nearest cylinders with the lightest fractions which, as mentioned previously, tend to have the lower octane numbers.

Consequently, there is a third octane rating, termed the CFR Road octane number, and this is determined for individual engines, to specify more accurately their fuel requirement. The initials CFR stand for Co-operative Fuel Research, and were introduced because Road octane number is determined co-operatively by a group of the major national and international oil producing companies, who test a large number of cars of each model and pool their results to produce a comprehensive set of data from which they can decide what fuel quality is needed to satisfy the demands of their markets.

We do not need to go into detail here on any of the test methods other than to say that, in all instances, the octane number is the lowest percentage of *iso*-octane mixed with *n*-heptane at which the engine will detonate under strictly controlled conditions of engine operation. In other words, as mentioned in Chapter 1, *iso*-octane C_8H_{18} (2,2,4-trimethypentane) is regarded as having an octane number of 100 and *n*-heptane C_7H_{16}, is taken as having a zero value.

2.3 Boiling point and vapour lock

Having the right mix of fractions in the fuel is important. Their individual boiling points affect not only its suitability for cold starting and use in both hot and cold ambient temperatures but also, if too high a proportion of the fractions have low boiling points, a risk arises of vapour lock occurring in the supply system through which the fuel is lifted from the tank to the carburettor.

Vapour lock is, as its name suggests, the formation of vapour in the system, usually in either the pipeline adjacent to the suction side of the pump or actually inside the pump chamber. It is unlikely to occur if the fuel pump is in the tank and therefore pressurises the fuel to lift it up to the carburettor or injection equipment, but is liable to do so if the pump is of the suction type mounted on or near the engine.

Reducing the pressure both inside and on the suction side of the pump lowers the boiling point of the fuel. Therefore, radiation or, in some circumstances, even conduction of heat to these components, from a nearby part of the exhaust system, may cause the fuel in them to boil. If therefore, the pump or pipes are too close to or, alternatively, not screened from the exhaust, vapour lock is liable to be severe and to occur frequently.

Since the pump is not designed for delivering vapour, the supply of fuel to the carburettor or injection system dries up completely and the engine stops. This is particularly likely to happen on a very hot day when the vehicle is climbing a long steep ascent. In these circumstances, the vehicle is generally moving only slowly, so there is relatively little ram effect to speed the air flow through the engine compartment so the rate of cooling is lower than normal. Moreover, the fan may be rotating relatively slowly too.

If the driver of a car with an engine-driven fan stops for a short time at the top of such an ascent, perhaps to admire the view, he may find that he cannot restart his engine when he wants to move off, even though he did not experience any trouble during the ascent. This is because, with neither the engine fan running nor any ram air flow, the heat that has been generated in the engine continues to be conducted through the metal structure into the engine-driven pump and even into the carburettor, in which case all the fuel may boil out of the carburettor bowl and, in some instances, flood the cylinders, which further increases difficulties in starting. Only when the engine has cooled down again will he be able to get it going by cranking it and thus actuating the fuel pump. Lift pumps are generally designed so that, in such circumstances, at least a little fuel remains in them to keep them primed. Drivers unaware of the cause of the problem, can be utterly at loss as to what to do, but a good remedy is to pour cold water over the pump and adjacent fuel pipes.

2.4 Carburettor icing

Carburettor icing is another phenomenon that can fool the uninitiated motorist, partly because it never occurs in very cold weather. In such conditions, the frozen particles of moisture in the atmosphere bounce straight through the carburettor into the engine. If, on the other hand, the ambient temperature is a little above freezing and the relative humidity high, the result is totally different. The moisture in the air on its way past the carburettor is deposited on the throttle valve and walls of the venturi and then, because it has been cooled below freezing point by the latent heat of vaporisation of the fuel, it freezes on to these metal parts. As the ice deposits progressively build up, they restrict the induction passage, causing the engine first to lose power and, ultimately, to stall. The humid conditions may be associated with fog or rain, without any sign of freezing, so the driver is totally unsuspecting. He tries to restart the engine and fails. Next, he looks under the bonnet and can see nothing wrong. Perhaps he will try once more to restart and, because by this time the ice has had time to be melted by heat conducted or radiated from the surrounding components, much to his astonishment the engine fires and runs normally.

2.5 Fuel composition

Oil companies generally vary the mix of hydrocarbons in the fuel they supply, to suit both the climate and the season of the year. They include more components of low boiling point in cold climates and in winter, and *vice versa* in hot conditions. Properties of a high octane gasoline for use in the UK might be as shown in Table 2.1 though, with the introduction of unleaded fuels, there was a trend towards increasing the proportions of the lighter fractions having high octane numbers. Such a fuel might contain between 24% and 45% aromatics, and from zero up to 26% olefins. If it were 92 octane leaded fuel, the corresponding contents might be respectively 9-41% aromatics and up to 37% olefins. In both instances, the remainder would be made up by mainly naphthene and alkane saturates, the latter being fractions whose molecules comprise atoms all of which are connected together by single arm bonds, as described in Section 1.1. Incidentally, because benzene in high concentrations has been implicated as a possible cause of leukaemia, its content in fuels is in some countries limited to 5% by volume.

In the USA, to meet the emissions regulations, fuel injection with closed loop control over fuel air ratio and catalytic conversion of exhaust gases is essential, so evaporation of fuel from carburettor float chambers is no longer

Table 2.1: PROPERTIES OF A TYPICAL PREMIUM LEADED GASOLINE FUEL FOR THE UK

Property	Summer	Winter
Specific gravity	0.734	0.732
Octane No.	97	97
Reid vapour pressure, kN/m^2	13.5	7.7
Initial boiling point, deg C	34	30
10% fraction boils of at, deg C	55	51
25%	74.4	63.5
50%	104.8	92.8
75%	139.2	129.4
Final boiling point	184	185

a problem. Consequently, there has been a trend towards the use of blends of fuels containing a higher proportion of light fractions than formerly, and even including butane. These light fractions generally offer the added advantage of having high Octane numbers.

ADDITIVES

2.6 The function and origins of additives

Additives are chemicals introduced in very small proportions to the fuel to improve performance, enhance it in respect of its desirable characteristics and to reduce the effects of its undesirable ones. The extent to which they are used, or indeed if at all, depends on the circumstances in each different part of the world at any given time. For instance, at the time of writing, most oil companies are supplying gasoline with few, if any, additives in the UK, but various additives are being used in their fuels supplied to some other parts of the world.

By the early 1920s, the demand for gasoline was expanding rapidly, and the oil companies found that they could no longer satisfy it with straight distilled hydrocarbons. Consequently they introduced other processes, such as cracking, to break down some of the heavier fractions to convert them into lighter ones, and thus balance their total outputs against the relative demands for the various types of product. It was found, however, that the cracked products were less stable than the straight distilled ones and tended to react with oxygen, to form gummy deposits that could block the jets of carburettors and even cause troubles in other components such as filters and pumps. The first additives, therefore, were the anti-oxidants introduced at that time.

2.7 Lead compounds

The best known additives, however, are probably the lead compounds for increasing the resistance of a fuel to detonation. Of these, tetraethyl lead (TEL) was the first to be used, its beneficial effect having been discovered in the early 1920s by Midgley, in the USA. It became widely used shortly before 1930, in those days generally at about 0.6 g/litre, as a low cost way of increasing the octane rating of fuels, the maximum increase, depending on the nature of the base fuel, being about 10 octane numbers. An addition of about 0.4 g/litre of TEL to a typical gasoline will increase its octane number by about 6 units. A level of about 0.3 g/litre is the lowest that can be tolerated by engines not specifically designed for unleaded gasoline, otherwise their exhaust valves, which require a film of lead deposit on their seats to prevent local welding of the peaks of their surface texture, may wear rapidly.

By about 1960, tetramethyl lead (TML), which has a similar effect, began to come into use. This compound has a lower boiling point than TEL, so it will evaporate with the lower fractions in a fuel and therefore, during acceleration, it will be drawn preferentially into the cylinders to increase the anti-knock effect.

The mechanism by which these lead compounds inhibit detonation is believed to be as follows. When a gas is heated, as for example in an engine combustion chamber, its molecules vibrate increasingly violently with the rise in temperature. Because the molecules of the lead compound are very heavy relative to those of the hydrocarbon fuels, they damp down the vibrations of the latter and thus reduce their activity, which is the reason for the tendency to detonate.

By the mid 1980s, pressures intensifed for the total elimination of lead compounds from fuel, on grounds that they are a health risk. However, no evidence of deterioration of any individual's health from this source has ever been produced, despite the fact that various government and other research centres have been searching for such evidence for at least twenty years. Even so, at the time of writing, it seems likely that lead-free gasoline will become predominant during the 1990s. A major influencing factor is undoubtedly that lead in gasoline renders it virtually impossible to use catalytic converters to cleanse the exhaust gases, so the producers of catalysts and converters have brought their considerable financial weight and promotional expertise to bear in support of those who believe that lead additives should be abolished.

2.8 Alternatives to lead—oxygenates

Pressure to eliminate lead stimulated research to find the best ways of improving the octane number of unleaded fuels. Blending in the existing high octane hydrocarbons such as the aromatics is not an easy option, since these constituents are in great demand for the production of petro-chemicals. Even if there were plenty for both the chemical companies and the motorists, which there is not, the price inevitably would be driven up. Eventually, the proportions of aromatics in current fuels could range from 25 to 50%.

Higher octane number can be obtained also by catalytically reforming and isomerisation of the feedstock, to produce higher octane gasoline. This extra processing, however, consumes energy which not only is in itself costly but also calls for very considerable extra investment in refinery plant, the capital for which can be obtained in the long term only in the form of higher prices for the fuel to the customer. Although high octane unleaded fuels are costly, so also is the use of low octane fuels in internal combustion engines that have low compression ratios and therefore high rates of fuel consumption. Therefore, since the driver will have to foot the whole bill, the setting of octane number will have to be a compromise between the two sets of costs. According to Shell, the optimum is 95 RON/85 MON.

Another possibility but, at the time of writing even more costly, is to blend in some oxygenates. Even so, as the price of crude oil rises, the use of oxygenate additives might in the future become more attractive than additional refining of the distillates. These additives include alcohols such as methanol, ethanol, and tertiary butyl alcohol (TBA), which is 2-methyl-2-propanol, or $(CH_3)_3COH$, and certain ethers, the most commonly used among which is methyl tertiary butyl ether (MTBE), or $C(CH_3)_3 OCH_3$, made from isobutylene (2-methyl-propene). All of these have high octane numbers. As can be seen from the diagrams below, TBA is a simple isomer, but the MTBE group is more complex, taking the form of an ether (R-O-R). In the diagram representing MTBE, the radical methoxyl (OCH_3) is on the left and the portion on the right is butyl (C_4H_9).

Tertiary Butyl Alcohol   Methyl Tertiary Butyl Ether

Alcohols, however, absorb water and separate out with a layer of gasoline on top of a layer of alcohol-water mixture so, as explained in Chapter 3, they cannot be used satisfactorily in quantities higher than about 5.5% in the fuels supplied for distribution from service station forecourts. Methanol is the most difficult in this respect so, to alleviate the problem, it has to be dissolved in a higher alcohol such as TBA. Some of the oxygenates tend partially to break down to form hydroperoxides which, although present in only very small quantities, are chemically active and therefore tend to corrode or otherwise degrade some of the components in the fuel systems.

2.9 Anti-oxidants

Just as the rusting of iron in air is very slow so also is the oxidation of hydrocarbons and mono-olefins. However, if traces of metallic salts including cobalt, copper, iron or manganese are introduced, they act as catalysts or as carriers of oxygen and accelerate the process. Copper is present in most crude oils and, after their refinement, may remain in the fuel in quantities between about 0.01 to 0.9 mg/litre. More may be added later owing to arcing of the commutator in an immersed fuel lift pump delivering the fuel to the carburettor or injection equipment. Another source of metallic salts, such as iron, zinc and nickel, is corrosive attack by the peroxides on metal pipes and other components in the fuel system and storage facilities.

Amine anti-oxidants have been used with hydrocarbon fuels, in proportions between 8 and 40 parts per million (ppm). However, with the trend, in the 1980s, towards reduction of the olefinic content of the gasolines from 20% to between 5 and 10%, the proportions of amines were reduced to between 5 and 10 ppm. In fuels that contain alcohol, the amines rapidly break down the hydroperoxides. More widely employed, however, are the phenolic anti-oxidants, which retard the rate of decomposition into hydroperoxides for periods exceeding the normal storage life of the fuel.

A problem that has arisen with some modern gasoline injection systems in which the gasoline is continuously circulated through fuel rails, and only a proportion drawn off for delivery to the injectors, is that the gasoline returning to the tank is warm. This significantly increases the rate of formation of hydroperoxides and rapidly exhausts all the anti-oxidant present. Quantities recycled vary up to between about 70 and 90%, depending on the load on the engine and thus its rate of fuel consumption.

2.10 Detergent and anti-icing additives

Detergent additives were introduced in the 1970s to clean the inlet valves and combustion chambers. Soon afterwards, others came in, for cleaning the carburettor and its jets. These had to be introduced in a carrier oil so that they would mix with the gasoline. Such detergents were particularly useful when, to reduce atmospheric pollution, the practice was adopted of removing from the crankcase the gases that blow by the piston rings and which hitherto had been discharged into the atmosphere through the crankcase breather. These gases are now discharged into the air intake, usually downstream of the air filter and therefore, without detergent additives, significantly increase the tendency to fouling of the components in the passages along which they are carried into the engine.

To combat the problem of freezing of moisture in carburettors and induction systems, glycols are added to gasoline. By the mid-1950s a problem arose due to deposits from the various additives themselves, particularly from the lead compounds, on both spark plugs and exhaust valve seats. These were countered by the introduction of phosphorous compounds. Since then, however, the lowering of the lead content and improvements in spark plug design have rendered these additives unnecessary. The precise nature of the many additives are closely guarded company secrets, Shell for example having described their detergent and phosphorus compounds, simply by the initials ASD and ICA.

2.11 Driveability, spark aiders and alcohol blends

Another of the additive packages, known as Formula Shell, was introduced in the early 1970s, before the advent of the energy crisis. Then, by about 1986, it was dropped because engine design measures had caught up and dealt adequately with what had previously become a problem. Before the energy crisis, most engines were with air:fuel ratios of about 13:1 at throttle openings approaching idling and wide open; afterwards, however, the mixtures had to be weakened throughout the throttle range, those for cruising falling to about 15:1, not only to economise on fuel consumption but also to help clean up the environment. With such weak mixtures, any wear or other in-service impairment of carburation, injection or other equipment in the fuel system could have a seriously deleterious effect on driveability.

Driveability, owing to its largely subjective nature, is difficult to define accurately, but it can be said to be a measure of how smoothly the engine responds to signals transmitted to it through the accelerator pedal. It also includes the qualities of starting, idling and warm-up, as well as acceleration. Symptoms include: hesitation, or a delay in response to the opening of the throttle; stumble, or a drop in speed immediately after the throttle has been opened; and surge, or an alternate gain and loss in speed at constant throttle opening.

A crucial factor influencing driveability is the speed with which the flame kernel initiated by the spark attains a critical size. If it does not develop rapidly enough, it can be blown out owing to rapid conduction of the heat it contains, into the turbulent gases in the combustion chamber, or it can loose heat by radiation to all its surroundings so rapidly that, again, it is extinguished.

Alternatively, a feeble initial rate of expansion of the flame kernel can cause the subsequent combustion of the whole charge to develop only slowly and the engine therefore to function inefficiently. An engine running on a weak mixture is particularly prone to defective ignition, because of the difficulty of distributing the mixture in combustible proportions equally to each cylinder: in contrast, given the richer mixtures of former times, even the cylinder receiving the leanest charge will fire effectively and its contents burn rapidly. To strengthen and accelerate the development of the flame kernel, therefore, what were termed spark-aiders were introduced into the Formula Shell package.

Another requirement for driveability when burning weak mixtures is better detergency, so improved detergents were also included in the package. They were needed to prevent the build-up of gummy accumulations of carbonaceous deposits from the gasoline and lubricant in ports, manifolds, combustion chambers and on valves. Such build-ups can cause an engine to need fuels of progressively increasing octane number as it ages. In extreme cases, this can happen in as little as 5000 km of motoring. The result can be uneven running, detonation, engine damage and poor fuel economy.

Entirely different problems can arise in countries in which high proportions of alcohols are blended with the conventional hydrocarbon fuels. This is a measure generally undertaken to reduce a drain on national reserves of hard currencies. An unfortunate side effect is a reduction in the effectiveness of conventional detergent additives. Consequently, research is being undertaken to find more suitable additives for such fuels.

Chapter 3

Alternative engines and fuels, including for racing

Currently, very few vehicles are run on fuels other than gasoline and diesel oil, the principal alternative being liquefied petroleum gas (LPG). However, in view of the prospect of our crude oil supplies running out in the 21st century, others are being investigated. All except about 5% of cars in Europe are still powered by gasoline engines because this type offers the highest specific power output, on the basis of both weight and bulk, at the lowest cost. On the other hand, by virtue of advances in diesel engine design, it has been forecast that this 5% of diesel cars could rise to as much as 20% during the 1990s and, with the progressive tightening of the controls over exhaust emissions, even this could be an under estimate.

ALTERNATIVE POWER UNITS

3.1 Merrit MCC and Sterling engines, gas turbines and electric power

This situation worldwide could change, however, following the appearance on the scene, in 1987, of the Merritt MCC engine. The future of this power unit depends to a major extent on whether investment is forthcoming for its further development to bring it into production.

Apart from this possibility, there is at the moment, no prospect of any other serious challenge to the conventional engines. It can be said that the Stirling unit is too heavy and bulky for automotive use, particularly in view of the fact that 50% of the heat generated has to be dissipated through a heat exchanger, which is inherently a costly item: this heat dissipation figure is about double that for and internal combustion engine. Increasing the maximum temperature in the cycle, however, could improve the prospects for the Stirling engine, Fig. 3.1, but would entail further development of ceramic or other materials resistant to high temperatures.

The gas turbine is efficient only as it approaches the upper end of its speed range, so it is suitable principally for relatively constant high speed operation though there are of course other factors mitigating against it, including cost and slow response to the control pedal owing to the very wide speed range over which compressor the rotor has to be accelerated to to provide the extra air needed to generate the extra power.

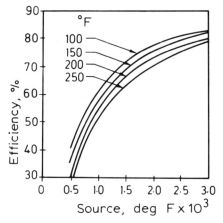

Fig. 3.1 *Diagram showing the ideal efficiencies of the Stirling engine in relation to temperature of heat source and heat sink*

Electric energy is impracticable, too, except for a few special categories of operation, at least until a storage battery considerably better than the lead-acid type is developed. No battery of adequate capacity is likely to be available in the short term nor is the prospect at all bright in the long term, Fig. 3.2. At the time of writing, optimistic claims are being made for

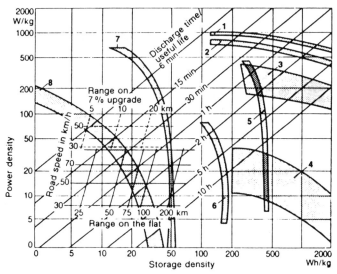

Fig. 3.2 *The Morse Report entitled "The Automobile and Air Pollution", published by the US Department of Commerce, includes this diagram comparing the power and storage densities of various drive systems*
1. Gas turbine, 2. Internal combustion engine, 3. Engine with external combustion, 4. Electric motor with fuel cell, 5. with lithium chloride battery, 6. with zinc air battery, 7. with nickel cadmium battery, 8. with lead acid battery

projected cars powered by AC electric motors. Although this cuts out the loss of efficiency in conversion of DC into AC current, the energy storage capacity hurdle remains to be crossed.

A first consideration in relation to the use of electrical traction is that the efficiency of conversion of primary fuel into electricity by a modern conventional power station dependent upon fossil fuels is between 23 and 30%. Secondly, it takes about eight hours to charge fully a lead-acid battery, and even then its energy content is enough to drive a vehicle for only about 30-40 miles.

In contrast, ten pumps on the forecourt of a service station, supplying gasoline simultaneously into the tanks of ten cars, deliver energy at a rate higher than that of a typical electricity generating station in a major city during a peak load period. This might seem astonishing, but one should bear in mind the efficiencies of use of the energy supplied to the two types of vehicle. Electrical energy is used largely at an efficiency of about 80 to 90% or even higher. In contrast, the chemical energy delivered to the cars in the form of gasoline is in general utilised at a maximum efficiency of only about 25%, and the average over all modes of operation, at between 12 and 15%, is approximately half this value. This is because, at 60 mph a family saloon car needs only about 20% of its maximum power, which means it is operating inefficiently, at small throttle openings. Consequently, even to compete just on equal terms, each car needs to be supplied with much more energy. Furthermore, each of the ten cars leaving the forecourt will normally travel at considerably higher speeds than any electric vehicle and for distances of 250 to 440 miles (400 to 700 km) on one full tank. It follows therefore that liquid fuel is overwhelmingly more attractive than electrical energy supplied through the medium of a battery.

Supplying electricity directly through the inevitably very costly overhead cable or live rail installations to vehicles is economically only where the density of traffic is high. Furthermore, overtaking is impossible and adverse safety and environmental considerations can arise. Even so, it is still used by some public transport undertakings.

POTENTIAL ALTERNATIVE FUELS

3.2 Liquid, liquefied gases and gaseous fuels

Alternative fuels of immediate interest are:

(1) Synthetic hydrocarbons, mainly made from coal.
(2) Alcohol, mostly methanol CH_3OH, made from natural gas or coal, or ethanol, the latter being ethyl alcohol or methylated spirits, C_2H_5OH, obtained by fomening vegetable matter, the hydration of ethylene or acetylene or by catalytic synthesis from ethylene and water.

(3) Gasohol, which originated in Brasil, is a mixture of gasoline and ethanol.

(4) Liquefied petroleum gas (LPG). This occurs naturally in the ground. It is mainly propane C_3H_8 but may also contain a small proportion of butane C_4H_{10} and possibly some ethane C_2H_6 and even a little pentane and slightly heavier fractions in vapour form. The heavier fractions tend to occur in LPG produced by distillation of crude oil or obtained from a natural reservoir of gas that contains also oil.

(5) Liquefied natural gas (LNG). This comes principally from dry natural reservoirs (those that do not also contain oil). LNG is generally mainly methane (CH_4) but, in some circumstances, with very small proportions of ethane and propane. Methane is better known as originating from decaying vegetable matter in, for example, sewage works, rubbish tips, or marshland, which is why it is sometimes called marsh gas. The latter is also termed biogas and contains significant impurities including CO_2.

(6) Producer gas, or water gas. This is a mixture of hydrogen, carbon monoxide and nitrogen, the latter being a product of the manufacturing process in which air and steam are passed over very hot coke to form mainly CO, with H_2 and some light hydrocarbons.

Although oil extraction from shale or oil-sands is often quoted as a possible alternative, it is not really practicable. This is because of the huge tonnages of shale or sand that have to be shifted and processed, and the consequent enormous costs in terms of capital investment and labour. Even if the handling and processing were to be virtually totally automated, the interest charge on the capital required for setting up the plant would still amount to an on-cost, on the charge per litre on the filling station forecourt, of about as much as the retail price of conventionally obtained gasoline. On top of this, the exploration, development, refining, transport and marketing costs would still have to be added to obtain the final selling price of the fuel extracted from shale or sand.

Compared with liquid fuels, which of course are fairly easily dispensed and mixed with air, by means of either a carburettor or an injection system, the gaseous ones are not at too great a disadvantage provided they can be dispensed in liquid form into the tank and retained there in that form at least until conversion into a gas during its passage to a simple gas carburettor and thence the engine. LPG and LNG are, as their names suggest, among the most attractive in this respect. LPG is covered in detail in Chapter 10. So far, LNG has not made any significant inroad into the automotive fuel market, but a very recent interesting development in connection with its containment in porous carbon, as adsorbed natural gas (ANG), has been described in articles in the April/May 1990 and 1991 issues of Automotive Engineer. For the longer term, we should, however, at least consider hydrogen as a replacement for gasoline.

3.3 Operation on LPG

Let us examine why operation on liquefied petroleum gas (LPG) is confined to only a very small minority of vehicles comprising mainly some taxis, and commercial and industrial vehicles, all travelling relatively short distances from base and, in many instances, on pre-planned runs. Indeed, because of the sparsity of potential refuelling points, a prerequisite for running on LPG in most territories is ownership of a bulk storage facility at base, to which drivers can return periodically for refuelling.

On the other hand, three factors favour LPG as a viable alternative. First it is much less costly than either gasoline or diesel oil, and this makes it attractive for all applications. Secondly, its exhaust gas is of low toxicity, hence the attraction for certain industrial applications. Thirdly, it occurs naturally in very large quantities and is easy to extract.

However, in general the overall cost of the fuel system on the vehicle (see Chapter 10) is significantly higher than that for a gasoline engine equipped with a simple carburettor. Furthermore, even in liquid form, it is significantly less dense than the liquid hydrocarbon fuels such as gasoline and diesel oil and its bulk calorific value less. Consequently, to fit a tank large enough to give an acceptable range is inconvenient or, in many instances even impracticable. It is this, together with the sparsity of refuelling points, that rules LPG out for long distance haulage.

If it were not for the fact that the price of fuels is to a major extent dependent on what tax is levied on them, undoubtedly more LPG refuelling points would be installed. To provide them now would certainly, by broadening the potential applications for the fuel, attract more tax to it until it was no longer cheaper, and could even become dearer, than the more conventional fuels. Because of the high volatility and inflammability of LPG, the dispensing equipment is required by law to be at least 3 m from the bulk storage tank and the whole installation at least 7.6 m from the nearest building or boundary fence, Fig. 3.3. This makes investment in refuelling facilities impracticable for many service stations, particularly in urban situations, where space for such a large installation is costly and, in any case, may not be available within the bounds of existing premises.

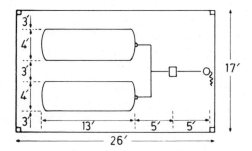

Fig. 3.3   Legal requirements for the bulk storage of LPG in the UK

3.4 Alternative sources and production processes

For many years, synthetic diesel and gasoline fuels have been made from coal. Among the first to go into production commercially was ICI in the United Kingdom. During World War II, larger quantities were made in Germany and, more recently, South Africa has improved the processing and by this means is satisfying much of its needs for liquid hydrocarbons.

LPG is in use in the UK, Holland and some other countries where reserves of the gas, often in association with crude oil, are to be found underground. Compressed natural gas (CNG), or more commonly biogas, is employed in vehicles run locally by, for example, sewage and other waste disposal undertakings, where methane gas is a byproduct of the processing of the waste. It does occur naturally underground too, in much the same way as does crude oil.

Among the alcohols, ethanol is less aggressive than methanol. In the USA, a 10% blend of ethanol in gasoline is sold under the name Gasohol. Alcohols are economically attractive, however, principally in countries having no natural reserves of crude oil or gas, and whose climate is so favourable for agriculture that several crops can be harvested per growing season. In such countries, not only can waste products from food crops be used, but also special crops can be grown solely for conversion into alcohol. In Brasil, 20% of ethanol is blended with all gasolines, and is also available neat as an automotive fuel. Indeed, 90% of all new cars sold in that country are designed to run on ethanol. The reasons why they have to be so designed are explained in the next paragraphs.

As previously mentioned, alcohol has a high octane number (104 to 106) so it is suitable for blending with gasoline. However, even when blended, the alcohols have the disadvantage that they tend to absorb moisture, in which they dissolve and then separate out in the bottom of the tank. Consequently, unless measures are taken to protect the metal components in the fuel system, trouble can be experienced with corrosion. Another difficulty that arises is that the air:fuel ratio required for complete combustion of alcohol is significantly lower than that for the hydrocarbon fuels, so blending the two can lead to combustion problems.

The latent heat of vaporisation of alcohol is 8 to 9 times that of gasoline, so cold starting and driving away with a cold engine at ambient temperatures any lower than 10 deg C tends to be difficult. Even at higher temperatures, ice may form in the induction system. On the other hand, the cooling of the ingoing charge increases volumetric efficiency but, if the icing problem has to be solved by heating the induction manifold, this advantage can be lost. The addition of about 5.5% of iso-pentane, however, can improve volatility and thus cold starting.

Methanol, which was first prepared by Boyle in 1661, has been proposed as an alternative fuel. It has been most actively promoted in countries that have readily available cheap supplies of natural gas, from which it can be produced together with some other petrochemicals. On the other hand, the energy requirement for conversion amounts to about 40% of that contained in the original gas, as compared with perhaps 20% when gasoline is prepared from crude oil. Furthermore if, prior to conversion, the natural gas has to be transported over long distances (as a liquid at a temperature of −162°C), the cost becomes prohibitive. Other possibilities include synthesis from carbon monoxide and hydrogen or methane and oxygen.

Yet another method of manufacture is by destructive distillation from wood, which is why it is sometimes called wood alcohol. The distillation is effected at between 370 and 500°C in an inert atmosphere, to form hydrocarbon gases and two layers of liquid, one tarry and the other aqueous. These liquids are distilled over, leaving a charcoal residue. The aqueous fraction of the distillate initially contains about 6% methanol, 10% acetic acid and a small amount of acetone. By the addition of calcium chloride to the aqueous fraction, the methanol is fixed as $CaCl_2.CH_3OH$. This is then distilled off and thermally decomposed into methanol and $CaCl_2$. The yield of methanol is approximately 20% by mass of the wood, and therefore is economic only as a byproduct, in relatively small quantities, of the manufacture of other chemicals.

Perhaps a more attractive method of production in the very large quantities needed for its use as a substitute fuel for motor vehicles is to combine catalytically hydrogen and carbon dioxide, at about 420°C. The hydrogen might be obtained from water and the carbon dioxide by thermal decomposition of limestone ($CaCO_3$). However, even if the hydrogen could be produced cheaply enough, the quarrying of the huge quantities of limestone required would tend to be either energy or labour intensive, or both, and to present major problems, as also would the disposal of the quicklime residue.

Although methanol has the advantage of being liquid at normal temperatures and pressures, it has several significant disadvantages. Its energy content is low (19.7 as compared with 43.5 MJ/kg for gasoline), so it would call for a fuel tank about twice the size of that for a gasoline or diesel engine; cold starting of engines running on it is difficult, but can be improved by blending with it abut 5.5% of the highly volatile isopentane; although its Research Octane number is between 104 and 106, its Motor Octane number is only about 94 and is not improved by the addition of either TML or TEL; furthermore, there are doubts concerning its toxicity, especially since it can even be absorbed through the skin. Even so, in the event of a sudden world shortage of crude oil, it seems quite likely that a 15% blend of methanol in gasoline, the M15 blend, would be used in some countries, so fuel system designers are tending to take this into consideration as regards their selection of materials, for example, for tanks.

3.5 Energy content

Perhaps the most important property of any fuel is its energy density, since this determines its commercial value in terms of ton-km of operation obtainable per litre of fuel in the tank. Gasoline and diesel oil are extremely energy-rich and, moreover, easy to distribute and to handle. Some relative energy contents on both a per volume and per weight basis are given in Table 3.1.

Table 3.1: ENERGY CONTENTS OF SOME FUELS

Fuel	(MJ/kg)	(MJ/m³)
Liquid		
Gasoline	43.5	
DERV	42.5	
Ethanol	26.8	
Methanol	19.7	
Gaseous		
Methane	50.0	3.22
Butane	45.6	3.39
Propane	46.3	3.35
Hydrogen	120.0	2.97

Some other comparative data relating to fuels are of interest. First, the energy in one tonne of steam coal is approximately equal to that in four barrels of crude oil. Secondly, one barrel of crude oil weighs about 0.14 tonnes, and contains 35 Imperial or 42 US gallons. Thirdly, conversion of coal to methane or methanol is effected at an efficiency of only about 50-69%, while that of converting crude oil to liquid fuel is over 90%.

3.6 Hydrogen as a fuel

Hydrogen was used in the 1920s in what were basically Maybach gasoline engines and, in 1934, in Daimler Benz diesel engines, which in both instances were converted for operation on gas and installed in Zeppelin airships. Although helium was used for maintaining the buoyancy of some of these airships, many contained huge quantities of hydrogen gas, and all needed the lightest possible fuel.

For road vehicles, however, the main obstacles are the current high cost of hydrogen and, more significantly, the extreme difficulty of containing the gas safely in the fuel tank. Storing it as a compressed gas at a pressure of 138 bar calls for the use of a very heavy container. At atmospheric pressure, liquid hydrogen boils at 20.4°K, so it would appear that the best way to store it is at cryogenic temperatures in a Dewar (vacuum) flask. Even then, it boils off slowly and so, if a car were to be left unused for a week, about 7% of the fuel in its tank would be lost. On the other hand, given a resolution of the containment problem, it could be practicable for supersonic aircraft powered by gas turbines because it would reduce the weight of fuel needed by a factor of 2.5.

As regards cost, hydrogen, however, might not always be at such a great disadvantage. If, for instance, nuclear fission reactors are eventually employed for the generation of electrical energy, the heat that otherwise would be wasted might be used for thermal dissociation of water very economically. Moreover, since the dissociation process would produce both oxygen and hydrogen, a possibility arises of injecting both gases into the engine, which could be of especial interest for submarine power units and applications where pollution of the ambient atmosphere by oxides of nitrogen must be totally avoided. As regards atmospheric pollution in general, a major advantage of hydrogen is that, except for NO_x, water vapour is its only product of combustion.

3.7 Metal hydrides as an alternative fuel source

There are alternatives to the use of hydrogen in either gaseous or liquid form and, at first sight, these might appear to be more practicable. One is the storage of hydrogen in the form of metal hydride granules, the cheapest probably being magnesium hydride. For the average American car, the weight of the container and magnesium hydride granules with 40% voids between them would be about 316 kg and its volume 0.31 m^3. In contrast, the corresponding figures for hydrogen gas at 138 bar and gasoline respectively would be 1030 kg in 1.87 m^3 and 68.4 kg in 0.08 m^3.

For a given energy content, a tank containing such granules would weigh only twice as much as an equivalent tank full of gasoline. The hydrogen gas can be driven off by the application of heat. A separate heater would be required for starting, but then the engine exhaust system could take over. Subsequently, the granules could be exchanged for a fresh batch, the used ones being regenerated by heating them in an atmosphere of hydrogen under pressure.

3.8 Liquid hydrides

A second possibility is that methylcyclohexane, a liquid hydride, might be employed. The initials MTH have been used to describe the process because, from the methylcyclohexane, toluene and hydrogen are produced. A great deal of development and research have been carried out with this fuel by DERECO (Diesel Engine Research and Engineering Co Ltd, of CH-9320 Arbon, Switzerland).

This liquid has an energy content of about 9.6 to 12.0 MJ/kg. Although the system is too heavy and bulky for cars, it might be practicable for larger vehicles, such as trucks and city buses. The hydride is stable at normal atmospheric temperature and pressure, so the only extra provisions that have to be made on the vehicle is a catalytic dehydrogenation unit, a pump to return the residue (toluene) and a tank to contain it after the hydrogen has been extracted. Investigations are in progress into the possibility of using n-heptane instead of methylcyclohexane. This would still produce toluene as a residue, but the output of hydrogen ($4H_2$) is potentially four times greater.

A methylcyclohexane dehydrogenation unit has been designed to produce hydrogen at 12 bar, at which pressure it can be injected directly into the cylinders of diesel engines. A truck was running on this fuel as early as 1984 and a second in 1985, the hydrogenation unit of which was capable of supplying a 350 kW engine. In 1987, a more advanced system was installed in a 20/25 tonne truck by the Swiss Federal Institute for Reactor Research. Its experimental dehydrogenation unit weighed 750 kg and occupied 1 m³, for a diesel engine producing 150 kW. However, considerable reductions in weight should be possible eventually. The weight of hydride required for a journey of 300 km was 500 kg. This still highlights the advantages of liquid hydrocarbon fuels since, for the same distance, a tank of diesel fuel weighing only 90 kg would be required.

The price of toluene is relatively low and both it and methylcyclohexane can be stored at atmospheric pressure. On the vehicle, part of the heat required for the catalytic release of the hydrogen, at 400°C, could be derived from the exhaust. Less than 300 g of free hydrogen is contained within the system at any given moment and is burned at approximately the rate at which it is produced.

3.9   Prospects for other gaseous fuels

For the present, fuels such as propane and methane show some promise. Producer gas, on the other hand, has a very low calorific value and therefore the range of a vehicle run on it is very restricted. All the gases are clean burning, and therefore do not contaminate the lubricating oil as much as do gasoline or diesel oil. On the other hand, all are at a disadvantage as compared with the liquid fuels, in that they displace more air from the cylinders of the engine, especially if the liquid fuel is injected in droplets, as is the case in diesel engines. However, since many gaseous fuels have high octane numbers, the disadvantage of displaced air can be largely offset by operation at higher compression ratios. Properties of some gaseous fuels are given in Table 3.2.

Table 3.2:   PROPERTIES OF THE PRINCIPAL LIQUIFIED GASEOUS FUELS

Fuel	RON	Boiling pt, (°C)	Storage press, bar
Butane	94	−0.5	1.5
Propane	111	−42.2	10.8
Methane	124	−161.5	240.0 (or at low temp)
LPG	103-105	(Mixture)	6.8

3.10   Fuels from coal

World coal reserves are such that they seem likely to remain available for between about five and ten times as long as petroleum. Since coal is a carbon-rich fuel, hydrogen must be added if it is to be converted into a hydrocarbon. This can be done by either of two processes, both of which originated in Germany. The first was discovered in 1914, by Bergius. He liquefied coal by hydrogenation, exposing it in the presence of a catalyst to hydrogen at about 930°F and 700 bar pressure. By using different types of coal, or coal derived products, and different catalysts, the type of fuel produced can be varied from gasoline to fuel oil. Obviously, a considerable degree of cleansing of the coal derived ingredients is necessary, prior processing them, and the product is expensive because of the huge capital cost of the plant required.

Then, in 1915, Fischer and Tropsch synthesised liquid hydrocarbons from water gas obtained from coal, as described in Section 3.2. This process was not used commercially in Germany until 1927, and in more recent years has been considerably further developed in South Africa. It is much more economical than the hydrogenation of coal.

A mixture of one part by volume of carbon monoxide and two parts of hydrogen, some of which has to be added to that already in the water gas, again thoroughly cleansed, is passed over a catalyst under carefully controlled conditions. This produces a mixture of alyphatic hydrocarbons ranging from methane to waxes, among which the following are of most interest as automotive fuels: benzene, C_6H_6, toluene C_6H_5. CH_3 and xylene $C_6H_4.(CH_3)_2$. Benzol, or benzole, is a mixture of all three. The temperatures required are only about 180 to 200°C, and the catalyst originally used was cobalt. Pressures ranging from one to ten bar have been the general rule.

Subsequently, a more robust iron catalyst was developed, though this called for a temperature of 325°C and a pressure of 20 bar. Among the refinements that have been introduced are the use of fluidized bed equipment for containing the catalyst and the introduction of a gas prepared from natural gas by the partial combustion of methane under strictly controlled conditions. A fluidized bed, incidentally, is one in which the catalyst in powder form, or deposited on an inert powder, is supported on the gas introduced through a perforated plate beneath it, to lift it rather as water is lifted by the vapour produced as it boils.

3.11   Racing fuels and additives

Selection and blending of special fuels and additives for racing is a highly complex and specialised subject. In general, the decisions are based upon the type of race track, number of stops allowed for refuelling and other rules applying to a particular race. For instance, if range without refuelling stops is an overriding consideration, emphasis might be placed on energy density of the fuel. On the other hand, high compression ratios are the norm for racing engines, so high Motor Octane number is important. In most racing events, however, the use of exotic fuels and additives is banned.

Since the alcohols have high Octane ratings, rendering compression ratios of up to 15:1 practicable, they tend to be favoured despite their low calorific value. Additionally, their high latent heat of vaporisation, not only cools the charge and increases its density but also is held by some to contribute towards cooling the engine in general. Blends from 40% up to virtually all alcohol have been employed. Among them are methyl alcohol (methanol), ethyl alcohol (ethanol, or methylated spirits). These can be used neat or blended with hydrocarbon fuels.

Ether ($C_2H_5O.C_2H_5$), because of its low boiling point, may be useful for facilitating cold starting; acetone (CH_3COCH_3) may be added for its high anti-detonation value, and for inhibiting the strong tendency towards pre-ignition with methane; by virtue of its high energy content nitro-benzene ($C_6H_5NO_2$) may be added, but preferably in quantities no more than 5%; the even more dangerous nitromethane (CH_3NO_2) can explode if subjected to shocks even as light as those to which it can be subjected when being poured into the tank, but its value as an additive lies in the fact that its high oxygen content (52.5% by weight) will be released in the combustion chamber of the engine to combine with the other constituents of the fuel. Although it is only about 5% soluble in gasoline, it is very soluble in the alcohols. Power increases of up to 30% have been claimed with 40% blend of nitromethane in a gasoline-alcohol blended fuel. The proportion of nitromethane that can be used increases as the coolant jacket temperature is reduced and if water is introduced as an additional additive. Water, dissolved in alcohol, has been employed as an additive, mainly as a coolant and anti-detonant, but fell out of favour long ago.

Many of these fuels and additives are toxic: rubber gloves are advisable for handling methanol, benzole and nitro-benzene, and care has to be taken to avoid inhaling fumes from them. In the latter respect, care has to be taken also with ether. Various other measures may have to be taken. For example, carburettor jets and float valves usually need to be adjusted, and special anti-corrosion treatments applied to protect components in the fuel systems.

Chapter 4

Fuel Tanks and the Measurement of Their Contents

Legal requirements regarding safety measures to be taken in connection with fuel systems and the handling of fuel differ widely throughout the world. In general, the rules are laid down on the basis of sound common sense. To avoid becoming involved in the complexity of legislation on an international scale, however, we shall mainly view the design problems in terms of what is necessary for ensuring safety and efficiency of operation.

FUEL TANKS

4.1 Sizes of tanks

On a commercial vehicle, the size of the fuel tank will depend entirely on the type of operation for which it is designed. For cars, a range of about 200 miles came to be considered adequate in the early post World War II era in Europe but, following the building of the motorway networks, it became necessary by the end of the 1970s to make provision for covering approximately double this mileage without having to replenish the tank. Even then, an additional capacity of about 50% might have to be provided for countries in which methanol or ethanol are used for fuel and even more where filling stations are few and far between.

Vehicle manufacturers having to export their cars on a worldwide scale either have to make provision for installation of larger tanks for their products for export to some regions or to standardise on a large tank for all markets. They have generally taken the latter course in order to simplify production procedures. Consequently, by the mid 1980s, car tank capacities became such as to give ranges mostly between 450 and 650 km, which translated into 800 km when a diesel engine was offered as an option to the gasoline power unit. On the more expensive cars, the tanks have in any case always tended to be large, even for operation exclusively in Western Europe and North America.

34

4.2 Fuel tank evolution

Until about the mid 1930s, the extra costs associated with installing a pump were in some instances avoided by mounting the tank on the scuttle, so that the fuel could be fed by gravity to the engine below. This also obviated the risk of breakdowns owing to the failures of the pumps which, in those days, were unreliable. The provision for fuel contents gauging was in some instances, simply a metal tube connected from the tank to a vertical glass tube on the dash fascia, at a height such that it displayed to the driver the actual level of the fuel in the tank. With the tank not only in the engine compartment but also virtually above the laps of those in the front seats, the danger to the occupants from fire in an accident was considerable. Even so, vehicles with this layout were still on the road during World War II.

Long before that, however, the best place for the tank had come to be regarded as between the chassis side-members, to the rear of the back axle. This layout was virtually universal until the beginning of the 1980's when, in some cars, the tank was installed forward of the rear axle, under the back seat. As regards fire risk, there seems to be little to choose between these two positions: at the extreme rear, the tank is exposed to being pierced or fractured in the event of a shunt, while under the rear seat, it is far from ideal as regards passenger safety but, nevertheless, better protected from damage. A good compromise is possible with trailing arm rear suspension since, with the axle forward of the wheel centres, the tank can be placed between the wheels which, in conjuncion with the rear bumper, tend to protect it from both side and rear end impacts. Furthermore, the tank can usually be significantly deeper in this position than under the rear seats which, in the interests of both dynamic stability and keeping the roof profile down for minimal aerodynamic drag, must be as low as practicable.

On heavy commercial vehicles, there is much more space under the body, and a tank at the rear is liable to be damaged. Furthermore, need for easy access has generally dictated that it be mounted between the wheels, outboard of the side members, at any convenient point along the chassis but near the engine and well away from mid-span, where it could be damaged on very rough or humped terrain. To give the pump as little work as possible in lifting the fuel up to the carburettor or injection equipment, the tank has been in the past placed as high as practicable within the constraint imposed by the presence of the body floor immediately above the frame.

This of course applies to cars as well as commercial vehicles. Now, however, height of tank is of much less significance, since electric pumps that can function reliably immersed in fuel have been introduced and therefore may be installed inside the tanks. With gasoline, this largely obviates the risk of vapour lock.

4.3 Factors affecting tank position

It is of interest to note the changes that have influenced the positioning of tanks over the years. In the very early days, few cars had boots, so the tank was totally exposed at the rear: luggage was carried on racks, mostly at the back, over the fuel tanks, but sometimes on the roof or, in a few isolated instances, even on running boards. This continued on popular saloons and sports cars until approximately the end of the 1920s, and some sports cars, much later.

By the mid 1930s, however, most saloon cars had luggage boots, the sizes of which increased with the successive introduction of new models. In recent years, because the designers had gone as far as they could in lengthening the boot, the trend has been to deepen it by lowering the floor and raising the top deck. In some instances, this has led to the installation of fuel tanks in the otherwise virtually useless space above the rear wheelarches. A question of safety in the event of an accident arises, but the incidence of fire in these circumstances is not high except in the context of in high speed multiple crashes on motorways.

Other influencing factors have included the desire to improve handling characteristics and stability which, over many decades, has led to a progressive lowering of the body and, indeed, most of the heavy components, to bring down the overall centre of gravity. A major advance in this respect came with the introduction of chassisless construction.

The outcome of all these measures has been that there is now less space available for the tank between the floor and the ground, so tanks have tended to become less deep. Perhaps of greatest significance, however, was the introduction of front wheel drive, beginning with the Austin Mini at the end 1950s. This, by obviating the propeller shaft, opened the way for the tank to be brought into the space immediately to the rear of the heelboard, beneath the seat cushion and just in front of the back axle. However, it was not until the early 1980s that advantage began to be taken of both this opportunity and the ease of moulding plastics tanks into irregular shapes.

Prior to this except in the very early days, when cylindrical fuel tanks were not uncommon, they had almost invariably been of rectangular shape. Initially, their sizes and shapes were such that they could be slung snugly between the chassis side members. Partly because of the ease with which an existing rectangular tank can be adapted to fit into a new model, this practice was continued when integral construction (a vestigial frame welded to the underside of the body) was introduced and even into the era of chassisless construction (in which there is not even a vestigial frame).

CORROSION AND DESIGN

4.4 Tank construction

Some fuels, notably the alcohols, absorb water. Furthermore, hydrocarbons can react chemically with both dissolved oxygen and the alcohols, producing not only water but also chemically active hydroperoxides all of which can corrode tanks and other components in the fuel system. Mostly, however, moisture gets into fuel tanks either by overnight condensation from the air or directly by rain entering as they are being filled. To exclude potentially humid air, it is good practice to top up the tank with fuel at the end of each day. It is also possible for water to enter the bulk storage tanks from which vehicles are refuelled.

However the water entered, the outcome is usually that a few drops absorb chemical impurities from the fuel and collect in the bottom of the tank. Some of the chemicals, such as sulphur, may form highly corrosive compounds and solutions. As a result, therefore, of either chemical or electrolytic action, surprisingly rapid corrosion can occur.

It follows that steel tanks must be coated internally with a corrosion resistant material. This is why, though seemingly such simple components, they can be so costly. It also explains why soldering has been used in the past for joining the components of steel tanks, which are usually plated with tin, or Terne tin-lead alloy. Alternatives are zinc, zinc-aluminium, or Zintec coated internally. Zinc is not widely used because of the difficulty of seam-welding the flanges around the tank. Where low cost has been the prime consideration, steel tanks in a few instances, have even until relatively recently, been protected internally only by painting. To save weight, aluminium has been considered for some large tanks on heavy commercial vehicles. However it cannot be soldered, is not so easy to weld as is steel and, unless exceptionally pure, is easily corroded, especially by salt splashed up from the road in winter. Even so, a Mercedes car with an aluminium tank was introduced in 1991.

Clearly the simplest way to manufacture a fuel-tight metal tank, at least for quantity production, is to press its base into the form of a deep dish with flanges around its edges to which a shallow domed lid can be electrically seam-welded and from which it can be suspended, from either brackets or the adjacent structure. With such an arrangement, the dome contains only air, so there are no potentially leaking joints below the level of the fuel when the car is parked for long periods. Morever, the top of the tank can be carpeted to serve as part of the boot floor, though a covering of hardboard or plywood is an advantage both to protect it from damage and to form a flat surface above it. Where an exceptionally deeply drawn tank has to be used, it may have to be pressed in two stages, with an intermediate annealing process.

As intimated previously, the domed lid acts as a reserve to cater for contingencies, for example, after the tank has been filled at night and the vehicle is left the following day standing in very hot sun, so the fuel expands to occupy a significantly larger volume. Clearly, therefore, the filler tube has to extend down to a level no higher than that of top of the lower deep dished portion of the tank so that, as the fuel level rises during filling, the air trapped in the dome of the lid will cause the fuel entering to blow-back and thus to discourage overfilling. Recently, some manufacturers have incorporated buoyant ball type non-return valves in the lower ends of their filler tubes, to prevent both over-filling and blow-back.

Another consideration relating to the design of a tank is that the fuel needed for driving the vehicle off the production line, and subsequently delivering the car to the customer can represent a significant on-cost for both the manufacturer and his dealers. Consequently, some device is needed inside the tank, such as a well or collector pot into which the fuel passes preferentially, and the capacity of which is such as to enable the car to be driven reliably until only about 1 litre of fuel remains. This is an advantage, too, if ever the engine has to be restarted after a temporary refill from a small container after the tank has been inadvertently allowed to empty completely and the engine has consequently stalled.

4.5 Filling and venting requirements

With the development of plastics fuel tanks, sophisticated venting stystems became practicable. Consequently, by the early 1980s, some manufacturers, notably VW, who had been studying the requirements in great depth and establishing their design requirements, were producing some tanks of technically very advanced designs.

Among the first legal requirements to be established in the USA was that the vents must not allow fuel to spill out of the tank in the event of an accident with the vehicle, including if it is overturned. Practical considerations dictate also that fuel should not be spilled through the vents when the car is cornering, or climbing or descending on incline. A point that is liable to be overlooked is that, to position his car out of the way of other traffic, the driver might park it with the wheels on only one side on a bank by the roadside. The effect of this, especially in a hot climate where the volume of the fuel might also be temporarily increased by thermal expansion, could cause spillage with inappropriately arranged venting.

Since pistol type dispensers on service station forecourts are capable of delivering up to 60 litres/min, the tank must be vented to allow the air being displaced by the fuel to escape from it, and thus to avoid blow-back of fuel up the filler tube. Venting during filling, however, is only one of three distinctly different requirements. Another arises after the tank has been filled, perhaps late in the evening, and the car is immediately parked. The following day the temperature might rise, by as much as 40°C in some climates. Not only will the fuel expand at a rate of about 1.3% per 10°C rise, but also its vapour pressure will increase. Indeed, the pressure in a sealed tank could rise as high as 0.8 bar at 40°C (vapour pressures and boiling points of typical fuels are illustrated in Fig. 4.1). To avoid, at best, distortion and, at worst, leakage or perhaps even explosion of the tank as the pressure rises, it must be adequately vented.

With the introduction of fuel injection systems in which fuel is supplied to the injectors at rates higher than the engine can consume it, and which therefore have fuel rails in one end of which is a blow-off valve past which the excess fuel is returned to the tank, this returning fuel can be surprisingly warm. For example, after the vehicle has climbed a steep ascent, and has then been held up by traffic, with the engine idling, the high temperature of the engine will cause radiation and conduction of excessive quantities of heat

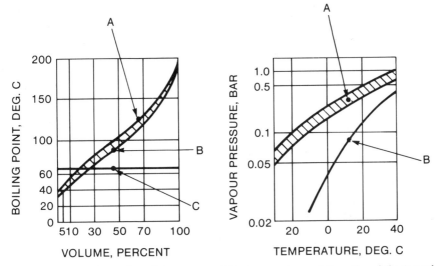

Fig 4.1   Left, boiling points of A summer and B winter grades, and C, methanol (horizontal line). Right, A and B, the summer and winter grades of a typical fuel

into the rail. Indeed, its temperature can be so high that the weight of the vapour released from it into the tank, and therefore passing out through the venting system, can in some circumstances exceed that of the fuel being consumed by the engine. In such cases, especially large carbon canisters are needed to absorb the vapour and thus prevent it from being discharged into the atmosphere. Carbon canister design is described in the Sections 13.22 to 13.25.

The third venting requirement arises as a result of fuel's being consumed as the vehicle is driven, ultimately emptying the tank. Without adequate venting, either the tank would implode or the engine would stall. In practice, it has been found that a venting capability of about 10 litres/h of air is generally adequate for preventing implosion. Although this is only a rough guide, it is a reasonably safe one since size of tank and rate of fuel consumption are in almost all instances interrelated.

4.6 Venting in practice

Consider first the requirements for venting while filling. The vent must be of a diameter large enough for the air in the tank to escape at a rate of at least 60 litres/min. When the tank is full, however, there must be enough back-pressure in the filler tube to activate the cut-off switch in the delivery pistol of the dispensing equipment.

This, of course would be difficult if the venting pipe for the parked and running conditions were too large. Consequently, each needs to be vented separately and, since emission legislation calls for low levels of evaporative emissions, the large vent for filling, phase 1, must of course be closed once filling has been completed, phase 2. For the same reason, as well as effectively to restrict the venting as the maximum permitted fuel level is attained during filling, the vent pipe for phase 2 must be limited in diameter.

To meet this requirement, VW have found that a vent restrictor of between 0.8 and 1.2 mm is a good compromise between avoiding failure of the dispensing pistol to cut-off when the tank is full at the end of a phase 1 venting operation, while maintaining adequate venting during phase 2. In a very hot climate, the rate of generation of fuel vapour in a tank can be typically as much as 600 litres/h.

Good examples how all these requirements can be met with plastics tanks are the 1984 VW Golf and Jetta models. The layout of the venting system is shown diagrammatically in Fig. 4.2. The tank itself is of moulded high density polyethylene (HDPE), and the filler neck extension is integral with the tank so that it is self supporting. This not only avoids the cost of having to attach its upper end rigidly to the bodywork but also, in the event of either a side or rear end impact, the filler neck and tank cannot be ripped apart, allowing fuel to spill out.

The VW filler tube is surrounded by a bulbous extension of the tank, serving as a chamber for accommodating thermal expansion of the fuel with increasing temperature. Thus, since a major part of the expansion volume is no longer in the top of the tank, either the top deck can be lower, to provide more space in the boot, or the depth of the tank can be increased to accommodate more fuel.

The filler tube itself extends from a funnel shape opening at the top, down to the level of the fuel in the tank when it is full. A ball-valve is accommodated in the lower end of the filler tube, the ball being of light weight so that, when the tank is full, it floats up and closes the fuel delivery port. This ensures that the delivery from the dispensing pistol is

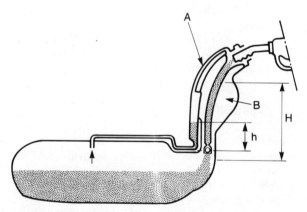

Fig. 4.2   Diagrammatic arrangement of the fuel tank of the 1984 VW Golf. In the vehicle, the vent pipes are situated forward instead of inboard of the filler neck
A: Vent, B: Ullage, H: Head of fuel in filler tube, h: Head of fuel in vent

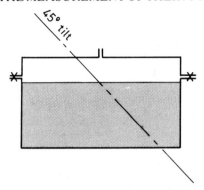

Fig. 4.3   Showing how, with a deep tank, the fuel level is well clear of a central vent, even at an angle of 45°. With a shallow tank of equal volume, it of course comes much closer, perhaps clearing it only up to about 30-35°

automatically cut off by the sudden increase in back-pressure, and overflow is further prevented by the extra capacity available in the funnel shaped section.

During filling, the outgoing air passes through a vent in the centre of the roof of the tank. A tube is connected between this vent and the base of a small vertical reservoir inboard of and parallel to the bulbous extension of the tank. From the top of this reservoir, the venting continues up through another tube into the open end of the funnel and out past the dispensing pistol.

Venting during the parked and running conditions is also effected through this tube. Because the vent is centrally positioned, the tendency for fuel to pass into it if the vehicle is on either a lateral or longitudinal incline is obviated, as can be seen from Fig. 4.3, which illustrates the principle diagrammatically. In the VW system, the lower portion of the tube is in fact in the form of a U-tube to seal the vent when the pressure differential between in and outside the tank is zero or very small, and the small vertical reservoir accommodates any excess fuel which, owing to the inertia of the incoming fuel during filling, might be forced into the system. The volume of the trap, together with action of a restrictor in the connector for the lower end of the vent pipe, ensures that the height h of the column of fuel in the trap will always be lower than that H in the filler tube. Should h, in exceptional circumstances, increase until it equals H, a hydraulic lock is formed, rendering it impossible for any more fuel to pass down the filler into the tank.

The upper end of the extension chamber is connected by a tube to a mushroom valve at a point adjacent to the lower end of the screw type filler cap. When the cap is open, this valve is closed but, as the cap is screwed home, to close the filler tube, its lower end pushes on the stem of the mushroom valve, opening it, as shown in Fig. 4.4. Consequently, when the filler cap is closed, the venting route is out through a gravity valve which, if the vehicle is turned upside down, shuts so that no fuel can escape.

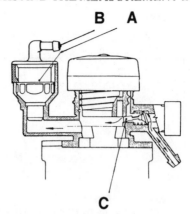

Fig. 4.4   When the filler cap is screwed home, it tilts the tank vent valve. This opens it to ensure that the tank cannot implode as the fuel is consumed. Removal of the cap, allows the spring to seat the vent valve so that the back pressure will trigger delivery cut-off in the event of the rate of filling becoming so rapid as potentially to lead to blow-back
A: Roll-over valve, B: To carbon canister, C: Tank vent valve

To meet legal requirements regarding evaporative emissions, the outlet from the valve must be taken into carbon canister vapour trap. In countries where evaporative emissions regulations are less stringent, however, it could be taken into the cavity that is closed by the filler flap. For safety, this cavity should be sealed in such a way that that neither fuel nor vapour can leak into the body.

For metal tanks, a system of venting that has been used by General Motors is to incorporate a two-way vent valve in the top of the tank. It is centrally positioned in the top panel of the tank so that, when the car is on an incline, either longitudinal or lateral, the valve will not normally be submerged below the fuel even if the tank is full. The main valve blows off to accommodate thermal expansion and vaporisation of the fuel, while a second valve housed coaxially with the first allows air to enter the tank, both to accommodate contraction with a fall in temperature of the fuel and to enable the space left by that which is consumed by the engine to be refilled with air.

With the introduction of fuel injection, in which fuel boil-off from carburettor float valves is not a consideration, the oil companies in the USA have been including increasing proportions of light fractions in the fuels they supply, even including butane and propane, to increase octane number without adding lead. Consequently, it has become necessary to set the main blow-off valve to open at a higher pressure.

Another example of a simple vent valve is that which, together with the fuel contents sender, is carried in the top cover of the 1981 VW Passat tank, Fig. 4.5. The weight of the valve is such that it compresses the light spring on which it is carried, so that it floats mid way between the upper and lower vent orifices. Should the vehicle roll over, the valve is closed by its spring as it

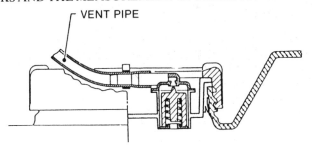

Fig. 4.5   Vent valve on the 1981 VW Passat. The screw-on top cover carries also the fuel contents sender, which is not shown here

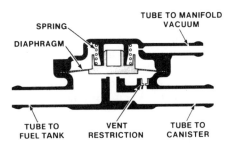

Fig. 4.6   This Delco fuel tank pressure control valve is intended for use in association with a comprehensive emissions control system

rolls up to 35° about its longitudinal axis and, by a combination of the spring and gravity from 45° onwards. This of course is to prevent any fuel from escaping.

More complex, and not necessarily mounted on the tank itself, is the GM unit for helping to control evaporative emissions, Fig. 4.6. When the engine is running, manifold depression lifts the diaphragm actuated valve open so that the vapour from the tank can vent to atmosphere or, more usually, into the carbon canister. However, when the engine is stopped, the vapour is sealed in the tank except in as much as any rise in pressure is bled off slowly, through the restriction, into the connection to the carbon canister. In the extremely unlikely event of an extraordinarily high pressure developing in the tank, it would lift the diaphragm and, again, open the main vent to the canister.

4.7   Filler necks

Compact moulded snap-in filler necks of filled acetal homopolymer resin, such as Delryn because of its good resistance to swelling and degradation by gasoline, are commonly mounted in the upper ends of the tank filler tubes, to simplify production. In some instances, these are fairly complex mouldings having anti-surge flap valves of the same material hinged inside them. Therefore, provided secure arrangements are made for venting, a low centrally mounted filler on the rear panel, which was earlier abandoned because of proneness to spillage during cornering or rapid acceleration, again becomes practicable. This had the advantage that the filler hose does not have to be dragged over the top of the car to allow it to reach a filler neck on the rear quarter remote from the dispensing pump.

Screw-caps, used with the moulded polyester or acetal filler necks need to be protected against overtightening, which could turn the filler neck out of its proper alignment or even damage it or its connection to the filler tube. When tightened, some of these filler caps therefore are designed to override a spring-loaded pawl, or ratchet like device, so that they cannot be overloaded. The external flaps that conceal filler neck assemblies are generally of metal. Nylon 66, which is easy to paint to match the colour of the surrounding metal panels, can also be used.

A German company, called Tem Tec ATV Fahrzeugtechnic Entwicklungs GmbH Vertrieb KG, has developed a moulded nylon filler neck that does not need a cap. Instead, its upper end is closed by a strong flap-valve, which is pushed open by the nozzle of the pump on the filling station forecourt, and which closes automatically when the nozzle is withdrawn. At the time of writing, however, this device has not appeared on any quantity produced car.

PLASTICS TANKS

4.8 History, design requirements and testing

Because plastics tanks are a relatively recent development, they will now be described in some detail. BASF developed the first plastics fuel tank in 1969. It was not until 1976, however, that VW pioneered its use in quantity produced cars, the first example in production being that in the 1976 Passat. The 1985 Ford Transit van was probably the first road-going commercial vehicle assembled in the UK with such a tank, though the Ford 4610 tractors produced at Basildon had plastics tanks in 1981. Later, the Ford tractors introduced in October 1985, had two plastics fuel tanks, one each side. They are interconnected, Fig. 4.7, so that both can be filled from one side and there is no risk of one tank emptying and the engine consequently stalling, before the driver has had time to switch over to the other tank. The gauge is of course calibrated to indicate the total volume of fuel in both tanks.

The legal situation is that the UK regulations stating that tanks must be of metal has been overriden by ECE Regulation 34. Annex 5 of this Regulation stipulates the tests that must be passed by plastics tanks to ensure their acceptability for use in road vehicles.

Surprisingly, it is virtually certain that many of the metal tanks in cars would fail some of these tests. For instance, in the impact test, a pendulum with a 15 kg steel head at its lower end is swung against the tank filled with a

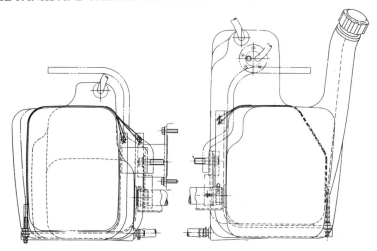

Fig. 4.7   Ford fit two plastics tanks, one each side, on some of their tractors. At sump level, they are interconnected towards the front by a small diameter hose and, slightly higher and further back, a larger diameter one to ensure rapid equalisation of the contents during filling

water-glycol anti-freeze mixture at $-40 \pm 2°C$, and fixed and supported as it would be in the road vehicle. The tank must absorb, without being penetrated, an energy of not less than 30 Nm. This would probably rupture a steel tank. The head has to be of pyramid shape on a square base with equilateral triangular faces, and its apex must be ground to a radius of 3 mm. In the USA, one specification decrees that the tank, filled as above, must not crack or leak after having been dropped from a height of 6 m in any orientation (i.e., on its corners, etc).

Among the other ECE requirements are a leak-test at 0.3 bar and $53 \pm 2°C$ for five hours, a permeability test and a fire test. In the latter, a tray of gasoline (15 litres/m^2 pan area) is kept burning for two minutes beneath a tank filled with fuel to 50% of its rated capacity. This is intended to represent an accident in which a severe spillage of fuel has caught fire beneath the vehicle. Consequently, for the test, the height of the tank above the surface of the petrol must equal the ground clearance beneath the tank when installed in the vehicle.

The regulations require also, a temperature-resistance test to be made at an ambient temperature of $95 \pm 2°C$ for one hour, but with the tank half full of water. At the end of each of these tests, there must be no leakage from the tank. The Japanese regulations, incidentally, are similar.

4.9   Evaporative emissions

As regards permeability, under the European and Japanese regulations on permeability in force almost up to the time of writing, the permissible loss was no more than 20 gm of fuel per 24 hours, over a period of 8 weeks, from a half filled sealed tank at a temperature of $40 \pm 2°C$, and at an internal pressure equal to ambient. However, the American EPA Regulation, Part 86, Control of Air Pollution from Motor Vehicles, Evaporative Emission Regulations, has now imposed stringent regulations limiting, as its name indicates, the total evaporative emissions from vehicles. Obviously, other countries are likely to follow along the same lines.

Under this regulation, what is termed the SHED (Sealed Housing Evaporations Determination) test has to be performed. The official specification for the test comprises six pages in closely printed small type, so what follows here is only a very brief resumé. First, the vehicle has to be taken through a complex preparation and preconditioning process, representing a period of normal running followed by part refuelling and parking either overnight or during daytime. This takes 14 hours or more, during the last ten of which it is parked. Only then is it then placed in an enclosure, or shed, in which the environment is controlled within certain limits. Generally, the shed is a light structure housed in a larger building in which the environment is controlled. It is large enough only to house the vehicle, with a little working space around it.

If the fuel tank were full, the rate of evaporation from it could be unrealistically low, possibly because either the exposed surface might be smaller, or the atmosphere in the smaller ullage space more highly saturated with vapour, or both. Consequently, it has to be about 40% full and, on starting the test, at a temperature of between $16 \pm 1.1°C$. Over the 1 hour duration of the test, however, its temperature is increased progressively, by $13.3 \pm 0.5°C$, by what is in effect an electric blanket beneath the tank. At the end of this period, the atmosphere in the shed is sampled so that the evaporative emissions in it can be measured. This first phase is called the *Diurnal Breathing Loss Test*.

Incidentally, the thermal output from the hot blanket is intended to represent heat radiated to the tank from the tarmac beneath the vehicle when parked in hot sun. This is of course almost certainly the worst possible case as regards evaporative emissions.

Then follows immediately the second phase, which is termed the *Hot Soak Test*. The car is removed from the sealed housing, or shed and put on to a chassis dynamometer, to be re-run through part of the EPA Test Schedule, which amounts to about 11.5 miles. It is then returned to the sealed housing for a further hour after which the emissions are again measured. This is to represent the losses when the vehicle is parked with the engine hot after a normal run. Over the two hours (two phases of the test) in the sealed housing, the weight of the emissions from the whole car must not exceed 2 gm. Since a high density polyethylene (HDPE) tank can account for a significant proportion of the total, its permeability is of major concern to the manufacturer, especially bearing in mind that 1.5 gm of hydrocarbons can be lost during a two hour test of a typical car having a steel tank and electronic fuel injection (no float chamber emissions).

4.10   Plastics tank materials and design

The main reason for fitting plastics tanks is to obtain a larger capacity than is practicable with steel ones. This advantage arises because the plastics tank is moulded and therefore can be more readily shaped to fit exactly into the space available than a pressed steel one. For example, on a rear wheel drive vehicle, it might be moulded to fit between the rear wheelarches and, perhaps, be dished in two places to clear a spare wheel and the final-drive casing, Fig. 4.8.

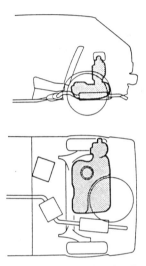

Fig. 4.8   A major advantage of plastics tanks is the fact that they can be moulded to clear items such as final drives, suspension components and spare wheels

Although cross-linked polyethylene has the best mechanical properties, it cannot be fusion welded and so is not used. The material pioneered for this application by BASF, and now widely employed, is high density polyethylene, for example Lupolen 4261, for blow-moulding, and medium density polyethylene for rotational moulding. To keep material costs down, it is desirable to re-cyle some rejects and off-cuts obtained when trimming mouldings. However, a certain quality level is essential for ensuring that the finished product, especially where welded, will meet all the test requirements and have adequate mechanical strength, impermeability, durability, fatigue resistance, and give reliable service. It is therefore necessary to limit the proportion of reground re-cycled material fed with the fresh stock into the moulding machine.

Since plastics tanks, if thick enough to withstand the fire and impact tests, will not necessarily flex easily enough to be sprung out of the moulds in which they are produced, draw angles must be incorporated in their design, to facilitate extraction. Thicknesses range from about 4 to 8 mm, but the trend is upwards from the 4 mm figure, to meet the fire test requirements. It is, however, permissible to use metal screening to enable the tank to pass the fire test, provided this screening is also a permanent feature in the vehicle. This measure may be necessary for the connections between pipes and the tank, especially where the pipes are of plastics and are simply a push-fit into them or are of metal with an elastic sleeve slid over them for making the connections.

Another test that plastics tanks have to pass is that of ECE regulation 34, as laid down in Annexes 3 and 4. These annexes cover front and rear impact tests at about 50 km/h with the tank installed in the vehicle. For this reason, it is important that there shall be no sharp edges of metal around the tank installation, that could pierce the plastics in a crash.

4.11   Plastics tank production

Two methods of manufacturing plastics tanks may be employed: extrusion blow-moulding, and rotational moulding. With either, the tank can be moulded in one piece. Vacuum moulding is not used because it would entail moulding in two pieces and then joining the halves together. Rotational moulding can be the more economical for limited quantities of small tanks, because the tooling costs are lower for quantities of up to 50,000. The last mentioned limit applies only where more than one component can be produced simultaneously on one rotary machine.

Owing to the absence of stretching of the material in the mould, uniform wall-thickness can be reasonably well maintained provided the tank is not too large and its shape is not such as to obstruct local flow of the plastics during rotation. On the other hand, although there is a tendency for a hard skin to form on both the interior and exterior surfaces, the material in between can be of doubtful consistency. Consequently, this process tends to be favoured only for development test vehicles, relatively large numbers of which may be built by large multi-national automotive manufacturers. The advantage is that a low cost tank can be utilised in test vehicles, leaving only the blow moulded production version of the tank to be proved, which can be done largely by rig testing.

For quantity production, extrusion blow moulding is employed. A tube of the high density polyethylene (HDPE), termed a *parison*, is extruded vertically downwards from the head. Compressed air is then introduced into it from below, above or even the side, and a female mould closed radially on to it. This moulds the tube into the shape of the tank and, during the last few cm of closure, pinches together some of the material between the flats that surround the impression of the tank in the halves of the mould. Approximately 30% of this flattened material is then cut off and reground for subsequent recycling. With this method, dependent on the air pressure in the parison and shape of the mould, there need not be any significant local thinning of the walls due to stretching.

4.12   Meeting evaporative emissions requirements

So far, the manufacturing process just described has been satisfactory and meets the requirements of EEC Regulations EME 34, Annex 5, as regards impact and general mechanical strength, high temperature, fire resistance, and permeability. However, most cars with HDPE tanks can only just pass the EPA permeability test, leaving minimal margins of safety to cover variations in production, especially with fuels containing oxygenates. Consequently, chemical barrier treatments are used but, over long periods in service, some tend to lose effectiveness.

Originally, there were two such treatments: one, at the time of writing favoured by Ford, Volvo and Saab, entails the use of sulphur trioxide; the other, in which fluorine is used, has been applied to tanks for some Daimler-Benz, VW, and French manufacturers' models. In all instances, the gases are introduced during blow moulding, to form a chemical barrier coating inside the tank. Sulphur trioxide, however, leaves a residue of sulphuric acid, which must be washed out, while the fluorine, even though diluted, is extremely toxic. Therefore both entail not only careful cleansing of the tank after the treatment, but also investment in costly ancillary equipment and the disposal of poisonous waste.

4.13   A simple, non-toxic barrier sealing process

A much better process, which is non-toxic, though possibly more costly, has been developed by Du Pont, who call it Laminar Barrier Technology. Up to about 4-5% of a barrier resin called Selar RB is moulded into the HDPE, where it forms a virtually impermeable lamination of closely packed overlapping platelets, Fig. 4.9. Other resins can be used, provided a suitable copolymer can be found to render them compatible with the HDPE.

Selar RD, developed initially as a barrier against unleaded gasoline, is basically a nylon 66/6 copolymer. Another copolymer is being developed for use as a barrier against ethanol and methanol fuel blends. A 15% blend of methanol in gasoline is the most permeable to HDPE and therefore is used

Fig. 4.9   Sealing with Selar RB is a one-shot injection blow moulding process in which a layer of overlapping nylon platelets (bottom right corner) within the HDPE forms a barrier against permeation by the fuel, represented by arrows

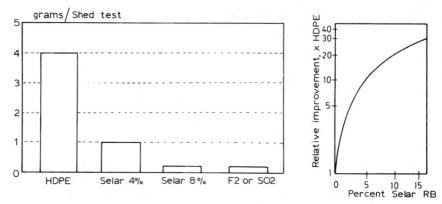

Fig. 4.10   Left, a column chart showing the relative permeability of HDPE untreated, and treated with 4% and 8% Selar RB, fluoride and sulphur dioxide. Right, curve showing reduction in permeability obtained as the proportion of Selar RB is increased

in tests on new materials. However, because other problems (described in Section 3.4) arise with blends of such alcohols, it seems that blends of about 7% will be most appropriate, at least in the medium term.

Only 4% of the Selar RB is needed to reduce the permeability of a car in the EPA test to about a quarter of its value with an untreated HDPE tank. The degree of permeability obtained can be controlled by varying, between about 3 and 8%, the proportion of barrier resin introduced, Fig, 4.10. However, a 4% concentration is the optimum and is so effective that if a shed test shows a need for a higher resistance to permeation, other areas of the fuel system should be examined before considering uprating the tank.

4.14   Method of lamination of Selar RB

For laminating Selar RB, standard blow moulding equipment is employed, but with a specially designed and patented low energy, moderate compression ratio screw in the extruder. This screw has no dispersive elements such as pins or kneading blocks, so that the Selar RB is introduced as discrete overlapping platelets within the HDPE. To enable the tank to pass the 6 m drop-test at −40°C, a fairly wide pinch-off flange is required between its halves. This is so that, during the closing of the mould on to the pinch-off, the HDPE is squeezed locally from between the laminations of

Fig. 4.11   The dimensions of the mould pinch line should be such that the layers of nylon platelets are bonded together as they approach the ground off end of the joint. Slightly recessing the joint reduces the stresses induced at the joint line during a drop test and presents a relatively unobstructed surface profile for ease of installation

Selar RB and backfills into the region of the inner edge of the junction between the halves. Consequently, the nylon laminations in the halves of the tank bond together, Fig. 4.11, leaving the strength of the pinch-off joint equal to that of a straight section of the tank.

4.15 Advantages of Laminar Barrier technique

With this process, the tanks are made by a one-step non-corrosive extrusion process in which the modified nylon is dry-blended with the HDPE using standard blow moulding machines. Consequently, in contrast with the chemical barrier treatments, the only extra investment required is that for the screw and, perhaps, slight modification of tools. The moulder is not faced with any problems as regards safety or disposal of toxic waste. Nor is there any likelihood of operator objection. Cost savings can benefit both the moulder and vehicle builder. Furthermore, the vehicle builder could even install a blow moulding machine alongside his assembly line, and thus save the cost of shipping tanks, containing nothing but large volumes of air, from a distant supplier.

Finally, quality control is simple and effective. Du Pont has developed two non-destructive tests capable of being completed in a minute or so, on the line. The simplest is an ultrasonic test by means of which simply the presence of the platelets can be verified. However, in the more comprehensive test, a fibre-optic probe is used in conjunction with a small computer programmed to assess, by spectral analysis, the lamination thickness, barrier resin concentration, and shape and distribution of the platelets, and to compare the results with data regarding corresponding permeability values in its memory. This quantifies the actual barrier properties to an accuracy of about 90%, which is vastly better than the procedure, used following the other treatments, which entails sectioning the tank and measuring the concentration of the chemicals. It can produce an accurate and meaningful result virtually instantly, thus avoiding production of tanks that subsequently have to be scrapped, and the consequent increased costs and loss of confidence in the product.

Hot-plate fusion-welding is employed for attaching brackets, pipe fittings and, in many instances, filler tubes to the tank. If the filler tube can be positioned so that it is bisected diametrically along its length by the parting line of the mould, it may be possible to incorporate it integrally with the rest of the tank. This has the advantage that it is generally unnecessary to attach the upper end to the body structure. For various reasons, however, the alternative of friction-welding circular polyethylene components to the tank is a better approach.

4.16 Plastics tank construction and assembly

A method of fixing to the tank the sub-assembly comprising the fuel gauge sender, fuel take off pipe and, if fitted, return pipe and submerged electric lift pump, is to mount it on a circular steel plate, which seats on a seal on a metal ring moulded into the top of the tank. The periphery of the ring is threaded to receive a ring-nut for holding the circular plate down on the sealing ring. In some instances, plastics ring-nuts have been screwed on to threads around a ring that is part of the tank moulding. If a steel ring and nut are used, the former could be moulded integrally into the top of the tank, but a good alternative is first to injection mould a polyethylene ring around it and then hot-plate weld the polyethylene ring to the tank. This simplifies the tank moulding, and facilitates making provision for the differential rates of expansion of the plastics and steel parts.

When designing plastics tanks in which metal components are incorporated it is necessary to bear in mind that the difference between the coefficients of thermal expansion of the plastics and the metal affects the overlap needed between the edges of the components. On the other hand, the coefficient of expansion of the plastics is not so different from that of the fuel, so the ullage space needed as provision for expansion is smaller than that in a metal tank, and the fuel capacity correspondingly larger relative to the total volume of the installation.

Two alternative methods of fixing the various components inside the tank have been used. One is to pass the sub-assembly through the top plate and screw it into a bayonet fitting attached to the floor of the tank. Such a method of attachment is perhaps easier in a metal than a plastics tank. The second method is the thermal bonding of a collector pot in the base of the tank during the blow moulding process.

Other components, can be either moulded integrally into the tank or, for example, ultrasonically welded on to it. Usually a metal filler neck is inserted into the upper end of the filler tube, since such a component, carrying the filler cap and various vent-tubes and, in some instances, non-return, blow-off and anti-implosion valves, is easier to make of metal. In many countries, unleaded fuel is becoming obligatory for vehicles having engines that can accept it. In these circumstances, both leaded and unleaded fuels are available at filling stations, but the dispenser nozzles for dispensing unleaded fuel on the forecourts may be of smaller diameter than those for leaded fuel, and cars that are designed for unleaded fuel have filler necks with restrictor plates or smaller apertures, so that only the dispenser guns for unleaded fuel can be inserted into them. This, however, is likely to be only a temporary measure, since unleaded fuel will almost certainly become universal in the course of little more than ten years.

Whereas metal tanks can be bolted up to the chassis or body structure, plastics ones are generally slung on steel straps. These are most conveniently held in store if they are flat. However, when a flat strap is wrapped round a rectangular tank, it tends to retain a partly circular shape: in other words, it will not seat snugly against the flat sides of the tank and is therefore difficult to locate and to retain in its correct position and, as dynamic loading causes the tank to settle, it may become loose in service. One method of overcoming this problem is to have, beside the assembly track, a jig on which the straps can be bent to the required shape prior to installation.

4.17   The advantages of plastics tanks

In addition to the previously mentioned ease with which a plastics tank of adequate capacity can be fitted into what ever space is available almost regardless of its shape, and then filled to a higher level, a number of other advantages accrue from the use of plastics. For instances, fatigue failures of such tanks are virtually unknown. This is attributable to three effects: first, the walls of plastics tanks are thicker (4 mm plus, as compared with about 0.8 mm for steel) and therefore stiffer than those of metal tanks; secondly, the inherent damping of the plastics material keeps amplitudes of vibration low; and, thirdly, if resonance occurs, the vibration generates heat in the plastics and the consequent local softening detunes it, causing it to drop out of resonance.

Plastics tanks do not suffer corrosion problems. Moreover, they are light in weight—a 4 mm thick HDPE tank can be 30% lighter than a 0.8 mm thick steel one of the same capacity, Fig. 4.12. The tooling cost for a steel tank is much higher than that for a plastics one, the overall cost of which can also be lower. On the other hand, unless the total installation cost is taken into account, misleading conclusions can be drawn: for instance, for a plastics tank, one generally has to produce also special support and protection brackets and then to assemble it on to them. The flanged rim of a pressed steel tank can be a useful bonus so far as ease of mounting is concerned.

Finally, some claim that a plastics tank is even safer than a steel one. The ground on which this claim is made is that whereas, under incendiary conditions, pressure can build up in a steel tank and a catastrophic rupture occur, causing its burning contents to be sprayed around and thoroughly mixed with the ambient air, the plastics tank softens before such a high pressure can be generated so it collapses rather than bursts, and the

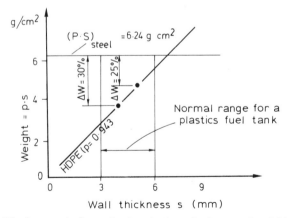

Fig. 4.12   BASF, who were the first to develop plastics tanks, have produced this graph showing the weight per cm³ of HDPE sheet, compared with steel sheet used for tanks (horizontal line at the top). For heavy duty applications, for example tractors, untreated HDPE tanks may have to be as thick as 8 mm

subsequent burning of the fuel it contains is of a progressive rather than an explosive nature.

INSIDE FUEL TANKS

4.18   Connections, drainage, instrumentation and surge pots

The uninitiated tend to think of a fuel tank, especially a metal one, as simply a box, possibly with some baffles in it to prevent the fuel from surging back and forth and from side to side. However, there is indeed much more to it than that. The outlet pipe to the engine may be taken from a small sump in the base of the tank, not only to enable maximum use to be made of its contents but also, as previously explained, to form a reservoir so that when the vehicle is on an incline, its engine will not be temporarily starved from fuel if the level in the tank is very low. There may be special provision for draining off any water that might collect in the base of the sump, though a simple drain plug is mostly used.

The outlet, or fuel take-off pipe may have a small filter on its lower end. Such a filter is generally of the non-ferrous metal gauze type, or a woven plastics, perhaps polyester, fine enough to prevent water from passing through.

A drain plug may never be used unless the tank has to be emptied prior to doing welding repairs on or near it, but in some dusty or very humid territories, its presence in the base of the well can be extremely reassuring to the owner. Obviously, the lower end of the outlet pipe and its filter must not come down too close to the plug, otherwise any water or debris that might have collected above it could either block the filter or, if none is fitted, enter the pipe. In some instances, the lower end of the fuel take-off pipe and filter assembly are telescopically attached to the connection to a submerged electric fuel pump, and spring loaded to press it down on to the floor of the tank. In this case, the function of the sump may be simply to trap any water that has contaminated the fuel and to keep it clear of the end of the pick-up pipe.

The tank also has to house a sensor, or sender, to serve the instrumentation for measuring its contents and, in some instances, an electrically driven fuel lift pump. These components are inserted as single sub-assembly, through an aperture in or near the top of the tank or, in a very few instances, mounted directly on the bottom of the tank or, even more rarely, on a cover plate bolted up to it.

4.19   Some recent developments

Plastics tanks have introduced some entirely new situations and requirements For instance, a plastics tank under the rear seats is of necessity wide and shallow. As a result, when the level in the tank has fallen and vehicle is on a road having a steep camber, and especially when cornering, all the fuel may swill to one side, leaving the end of the take-up pipe high and dry. To counter this, some manufacturers install inside the tank a large cylindrical surge-pot, usually having an open top, to surround the submerged petrol pump and its take-up pipe. Acetal homopolymer tends to be the favoured material for these pots, on account of its resistance to hydrocarbon fuels and ease of moulding to complex shapes. It is generally ultrasonically welded to the bottom of the tank but, as previously mentioned, it has also been inserted into the parison during, and bonded in position immediately prior to the end of the blow moulding operations.

In a square tank, holes or slots in the sides of the pot, but at the level of its base, allow the fuel to flow in and out. In wide flat tanks, however, they may be in the front and rear walls of the pot, so that the fuel does not flow out when the vehicle is cornering or running on a camber. In all cases, the holes are of a size such that the pot is filled at a rate much faster than that at which fuel is being consumed by the engine but will not empty rapidly under lateral or fore-and-aft acceleration.

An even more effective variant on this theme is in the VW Passat. The pot in this tank has two rectangular funnel shape ducts near its base, one on each

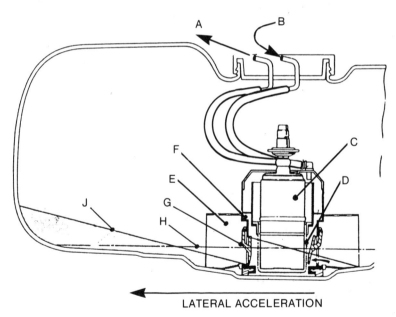

LATERAL ACCELERATION

4.13   The 1981 VW Passat tank, showing the effect of lateral acceleration on the fuel level in an almost empty tank with non-return flap-valves in rectangular collector ducts leading into the central pot
A: Fuel out, B: Fuel return, C: Electric fuel pump, D: Filter, E: Rectangular section collector ducts, F: Surge pot, G: Non-return flap-valve, closed, H: Static fuel level, tank almost empty, J: Fuel level when displaced by lateral acceleration

side, Fig. 4.13, with a non-return flap-valve in the aperture in the wall of the pot, to which the small ends of these funnels are welded. The open end of each duct is feathered and presses down on the floor of the tank so that, until the tank is virtually completely empty, it will continue to scoop up the residue of fuel swilling from side to side and direct it through the flap-valve into the surge pot.

4.20 Special requirements for fuel injection systems

An entirely different problem arises with fuel injection systems in which the gasoline for the injectors is drawn from a continuously circulating supply passed through a fuel manifold. If the fuel contains oxygenates, the surplus returning to the tank tends to be degraded, or soured, by the heat to which it has been subjected: chemically active hydroperoxides are formed in it, and

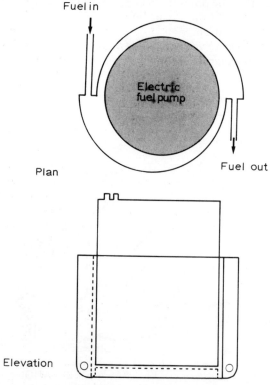

Fig. 4.14 *Returning fuel enters the surge pot tangentially and is cooled as it swirls around it, before being recirculated by the pump to the engine. The return pipe may be higher so that the warm fuel, tending to rise, will be better cooled before it sinks again to the pump inlet. If it is too high, however, hot fuel splashing into an almost empty tank would increase the rate of vaporisation. A small hole in the wall of the pot restricts the rate of flow from it when the vehicle is turning, braking or accelerating*

these can corrode or degrade some of the components of the fuel system. More details on the souring of petrol were given in Section 2.8.

To allow the warm fuel returning to drop down on to the surface would increase both its exposure to oxygen as the tank emptied and the generation of vapour. Moreover, the sooner the contaminated fuel can be cooled and then recirculated to the injection system and burned the better. These requirements can be met by returning fuel tangentially into the base of the swirl pot, Fig. 4.14, which may be a simple variation of the surge pot. This also cools the potentially sour fuel, restricts its exposure to oxygen, and also confines it to the region around the take-off pipe. Obviously such a pot should be made of a plastics, for example an acetal homopolymer such as Delrin, that is resistant to degradation by hydroperoxides.

In some General Motors cars, the return flow from the fuel rail on the engine is passed into the base of an acetal homopolymer collector pot in the tank, and is augmented by fuel drawn in from the tank by means of a venturi through which the return flow passes. The augmentation fuel enters through a radial port in the neck of the venturi, where the reduction in pressure due to the flow through it is at a maximum. A recent development, however, has been to drive the pump by a brushless motor, the speed of which is varied by the electronic engine-management system, to match the fuelling requirements of the engine as its speed and load vary, so that little is returned to the tank. A collector pot is still used, but fuel from the tank enters simply through a hole in its base.

4.21   Fuel contents gauging

Accurate gauging of fuel contents is extremely difficult. This is because of manufacturing tolerances, variations in temperature, and the complex shapes of some modern tanks which, as implied previously, may be fitted into spaces available around the independent rear suspension systems now almost universal. Aggravating the situation is the fact that the trend towards the introduction of on-board computers for the display of information, including average fuel consumption, is giving rise to a demand for more accurate measurement of tank contents than ever before.

4.22   Swinging arm type sensor

Until the late 1970s, almost all tank contents sensors comprised a bell crank lever, the long arm of which carried a float resting on, and rising and falling with the, surface of the fuel, Fig. 4.15. Its shorter arm swept over an arc-shape rheostat around the pivot. The resistance of the electrical circuit through the rheostat and the bell-crank arm to earth was an indication of the level of the fuel in the tank so, because almost all tanks were of rectangular form, calibration of the instrument to indicate the approximate volume of the contents was relatively easy. Early rheostats were wire-wound, but the modern versions have thick-film resistors, which are more durable, easier to

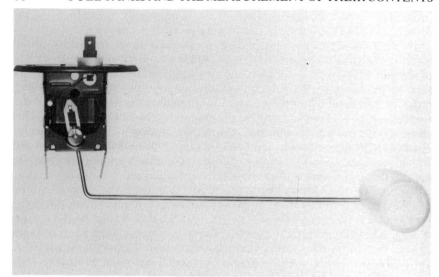

Fig. 4.15   A VDO float-and-arm type fuel level sensor sectioned to show its wire wound rheostat

Fig. 4.16   This VDO float-and-arm type sensor has been sectioned to show the thick film rheostat, a printed circuit board for which is shown to a larger scale above

produce in large quantities, and fairly readily calibrated for reading the contents of tanks of slightly irregular shapes.

The thick-film resistor circuits, of silver-paladium, are printed on to ceramic plates. They can be of either a zig-zag or a plain arc form, according to the magnitude of the resistance required. Mostly, a zig-zag is needed, but one or more printed resistors of fairly long rectangular shape are incorporated in the arc, Fig. 4.16. Such resistors can be easily calibrated by trimming, to compensate for irregularities in the shape of the tank. Trimming is affected by using a laser to cut a slot into the end of the resistor, and thus to change it from a rectangular into a U-shape resistor. The circuit, which originally ran straight through that end, then has to pass round the U-shape, which increases the effective length of the resistor and thus its resistance.

4.23   Float tube type sensor

A more recent development is the float tube type sensor, Fig. 4.17. It has a wire rheostat either vertically stretched or wound in the bore of a vertical plastics tube. This is traversed by a conductive flexible pick-up on periphery of a cylindrical float inside the tube. During its vertical motion, radial location of the float relative to the tube is effected by a stem passing co-axially through a hole through its centre. Another pickup, connected between the float and the stem, completes the circuit.

This type has the advantages of simplicity and compactness and being less vulnerable to damage, both on the vehicle assembly line and in service. It is

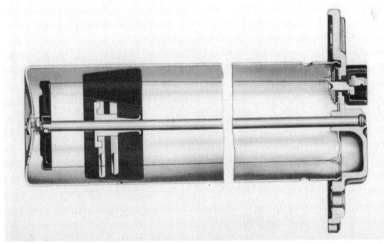

Fig. 4.17   VDO float-in-tube type sensor with a guided float carrying brushes that complete the circuit between a wire and the guide rod. Alternatives include winding the wire around inside the tube or substituting for it a printed thick film resistor. The height of the float defines the quantity of fuel in the tank. This unit is of course installed with its axis vertical.

easier to accommodate in most tanks. Moreover, the effects of surge in the tank can be easily obviated by sealing its ends and piercing small holes in the side of the tube to restrict the rate of flow of the fuel into and out of the tube.

4.24   A compound sensor

Ease of accommodation of a tube sensor is not, however, universal. In at least one vehicle having fuel tanks over the rear wheel arches, a combination of two sensors has been used. One is of the float-tube type, measuring the content in the lower part of the tank, while the other is a float-arm sensor measuring that in the upper part, because it was impracticable to install a float tube alone that would cater for measurement throughout both. The two sensors are mounted on a complex plastics moulding incorporating the filler and vent tubes and also carrying the electric fuel pump and filter. This, however, is a complicated and far from ideal arrangement, so a much simpler system was developed.

4.25   The electrothermal sensor

The latest sensor is the electrothermal type, which is simply a resistor circuit printed on to a plastics ribbon. Measurement is based on passing an electric current through the circuit. The resistance is dependent on the temperature of the conductor and therefore on what proportion of it is immersed in the fuel. Consequently, either the current flowing or the voltage drop across the circuit can be taken as a measure of the contents of the tank.

The ribbon can be housed in either a rigid, Fig. 4.18, or a flexible tube, in which case, it can be bent to pass into a hole in, for example, the side of a tank. In either, the circuit can be readily designed to match irregularities in the shape of the tank, and the complete sub-assembly, including other components such as filters and pumps, can be easily inserted into the tank.

This system has many other advantages. It is fully compatible with the electronic circuits in on-board computers and display devices. Damping by means of small holes in the tube in which it is housed, to allow the fuel restricted entry, obviates the effect of surge. The sensor is simple, compact, and is suitable for virtually any type of fuel, or indeed any other liquids, and has no moving parts at all.

Fig. 4.18   A VDO electro-thermal fuel contents indicator. The resistance of the resistor printed on to tape extending down the tube varies with its temperature, which is a function of the depth immersed

Chapter 5

Transferring the Fuel from Tank to Metering Unit

Although a single lift pump is normally used to transfer the fuel from the tank through the pipes to the carburettor, two may serve fuel to some injection systems. Traditionally, the pipes have been of a corrosion resistant metal such as copper but, in recent years, alloys of copper but, more especially, tin-coated steel have been most widely employed. Aluminium is not normally considered because it is neither adequately resistant to corrosion, particularly where it may come into contact with salt spray, nor to fatigue or chafing in installations where the pipes are subjected to vibration.

Now, however, a much wider range of materials, including plastics such as fluoro-elastomers and nitrile rubbers, are coming into use, either alone or as composites. The advantages of pipes made of suitable plastics include ease of connection, light weight, absence of corrosion and, because of their thickness and relatively good bearing properties, resistance also to leakage as a result of chafing. They can even be less costly, especially when handling and connection into the system are taken into account.

An important point needs to be borne in mind in relation to fuel injection systems in which the fuel is supplied at constant pressure in quantities larger than are needed by the engine, and there is therefore a constant return flow, of possibly fairly warm fuel, to the tank. It is that, if oxygenates are blended with the hydrocarbons, Section 2.8, hydroperoxides may be formed in the circulating fuel and these can attack some materials used for pipes. If inadequately protected steel pipes are used, these not only can corrode them but also cause the plating to flake off and block carburettor jets and injectors and even filters. Among plastics, the fluoro-elastomers are resistant to blends of methanol with hydrocarbons.

A requirement of major importance is that the bore of the pipe, metal or steel, shall not become contaminated with scale, corrosion or any other type of fouling since the fouling will inevitably break free and, possibly, block filters and the fuel metering equipment. Hydroperoxides can be very destructive of plated metal pipes, but methods of plating, notably using nickel on copper, have been improved to combat this problem, but of course they cost more. Were this not so, there would be little incentive to consider plastics pipes.

In general, care has to be taken to ensure that the pipe slopes continuously upwards from tank to engine, to avoid vapour or air lock. Furthermore, it must not sag or kink at any point, or water may be trapped in it and, in very cold weather, freeze and cause a total blockage.

Where the upper end of the pipe has to be connected to the carburettor or injection equipment, flexibility is necessary, to accommodate the rocking of the engine on its flexible mountings. With plastics pipes and connector sleeves, static electricity can be a problem: although the energies of such discharges across connections from the pipes to metal components are unlikely to be high enough to cause a fire, they might, by erosion of the pipes, eventually cause leaks. However, carbon impregnated grades of plastics can be used to obviate risk of static accumulation and sparking.

PLASTICS PIPES, FUEL RAILS

5.1   Requirements for elastomeric pipes

It is essential that plastics and elastomeric pipes for fuel systems are not degraded under the influence of both hydrocarbon or alcohol fuels and their additives. Other important factors include:

(1) Resistance to permeation and to high temperatures
(2) Absence of swelling
(3) Absence of any tendency to harden, become brittle and crack
(4) Retention of flexibility at low temperatures, and resistence to compression set.

Non-flammability is also a marked advantage and, in some countries, a legal requirement. Owing to the length of piping in some fuel systems, and particularly the fact that return flows from injection equipment may be warm, permeation is a serious consideration for meeting legal requirements (Sections 4.8 and 4.9).

Temperature resistance is of course important in engine compartments and where pipe runs go close to exhaust system components, including catalytic converters, but it also has a bearing on safety in the event of a fire. After all, what is the purpose of subjecting the tank to a fire test if the pipes connected to it will fail that test? A factor easily overlooked is that, if the pipe were to soften with rising temperature, it could sag on to a hot spot, on for example the engine, and weaken or melt and cause a serious fire.

Swelling, too is usually accompanied by softening and can lead to mechanical failure of the pipe, as also can hardening and cracking as a result of either ageing or subjection to low temperatures. Compression set should be marginal or zero, otherwise the security of squeeze type fastening devices or clamps may be impaired.

5.2   Plastics materials

A major problem faced by those considering substitution of new materials for existing ones is not only their cost but also that of the development needed to prove that not only will they be adequate in the first instance but also will not deteriorate significantly in the long term. Among the factors that need to be taken into consideration is how such materials behave when the fuels they might have to carry include either pure alcohols or blends of them, notably methanol, with the hydrocarbons.

Table 5.1 PROPERTIES OF SOME FLUORO-ELASTOMERS

Type	ASTM Spec	% Flourine	Properties
Dipolymer	FKM-EGOC	66	Satisfactory for straight hydrocarbon fuels
Terpolymer	FKM-6173	68	Resistant to swell and permeation in up to 85% methanol, and to compression set at high temps.
Terpolymer	FKM-6191	70	Low swell in methanol blends up to 85%
Tetrapolymer	FKM-GLT	65	Superior as regards flexibility and compression set at low temperatures, and resistance to swell in methanol blends
Tetrapolymer	FKM-GFLT	67	Ditto

Indeed, the selection of plastics for meeting all the requirements, including for both hot soak and for start-up, perhaps at $-30°C$ or lower, is a complex task so the advice of experts in the pastics field is needed. For instance, although the fluoro-elastomers, to ASTM specification FKM-E60, which contain 66% fluorine dipolymer, are good, there are newer ones such as the tetrapolymer FKM-GFLT that are better. All are available under the trade name Viton, though as different grades. For good performance at low temperatures, the last two listed in Table 5.1 are the best. However, a compromise has always to be made between swell resistance and low temperature flexibility, the latter affecting sealing capability.

Nylon 11 and 12 as well as 66 have been and in some instances still are used, but they present some problems, mainly because they are flammable. Also, however, they are hard and fairly rigid when cold but soften as their temperatures increase. This can make assembly difficult, since the temperature may vary widely from winter to summer. Moreover, in the engine compartment, where the route can be very complicated, it may come very close to heater pipes or be subjected to radiation from exhaust systems or turbochargers, the heat from which, as previously mentioned, can cause it to sag. Safety being an overriding consideration, this must not happen. Nylon 66, for example, produced by Du Pont as Zytel, is available in a wide range of grades, including some with added impact resistance and flexibility: 66/6 halogenated for flame retardancy, 612 for low moisture absorbency. Their melting points range from 255°C for nylon 66, to 232 and 212°C respectively for the flame retardant and 612 grades. ACI Griflex Creators Ltd, who manufacture both flexible and rigid hoses of Nylon 11 and 12, quote working pressures of 43 kg/cm^2 at 20°C, and 22.8 kg/cm^2 at 60°C, based on a factor of safety of 4:1. Maximum working temperatures for limited periods range from about 120 to 140°C. Tecalemit produce Nylon 12 pipes sheathed with Monsanto Santoprene, for flame resistance.

High quality tubing of other materials is available and employed. These include thick walled nitrile rubber, or even costly co-extrusions such as a Viton-lined Hypalon nitrile rubber, in some instances reinforced with glass fibre, polyester or even stainless steel braid. Viton, the costly component, gives excellent resistance to degradation by ozone and fuel. It contains halogen and is therefore flame retardant, but it will burn if continuously exposed to flame, as incidentally will flame retarded nylon. In dynamic conditions it is suitable for use at temperatures down to about −23°C, in static conditions at least −40°C, and should give satisfactory service at over 230°C. The nitrile rubber is strong, elastic and resistant to ozone, weathering, heat and compression set.

Braided nitrile rubber tubing has also been used. The braiding enables thinner rubber tubing to be used, so the pipe can be more flexible. Because of its good performance at fairly high temperatures, nitrile rubber is suitable for installation in the engine compartment.

Ptfe is another material that might be suitable for lining fuel pipes. Indeed, it is commonly used in heavy duty and high pressure flexible hydraulic hose.It has the disadvantage of high cost and therefore, to be cost competitive, would probably have to be applied as a thin lining. Its

Table 5.2   Plastics for fuel systems

Component	Plastics type	Principal relevant properties	Trade name
Tank filler caps, etc. Filter housings	Acetal copolymers	Resistant to HC, strong, moulds to complex shapes, low permeability to methanol	Delrin
Fuel pipe veneers Needle valve tips	Fluoro-elastomer	Resistant to fuel, temperature to 260°C, and compression. set	Viton
Fuel pipes	Chlorosulphonated polyethylene	Rubber resistant to 130°C and HC. Flexible at low temps.	Hypalon
Braided reinforcement	Para-aramid	Fibre	Kevlar
Induction manifolds and filler caps	Engineering thermoplastic	High impact strength Dimensionally stable Moulds to complex shapes	Minlon
Fuel rails Filter housings Emission canisters	Polyamide (Nylon)	Melts 170–184°C Fatigue and impact resistant, dimensionally stable	Zytel
Barrier resin for fuel tanks	Polyamide	Low permeability to HC Tough and strong Dimensionally stable	Selar
Fuel filters Fuel tanks	Polyester fibre HDPE	Makes fine fabric filters Strong, resistant to environment	Decron Lupolen

advantages are, suitability for use at temperatures from −200 to +200°C, extreme resistance to combustion, chemical degradation and permeation. In common with nylon and nitrile rubber, it is made under many trade names: those of ptfe include Foraflon, Halar, Kynar, and Solef, Teflon and Tefzel.

Where plastics pipes are intended for application in simple installations in large scale production, preformed rigid or semi-rigid components might be preferred to pliable ones. They have the advantages of ease of offering up and connecting on the assembly line, and of course do not sag so readily. On the other hand, for small volume production, or where very long runs of tubing are necessary, for example on commercial vehicles and buses, and the operators on the line are used to assembling electric cables to chassis, flexible plastics piping may still be both more economical and satisfactory. In such installations, it is generally possible to prevent sagging by cradling the pipes on the bottom flanges of chassis side members.

A selection of plastics for automotive applications is listed in Table 5.2.

5.3 Pipe connections

For metal pipes, the soldered, screwed, or other complex joints needed for connections are costly, unnecessarily difficult to assemble and, in extreme conditions, the pipes can fracture as a result of fatigue due to relative movement or vibration. The engine end of the pipe is virtually always above the level of the tank and there is no risk of syphoning, so a simple elastomeric or plastics sleeve or, to accommodate relative movement, a longer length of tubing may be used. Such a connector may be a simple push fit on to a barbed connector tube (sometimes termed *fir tree* type) screwed into or moulded integrally with the metal housing of the fuel pump or filter, if fitted. If the material can be shrink fitted after pushing over the barbed connection, the joint may be stronger in tension than the pipe itself. However, in service, it cannot be removed except by cutting it off and therefore cannot be re-fitted.

If the fuel delivery pressure is high, a push-fit arrangement or sleeve may be less acceptable unless supplemented by a clamping device. A wide range of such devices, including snap-on and toggle action types, is available, among the securest being the various wire- and band-clamps. Adhesives resistant to hydrocarbons and alcohols are available but, at the time of writing, none has been used. They too suffer the disadvantage that the pipes then cannot be removed in service. Another disincentive is uncertainty as to whether they might ultimately dissolve off into the fuel or flake and block fine filters, jets and valves and injector nozzles.

To ensure safety, most manufacturers require their fuel connections to resist a certain pull-off load. Indeed, it has been jokingly bandied around among the staff of one major manufacturer that their pull-off requirements are so high that they could use their fuel pipes instead of a sling to hoist their engines off their mountings! Security of the connection to the tank is of prime importance, to obviate risk of wastage and, more especially of fire, due to leakage. Consideration has to be given also to the possibility of pipes

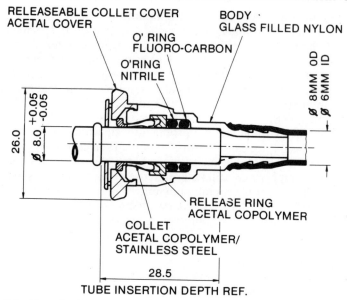

Fig. 5.1   The pull-off force of force of the Guest Speedfit pipe coupling is 450 Newtons

being wrenched off in an accident or when the vehicle is travelling over rough terrain.

An outstandingly good coupling for plastics fuel pipes is the John Guest Speedfit unit, Fig. 5.1. Among its advantages are that it is self aligning, easy to both assemble and inspect, secure with a pull-off force over 450 Newtons, and 100% quality assured.

From Fig. 5.1 it can be seen that its body, which is made of glass-fibre filled Nylon 12, houses on O-ring sealing element and a collet, the latter for locking the connection. Stainless steel knife-edge inserts are moulded into the bore of the each half of the collet to grip around and lock securely on to the spigot connection on to which the coupling is pushed. A wide range of variants is available, including colour-coded connectors. That illustrated has a barbed, or fir tree type, tubular extension at one end of its body, on to which the plastics tube is pushed. Normally the tube would be of a material, such as Nylon 11 or 12, that shrinks on to the barbs, so that the addition of a clamp of any kind is unnecessary. Consequently, producers of tubes can supply them, either singly or clipped together in sets, complete with these connectors on their ends, so that all the operator on the production line has to do is to push them on to the spigot connections on the tank and engine or fuel filter.

The tapered end of the barbed extension has a very smooth finish, so that the plastics pipe can be easily slid over it. This has been accomplished by designing the mould in a manner such that when the components are ejected, their ends pull straight out of an impression in its end plate, but of course there is a split line along the remainder of the mould. Both precision of moulding and compactness have been obtained by keeping the wall thickness of the component virtually constant for uniform shrinkage throughout its length.

Connectors can be supplied housing either a single or a pair of O-ring seals in a single groove. The least costly of course is a unit with a single seal, which can be of any suitable material such as Viton or a nitrile rubber. If a pair of O-rings is used, the one in direct contact with the fuel might be of Viton, which of course is highly resistant to swelling and degradation, and the other of nitrile rubber, since any slight swelling due to contact with fuel can be an advantage. Alternatively, two seals of nitrile rubber can be satisfactory. These will swell as soon as wetted with fuel so, provided they do not leak immediately the tank is filled, they can be relied upon to remain satisfactory in service. With Viton, on the other hand, there is a possibility that sealing may initially appear to be effective but a leak develop after it has become thoroughly wet.

The advantage of duplication of the O-rings is that, in the unlikely event of one having some slight imperfection, the back-up afforded by the second will ensure one hundred per cent reliability of the unit as a whole. To avoid confusion, the Viton O-rings are green and the nitrile ones black.

A feature of the Speedfit connector is that any attempt to withdraw it results in the collet's being pulled back into its taper seating, which closes the halves and prevents disconnection, and this will happen even before the spigot has entered the O-ring. Consequently, a requirement is a peripheral assembly mark or rib around the spigot, so that the operator knows whether he has pushed the connector right home.

This arrangement has four advantages. First, the operator has a positive indication that he has completed the connection which, unless he has the appropriate skill and sense of hearing and touch, he has not with a snap-on connector. Secondly, for quality control, the inspector on the assembly line needs only to check visually that the connectors are all inserted up to their assembly marks. Thirdly, it ensures that the end of the spigot is ultimately pushed well past the O-ring seals and therefore provides a good margin of safety. Fourthly, the device is tamper-proof because the collet cannot be released except by a special tool that has to be pushed into slots in the end of the housing to slide the collets clear of their taper seating.

One variant is available without these slots, making the connection permanent, and another has around its end a special collar, with lugs that can be pressed radially inwards to release the collet. These lugs have tapered inner ends which, by cam action on the end of the collet, push it axially clear of its taper seating. This type might be required where, for instance, a connector required to be removable must be mounted flush with a bulkhead and therefore provision for the insertion of the special tool might be difficult or even impossible.

5.4   Fuel rails

An area in which a rigid pipe is required is the fuel rail in a gasoline injection system. Mounted on the end remote from that into which the fuel is delivered by the pump is generally the fuel pressure relief valve, from the blow-off side of which a return pipe is taken to the tank, Fig. 11.17. To make the rail of either metal of plastics with joints throughout its length can be both costly to assemble and almost asking for leaks. An injection moulded component, of a reinforced Nylon 66, filled for reinforcement, is used by VW on some of their models. This can be much simpler and possibly also cheaper than a metal one. Even so, diecast or extruded aluminium is currently more widely preferred, and it has been suggested that the hard surface of an extrusion is more resistant to corrosive influences than is the cast material.

Various layouts have been employed, some very simple and others extremely compact and ingenious. For very small quantity production, the injectors may be interconnected by a series of short lengths of elastomeric tubing, which form the fuel rail, as shown in Fig. 5.2. The Jaguar 3890 cm^3 engine has a tubular rail, as shown in Fig. 5.3.

Fig. 5.2   For short production runs, a good arrangement is rubber hose interconnections between the injectors, to form the fuel rail, as on this Honda V-10 racing engine prepared by Cosworth. The pump delivers into one end and the return flows through a pressure regulator valve at the other to the tank

The fuel rail on the 2 litre, 16 valve engine installed in some of the Vauxhall Cavalier and Astra models does not have branch pipes: instead, the injectors screwed into the manifold have elastomeric seals around their upper ends, on to which the bolted-on aluminium fuel rail seats. This sort of arrangement has been adopted by several other manufacturers, including Ford for their Fiesta XR2i, Fig. 5.4. The rails are generally held down by brackets or clips bolted down on to either the manifold or the cylinder head.

*Fig. 5.3   The Jaguar 3890 cm³ engine has a tubular fuel rail, with a short pipe connection
between the right hand end and the pressure regulator valve*

*Fig. 5.4   Cast aluminium fuel rails are commonly employed and may be clamped down directly
on to the ends of the injectors, as on this Ford Fiesta XR2i engine*

Some V-engine layouts having cylinder blocks set at a fairly wide angle have
U-shape fuel rails.

FILTERS

5.5   Fuel filtration

As mentioned in Chapter 4, gauze filters are often fitted to the lower ends of
the pick-up pipes, inside the tanks, which is probably by far the best position

for introducing a filter into the fuel system. Its advantage is that the mesh is continually washed by fuel swilling around in the tank, so particles stopped by it fall back into the tank, leaving the filtration surface clear to allow free flow of fuel, yet instantly available for stopping either the same or other particles.

Instead of extremely fine metal mesh, woven filters made of polyester fibres can be used in fuel tanks. There is also an ingenious process for producing filter material from a fluoropolymer, such as polyvinyl difluoride, by mixing with the plastics a soluble finely granulated substance, for example starch, and producing a film from which the granules are subsequently dissolved out, leaving fine perforations in the material.

Fuel lift pumps serving gasoline engine metering equipment often have a small gauze filter in or near their inlet ports to trap any particles that might block jets. For the same reason, most carburettor manufacturers place, as an extra precaution, a thimble type filter in the inlet connection to the carburettor float valve. Another material that has been used is Dow Saran, which is a latex that can be converted into a porous carbon.

However, for vehicles that may have to be exported to countries where dust or water condensation is a serious problem, more thorough filtration may be virtually essential. In such cases, the risk of inadvertently exporting some vehicles without filters installed between their tanks and engines may be obviated by fitting the finest filters to all vehicles.

A separately mounted filter of the type most commonly used in gasoline systems is illustrated in Fig. 5.5. Such a filter generally comprises a head casting beneath which is a bowl, in most instances transparent. The rim around the bottom of the head may be internally threaded or incorporate a bayonet socket to receive the bowl, but more commonly the bowl is held up

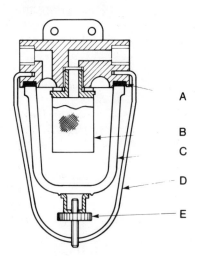

Fig. 5.5   For carburettors, this widely used type of filter with a glass bowl beneath it is adequate
A: Sealing washer, B: Gauze strainer, C: Glass bowl, D: Retaining stirrup, E: Adjuster nut

beneath the head by means of a wire clip. With a bowl that is transparent, one can easily see whether there is dirt or water inside. This can be drawn off either through a drain plug or by removing the bowl and cleaning it.

Fuel enters a port on one side of the head and is directed down into the bowl, where its velocity falls so that it loses kinetic energy and allows any water or solid particles in suspension to drop to the bottom. This sedimentation process may be helped by integral baffles, in the form of ribs extending down inside the sides of the bowl. Finally, under the pressure delivered by the lift pump, the fuel passes upwards, in some instances through a fine gauze filter, and out through a central port in the head casting. In some instances the filter is a gauze disc which, together with a sealing ring, is clamped between the head and the upper end of the cylindrical housing. In the unlikely event of droplets of water being swept upwards, they are stopped by the gauze and fall back into the base.

For gasoline injection, much better filtration is necessary, though it is still not of such critical importance to the proper functioning of the injectors as in diesel engine systems having reciprocating plunger type pumps. Fig. 5.6 is a typical gasoline filter: fuel enters on the left, passes around and radically inwards through a pleated resin impregnated paper element A, capable of straining particles of the order of 10μm diameter, into a tubular strainer D. Continuing to flow to the right, it passes through first another strainer and then a perforated end-support plate, ultimately leaving the unit through the connection on the right.

In general, most of the filter elements used are of very simple construction, comprising either a metal gauze, a fine woven polyester plastics cloth, or a resin-impregnated felt or paper element, possibly of pleated cylindrical shape, in a cylindrical plastics, pressed steel or cast metal housing. The resin impregnation is for increasing the wet strength of the element and, by partially bonding the fibres together, preventing any from becoming detached and passing downstream. A blow-off valve is unnecessary since total blockages are virtually unknown. In any case, the

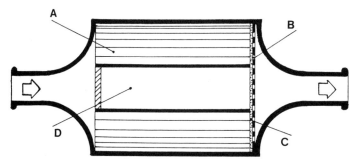

Fig. 5.6 Filters for injection systems require elements taking out particles from about 10 to 15µm diameter
A: Resin impregnated pleated paper filter element, B: Strainer, C: Perforated end-support plate, D: Tubular core

consequences would not be so serious as with filters in the lubrication system, which usually do have some sort of blow-off device to bypass the filter element and thus protect the engine from oil starvation.

On the other hand, vapour traps are sometimes incorporated where highly volatile alcohol blends of fuel are used for racing, where pipes or pumps are liable to be affected by heat radiated or conducted from the exhaust or turbocharger. For such applications, light weight is usually of overriding importance.

The housing of one such separator was made of acetal homopolymer the halves of which were joined by ultrasonic welding. It was sited in the highest point of the fuel system and comprised an upper and lower chamber separated by a fine polyester cloth filter diaphragm in an acetal homopolymer frame. Fuel entered at near the top and passed down through the filter and out to the carburettor. The filter was impervious to the vapour, which therefore rose to into a dome in the top of the casing, where it was vented through a ball-valve. As the liquid fuel rose, it lifted the light polyacetal ball and closed the valve port.

Cartridge type filters have the advantage that they can be simple, totally self contained, and their casings can be screwed into a very small connection or head. They are extremely easy to remove, discard and replace by a new unit as necessary. However, these screw-on types, unlike oil filters which can be very conveniently screwed into a connection on the crankcase, are more difficult to accommodate in a fuel system and generally need changing so rarely that they are hardly ever considered. Another though minor factor is that, whereas the lubricant is normally discarded and replaced when an oil filter is changed, the fuel in a similar filter will be wasted.

PUMPS

5.6 Fuel lift

In modern cars, the fuel may have to be lifted to a height of about 0.6 m from the tank to the metering unit and, on commercial vehicles, even higher. Some early vehicles had sealed fuel tanks and manually actuated air-pumps for pressurising them and thus forcing the fuel up to the level required. A more sensible device, which became very widely used, was the Autovac, in which induction manifold depression was utilised to suck the fuel up into a small tank at a level slightly higher than that of the carburettor, to which it was then gravity fed. This system was still to be found on commercial vehicles up to about the late 1920s. In the meantime, mechanically actuated positive displacement fuel lift pumps had been developed to a high degree of reliability and, by about 1928, had become virtually the industry standard, though electrically actuated versions were also employed, notably on Morris cars as early as well before World-War II.

The main advantage of the electrically driven pump was that it did not depend on an engine-driven cam for its drive, so it could be sited anywhere on the vehicle. It was usually installed in an accessible position in the boot, just above the tank, so that it pumped against both a pressure and a suction head, each of modest proportions, the suction head being nowhere near as large as that beneath a pump mounted on the engine. In consequence, the likelihood of the occurrence of vapour lock was greatly reduced, and these pumps tended to remain primed for longer periods than the engine-actuated type. Another major advantage was that the pump motor could be wired through the ignition switch and therefore could begin to function immediately the ignition was switched on. In contrast, even if still primed, a cam-actuated pump on a vehicle that had been standing for a long time might not begin to deliver until after the engine had been cranked for several revolutions, so starting from cold could be a difficult operation and impose a heavy load on the battery.

However, although electically driven fuel lift pumps have been available for well over half a century, by far the greatest majority of cars and commercial vehicles have had mechanically actuated ones, because they were cheaper and, at least until after World War II, much more reliable. Only when gasoline injection began to be taken seriously, and therefore pulse-free pumps became essential, did electric fuel pumps really become popular.

5.7 Mechanical positive displacement fuel lift pumps

AC introduced the first successful mechanically actuated fuel lift pump in 1927. A typical modern AC-Delco pump is illustrated in Fig. 5.7, and two SU units in Fig. 5.8. They all operate on broadly similar principles and each is driven by an eccentric on the engine camshaft. All three are diaphragm type, positive displacement pumps. They are the simplest and the least costly, and are extremely reliable, even in very wet and dirty ambient conditions. Their disadvantages are: a pulsating output, the need to mount them on the engine to obtain a mechanical drive, and their consequent vulnerability to vapour lock owing not only to the large suction head between them and their tanks, but also their proximity to sources of radiated and conducted heat.

Weber have a simple answer to the vapour problem (Fig. 5.9). The fuel is delivered down into the top of a float chamber, the needle valve of which is mounted on top of the float. Taken from the delivery pipe immediately above the inlet port to the needle valve is a branch back to the tank. A restrictor in the branch pipe ensures that only a small proportion of the fuel delivered passes in to it to be returned, but any vapour that it contains passes much more freely. In any case, the fuel naturally tends to drop down into the unit and the vapour to rise up the branch pipe.

Should the vapour flow temporarily exceed the capacity of the restrictor to allow it to pass, it accumulates in the float chamber, but continuously returns to the tank so long as the needle valve is open. The delivery passes through a second, but larger, restrictor to ensure that there is always a back

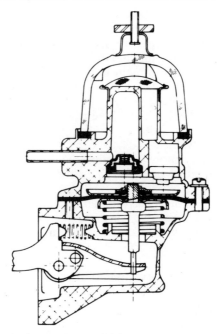

Fig. 5.7   The AC-Delco fuel lift pump, with the inlet valve on the right and the delivery valve, sectioned, on the left. It has a glass dome retained by a stirrup. Under the dome is the inlet stack pipe, capped by a fine mesh filter for trapping water

pressure in the float chamber to drive the vapour out. Obviously this could be used to solve a chronic vapour lock problem, but the correct solution is to design the problem out in the first instance, by removing its root cause. It was intended, however, for use in the line returning warm fuel from the injection rail to the tank.

Fuel lift pumps of the reciprocating type may reciprocate about 100 million times throughout the lives of the vehicles on which they are fitted. Consequently, in the early days, when either metal bellows or fabric diaphragms were used, ruptures were frequent. Modern diaphragms, on the other hand, reinforced with very strong, fatigue resistant fabrics, are extremely reliable. Diaphragms are preferred to pistons because they are simpler, lighter, less costly, more easily sealed and do not call for close clearances or machining to tight tolerances.

Mostly, these pumps are actuated by an eccentric on the engine camshaft, with a rocker follower, the end of the other arm of which has a slotted connection to a pull-rod attached to the centre of a diaphragm; the slot serves as a lost motion device. This lost motion extends between the lowest and uppermost ends of stroke, the rocker arm being returned upwards by a small diameter spring installed horizontally to keep the follower in contact with the eccentric, as can be seen from the illustrations.

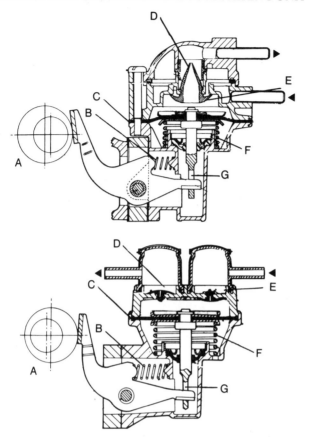

Fig. 5.8   (a) SU AF700, and (b), SU AF800 fuel lift pumps
A: Eccentric on camshaft, B: Follower rocker return spring, C: Diaphragm, D: Delivery valve,
E: Inlet valve, F: Diaphragm return spring, G: Lost motion slot

The rocker pulls the diaphragm downwards, drawing fuel into the chamber above it. Then the diaphragm is returned upwards by a large diameter spring installed coaxially beneath it, but its stroke is determined by the quantity of the fuel that has been delivered from the chamber above it to the engine. It follows that, if the engine were being motored on a dynamometer, the rocker could reciprocate with the limits of the slot indefinitely without actually doing any pumping.

Arrangements of valves differ from make-to-make, but they are almost invariably in the roof of the diaphragm chamber. In the SU AUF 700 unit, a single hollow valve is employed. Around its lower end is a mushroom head and, inside its upper end, a reed type delivery valve. Both valves are flexible and centred directly above the diaphragm. In each of the diagrams of the other two pumps, the inlet valve is on the right and the delivery valve to the left of centre. One has flexible mushroom and the other disc type valves.

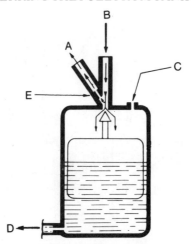

Fig. 5.9   *Weber device for removing vapour from the warm return flow from fuel rail to tank; it could be used for solving a chronic vapour lock problem if no better remedy is practicable*
A: Vapour return to tank, B: Fuel in, C: Float chamber vent, D: Fuel out, E: Restrictor

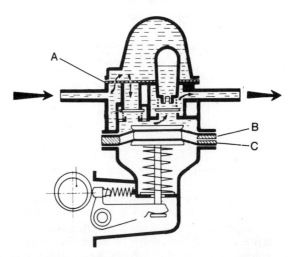

5.10   *Weber double diaphragm fuel lift pump. The inlet valve is on the left and the outlet on the right with, above it, a domed accumulator to damp out pulsations*
A: Filter, B: Pumping diaphragm, C: Sealing diaphragm

Most pumps of the diaphragm type have a filter over the inlet valve. In the AC-Delco unit, it is a slightly domed gauze on top of what amounts to a stack pipe that forms a water trap inside the large domed glass top cover. This cover is retained by a spring-clip, part of which can be seen on top of the dome. In the SU AUF 800 unit, a thimble type filter can be inserted in the small dome into which the inlet pipe is fitted, and on the 700 unit, it is a gauze

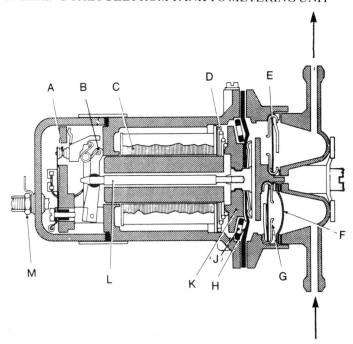

5.11   The SU electric fuel-lift pump
A: Contacts, B: Scissors type flick-over mechanism, with hairpin spring, C: Winding, D: Diaph-
rgam return spring, E: Delivery valve, F: Fine mesh filter, G: Inlet valve, H: Diaphragm, J:
Rollers, K: Armature, L: Push rod, M: electrical connections

disc clamped between the washer that seals the rim of the top cover and the
upper half of the diaphragm housing.

An interesting version of the diaphragm pump is the Weber unit
illustrated in Fig. 5.10. This functions in much the same way, but it has a
double diaphragm. The lower one ensures that fuel, if it leaks past the upper
one, which does the pumping, will not leak into the engine. The ingoing fuel
passes up into the domed chamber and then down through the inlet valve,
passing twice through the filter as it does so. Above the delivery valve is a
thimble containing air, for attenuating the pulsations.

5.8   Electrical positive displacement fuel lift pumps

Following the success of the mechanically actuated diaphragm type pump,
several electrically driven versions were introduced, notably by SU in the
UK and Bendix in the USA. The SU pump illustrated in Fig. 5.11, is typical.
Basically, it comprises a valve unit, a solenoid-actuated diaphragm, and a
flick-over make-and-break switch.

On the right in the illustration, is the inlet chamber with, in its base, a water drain plug and filter, which cannot be seen in this section. Fuel entering this chamber passes through the filter, and on up past a disc-valve into a second chamber whence, each time the diaphragm is pulled to the left by the solenoid, it is drawn into the diaphragm chamber. When the solenoid is moved to the right again, by its return spring, the previously mentioned disc-valve closes and another, above it, opens to allow the fuel to pass out to the carburettor as the diaphragm is forced back again by its return spring.

Attached to the centre of the diaphragm is an armature disc with a large peripheral groove. Carried in this groove are a number of discs the edges of which are rounded. These have three functions. One is to centre the armature in the magnetic pot in which the solenoid winding is housed. Secondly, they back up the diaphragm, helping to prevent it from ballooning under the pressure generated in the fuel by its return spring. Thirdly, by virtue of the profiles of their rounded edges and of the counterbore in which they seat in the magnet pot, they regulate the density of the magnetic flux passing through them, to maintain an approximately constant axial pull on the armature throughout its stroke. A fibre disc in a counterbore in the centre of the armature prevents metal-to-metal contact between it and the tubular core of the solenoid.

This tubular core for the winding houses a push rod interconnecting the centre of the armature and a flick-over switch at the opposite end of the unit. The left hand end of the rod is connected to one of two rocker arms, pivoted scissors fashion at their lower ends. Carried on the upper end of one of these arms is the earth contact of the switch for energising the solenoid, the positive contact being mounted on the switch base-plate, which is of insulating material. Interconnecting the upper ends of both arms is a floating spring of the coiled hairpin type. As can be seen from Fig. 5.11, this spring

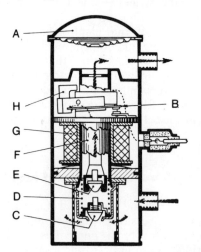

Fig. 5.12   Weber plunger type electric fuel-lift pump
A: Air space with separator diaphragm below it, B: Contacts, C: Inlet valve, D: Plunger return spring, E: Delivery valve, F: Plunger, G: Winding, H: Permanent magnet

flicks alternately back and forth, to serve the dual function of holding the contacts closed while the rod is at one end of its stroke and open while it is at the other end.

While Delco make a plunger type pump for diesel systems, Weber offer one for gasoline, Fig. 5.12. In the latter, the cast iron armature serves as the pump plunger, which reciprocates in a non-magnetic tubular core around which the solenoid is wound. The inlet valve seats on a port in the base of a thimble shape chamber, surrounded by a filter sleeve, beneath the plunger, while the delivery valve is above it, in the lower end of the hollow plunger.

When the current to the solenoid is cut off, the plunger is forced upwards by the return spring seating in the thimble below. This opens the inlet valve and fills the chamber beneath the plunger with fuel; at the same time, it forces the fuel above it into the delivery chamber an thence out to the carburettor. Above the separation diaphragm, the space in the domed top of the delivery chamber, is filled with air to attenuate the pulsations. As the iron plunger approaches the top of its stroke, the magnet is attracted to it, thus actuating the rocker that closes the contacts for the solenoid. This energises the solenoid to pull the plunger down again, appropriately closing the inlet and opening the delivery valve.

5.9 Requirements for pumps in fuel injection systems

For gasoline injection systems, it is important that neither air nor vapour (Section 2.3) is sucked into the system. Moreover, after for example a long climb up a mountain road, followed by a halt, perhaps to admire the view, the heat from the engine is conducted and radiated into an already warm fuel system and this, together with the low atmospheric pressure at altitude, causes a proportion of the fuel in the system to vaporise. This vapour can be in quantities large enough to drive all the fuel back down the pipe into the tank, leaving the pump full of vapour which, when an attempt is made to restart the engine, it cannot handle.

To obviate this problem, several arrangements of pumps have been used, Fig. 5.13. For instance, the 1984 Audi 80 had an external low-level pump fed by gravity from the tank. This ensured that even if the whole pipeline and pump system contained only vapour, fuel under the influence of gravity, quickly dropped back into the pump when it was switched on. For the same reason, the 1983 Golf had what was in effect a closed tank. A pressure relief valve in the venting system opened only when the pressure due to evaporation of the fuel in the tank attained the value necessary for ensuring that, in the event of vapour blow-back, the pump would always be primed. This valve was of the two-way type for the prevention also of implosion. The pump is installed at a level about mid-way between those of the fuel when the tank is full and empty, instead of lower than the tank. On the other hand, the 1981 Passat had a single pump mounted inside on the base of the tank.

An entirely different system has been used on the BMW 320i and Porsche Turbo. These have a low pressure lift-pump submerged in the tank, serving

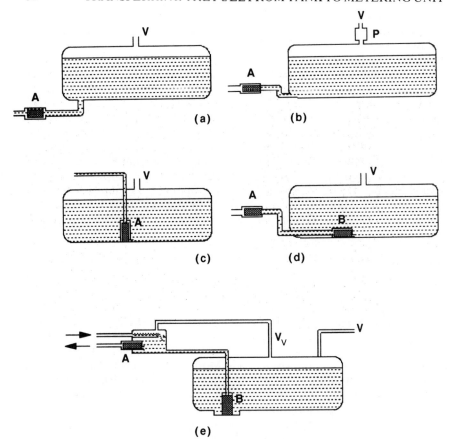

Fig. 5.13 Diagrammatic illustrations of five different fuel pump arrangements: (a) gravity feed to pump such as has been used for the Audi 80; (b) Pressurised tank as in 1983 Golf GTi; (c) The common arrangement of an in-tank pump (d) Lift pump in tank, pressure pump outside at mean level of fuel such as in BMW 320i and Porsche Turbo; (e) 1984 VW Golf system with in-tank lift pump and, outside, in a 0.7 litre combined vapour separator and priming reservoir, a pressure pump on which were mounted a filter and pressure relief valve (not shown here). The return flow from the fuel rail is discharged into the small reservoir, vapour from which is vented back to the tank
A: Pressure pump, B: Lift pump, V: Vent, P: Pressure regulating valve

an external main delivery pump set at a height mid-way between the full and empty tank fuel levels. The function of the submerged pump is always to deliver at a positive pressure to the main pump. It would appear, however, even this might not be adequate to cater for the problem arising from a complete emptying of the fuel tank. Before the engine can be restarted, first all the vapour and air has to be cleared from the system, then the pump has to be primed, next the pressure must be built up to its normal operational level, and only then can the engine be started. Another point is that all fuel pumps generate noise, and most tend to become noisier as their temperatures rise, so the fewer there are in the system the quieter it will be. In any case, there is little incentive to use two fuel pumps when one will suffice.

Even so, VW must have decided that the extra reliability of having two pumps was worth the extra cost, since they used just such a system in the 1984 Golf, Fig. 5.13. However, it was an improvement on the earlier systems in that the main pump was integral with a small reservoir of about 0.7 litres capacity. This reservoir was divided horizontally into two chambers. The pump inlet was in the lower chamber and the return from the injection system was delivered into the upper chamber. Consequently, any bubbles of vapour that might be in the return flow could be easily vented off into the main fuel tank, and there was no risk of their being drawn immediately into the pump inlet. Furthermore, even if the main tank were to empty completely, there would always be enough fuel left in the main pump reservoir to prime it.

Other measures for overcoming the tendency of air to be sucked in with the fuel when the tank is almost empty include the installation of a collector, swirl or surge pot in the tank. These have been described in the last three paragraphs in Section 4.18 and the whole of Section 4.19.

The addition by the oil companies of light fractions to their unleaded fuels, to increase octane number, has of course increased the tendency of vapour to form as temperatures rise. To overcome this, manufacturers have tended to increase fuel pump delivery pressures. However, this tended to encourage the oil companies to add even higher proportions of light fractions, and it became clear that agreement on what is the best compromise is necessary. At the time of writing, however, no lasting and clear cut decisions have been taken.

5.10   A rotary positive displacement pump

A positive displacement type of pump totally different from the reciprocating type, designed for relatively high pressure operation and much less pulsation of output, is a Weber electrically driven, roller-cell type unit, Fig. 5.14 produced by Magneti Mavelli. This is used in their gasoline injection systems. It has all the advantages previously described as being attributable to electric drive and, in addition, can be installed actually inside the fuel tank, where it is well protected from damage, leakage and fire risk, and is constantly cooled by the fuel flowing through and around it. The absence of fire risk is attributable to the fact that its electrical components cannot come into contact with a combustible mixture of air and fuel since, even if the tank becomes empty, the pump cannot deliver air against the head of fuel remaining in the system upstream of it.

As can be seen from Fig. 5.14, this unit comprises two sub-assemblies within a common cylindrical housing. One is a power unit and the other, mounted axially in line with it, the pump. The power unit is a permanent magnet, d.c. electric motor. It drives a radially slotted disc in the pump unit. This disc rotates in a short cylindrical housing, the bore of which is eccentric relative to the disc and shaft. Contained in each of five slots, machined radially inwards from the periphery of the disc, is a metal roller.

As the disc rotates, the slots revolve past an outlet port, the eccentricity of the housing simultaneously moving each roller in turn, as it approaches the port, radially inwards against centrifugal force. Thus the fuel beneath it is displaced out through the port, past the motor and away through the main delivery port at the far end of the pump. Further rotation causes the rollers to move out again, while the slots, or cells, in which they are contained revolve past an inlet port, drawing fuel in from the opposite end of the pump. Since fuel is always delivered in excess of the requirements of the

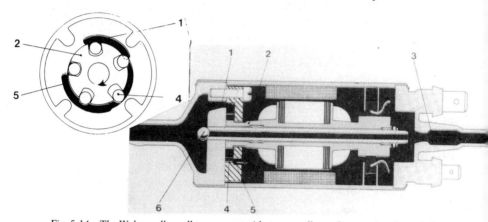

Fig. 5.14   The Weber roller-cell type pump with, to a smaller scale, a section through the roller chamber
1. Inlet port, 2. Pump rotor, 3. Non-return valve, 4. Rollers, 5. Delivery port, 6. Pressure relief valve

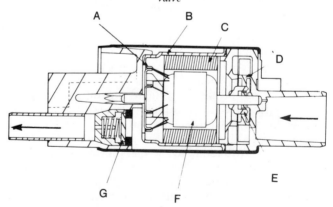

Fig. 5.15   AC in-tank fuel pump
A: Commutator, B: Flux carrier, C: Magnet, D: Impeller, E: Drive spigot, F: Armature, G: Check-valve

engine, a relief valve in the wall between the armature housing and the fuel inlet chamber limits the pressure to 5 bar. At the opposite end of the unit, the main fuel delivery port houses a check-valve to ensure that the pump remains primed after it is switched off. The motor is wired through the ignition switch, and there is a safety override switch to cut the pump out of operation if the engine should be stalled, for example in an accident.

5.11 Some other rotary fuel lift pumps

A number of different types of rotary fuel lift pump have been produced. Most are of the hydrodynamic type, with either a radial or an axial flow impeller. Their outputs are almost always pulsating at high frequency but low amplitude, owing to the passage of parts of such as vanes past the ports.

Among the simplest is a unit that was used in the Tecalemit-Jackson fuel injection system, described in *Automobile Engineer*, Vol. 54, July 1964. It had a plain rotor disc, on one side of which were machined, next to each other in a circle adjacent to the periphery, 20 small cells. Machined in the wall of the casing adjacent to the cells was an arcuate groove around 305°, the whole of length which was traversed by the cells as the rotor turned. The cells simply accelerated the gasoline entering from the inlet at one end of the

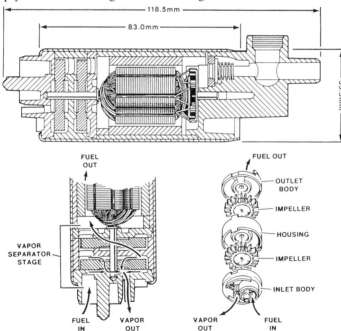

Fig. 5.16 *In this AC medium pressure twin turbine fuel pump, the first stage impeller removes vapour by centrifuging the fuel outwards and thus leaving the vapour in the centre, whence it is returned to the tank. The delivery pressure is about 1 bar*

groove until, by the time it left at the other end, it was rotating at the speed of the rotor. As it left through the outlet, the velocity energy that it had picked up was converted into pressure energy. This pump was intended to supply fuel at a pressure proportional to the square of the speed of the engine driving it.

An AC fuel pump is illustrated in Fig. 5.15. Fuel from the inlet is passed by a radial vane impeller axially through the motor housing to the outlet. In another version, Fig. 5.16, there are two stages driven in tandem: one for freeing the fuel from any vapour that might be present and the other for handling the liquid gasoline. The first stage has a radial impeller, the vapour being drawn off from its centre. Fuel leaving at the periphery of this first stage is then passed on by an eccentric rotor type pump through the motor housing and out at the other end. The need for separation arises in some American limousines, in which the tanks are so large that even when nearly empty, there is still a lot of fuel swilling around on the bottom, from which the pump may continue for some time to draw a mixture of air and fuel.

A Bosch two-stage, low pressure pump for installation in the fuel tank is used in the Mono-Jetronic injection system described in Section 11.29. As can be seen from Fig. 5.17, the fuel enters the first stage, which comprises radial vanes in the disc. In this stage its pressure is increased sufficiently to avoid vapour formation as it enters the second stage, where peripheral vanes boost its pressure to 1 bar. It then passes into the housing for the permanent magnet motor, which it cools, and finally out through a check valve, which prevents fuel from flowing back through the pump into the tank when the engine is stopped.

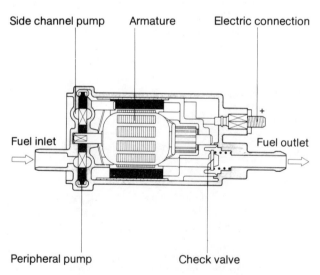

Fig. 5.17   Bosch low pressure electric fuel pump

Chapter 6

The Fundamental Principles of Carburation

Metaphorically, an engine breaths air, consumes food (albeit only liquid), digests it (combustion), has a circulation system (lubrication), and performs work. The critical role of metering the liquid foodstuffs in the correct proportions relative to the air that it breathes is done by either a carburation or an injection unit. This unit also makes a major contribution to their mixing in preparation for combustion. Since the carburettor was the first of the two types of metering system to become firmly established, it will be dealt with in this and the next two chapters. Injection will covered in Chapter 11.

REQUIREMENTS AND HISTORY

6.1   The functions of a carburettor

Carburation entails the supply of a mixture of fuel and air to the engine in proportions such that it will be easily ignited by the spark and then the fuel completely oxidised. The aim is primarily at converting as much as possible of the chemical energy in the fuel into heat in the combustion chamber of the engine. Total combustion of course implies total absence of carbon monoxide and unburned hydrocarbons in the exhaust. However, the formation of oxides of nitrogen must be avoided too since although not toxic themselves, when released into the atmosphere they can, in bright sunshine, contribute to the production of toxic gases, as explained in Section 13.4.

In automotive applications, load and speed of operation vary continuously, so the fuel and air metering and mixing function of the carburettor for matching exactly the requirements of the engine and satisfying the demands of the driver for torque is not simple. As the fuel is delivered into the airstream, it must be broken up into a fine spray. It must then be mixed intimately with the air as it is drawn on into the engine, and the mixtures ultimately distributed into each of the cylinders must be of identical volumes, strengths and consistencies. Finally, the carburettor must also provide for the transfer of enough heat to the mixture for the conversion of the liquid fuel to vapour, to facilitate the production of a homogeneous mixture prior to ignition. On the other hand, overheating of the mixture

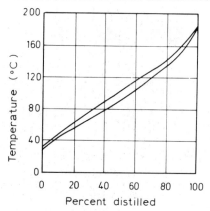

Fig. 6.1   Fractional distillation curve of typical leaded gasolines: top, summer grade; bottom, winter grade

must be avoided too, since this would reduce its density and therefore the weight of charge per induction stroke.

A number of problems have to be overcome. First, while one of the fluids to be metered is a mixture of the gases oxygen and nitrogen, the other is a liquid containing, if we include all the isomers, up to as many as 300 different hydrocarbons the boiling points of which differ over a range of perhaps 25 to 220°C, Fig. 6.1. Other factors include the variations in relative humidity, ambient temperature, engine temperature, and atmospheric pressure including the effects of changes in altitude. Then there are effects of the size, shape and layout of the induction manifold that conducts the mixture from the metering equipment and distributes it to the inlet ports, of the pulsations in flow due to the opening and closing of the inlet valves, and resonant vibrations of the gases throughout the whole induction pipe system.

6.2   Some early carburettors

Carburettors in use in the mid 1890s were designed for industrial engines, mostly required to operate at relatively constant loads and speeds, so they tended to be very simple. For instance, some were based on the use of wicks, over which the air was drawn, to vaporise the fuel as it passed on into the engine cylinders. A later refinement was the addition of a manual control by means of which the wick or wicks dipping in the fuel could be raised or lowered so that the area of wick exposed to the air flow could be varied. Thus, a rich mixture could be supplied for cold starting and then, as the engine warmed up, progressively weakened to eliminate black smoke from the exhaust.

The system illustrated in Fig. 6.2, entailed passing an exhaust bypass pipe through the base of a small reservoir, to encourage evaporation of the fuel it contained. Control of the rate of flow of air through an inlet pipe into the

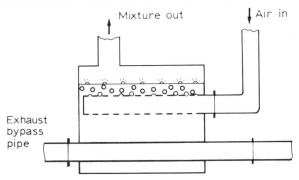

Fig. 6.2 Diagrammatic illustration showing the principle of an early diffusion tube carburettor with exhaust heat

reservoir, over the surface of the fuel, and then out to the engine was effected by a rotary mixture-control valve. In early devices, the lower end of the inlet pipe was below the surface of the fuel and was perforated, so that the incoming air emerging through the perforations bubbled up through the liquid.

Later came the surface carburettor, introduced by Gottlieb Daimler and Karl Benz in 1885, in which a float in the reservoir kept the level of the fuel constantly just below a plate, or very large flange, around the lower end of the inlet pipe to the reservoir, Fig. 6.3. The function of this plate, or flange, was to distribute the flow at relatively high velocity over a large area of the surface of the fuel. In some instances the reservoir was the actual fuel tank, while in others it was a separate and much smaller compartment. Cold starting was difficult with both variants of this system owing to the initial absence of exhaust heat.

In any case, however, the continuously varying load and speed entailed in the operation of road vehicles called for the development of something more

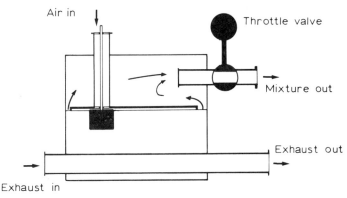

Fig. 6.3 Illustration of the principle of an 1885 Daimler-Benz surface carburettor with exhaust heating

sophisticated. Simple carburettors began to be used in which the flow of air over the jets created a depression which sucked the fuel out automatically in approximate proportion to the velocity of that flow. It was soon discovered that a single jet was not enough, and thus began a process of refinement that, even now, continues.

ENGINE CONTROL AND VOLUMETRIC EFFICIENCY

6.3 Breathing and ingestion of the air-fuel mixture

In this context, the term gas is used for the mixture of both air and fuel drawn into the engine so, as regards both volume and mass, the quantity is slightly different from that of the actual air consumed. However, given a chemically correct mixture of 14.7 parts of air to one part of fuel by weight, only about 2.2% of the volume of gas drawn in is fuel vapour.

Regardless of whether the engine is being cranked, for starting, or rotating under its own power, and so long as the inlet valve is open and the exhaust valve closed, the gas is drawn in through the induction system by the movement of the piston away from top (or inner) dead centre. The outward movement of the piston reduces the pressure of the air in the cylinder, so it is the ambient pressure that pushes the gas in. Therefore, the expression *depression*, not *vacuum*, should be used for describing the lowered state of pressure inside the cylinder, or the induction manifold.

The pressure differential increases with the speed of rotation of the engine. It is, however, influenced also by friction of the flowing gas on the walls of the passages through which it is passing, the sizes of the apertures, the turbulence in the flow at the various stages throughout the induction system and, at wide open throttle, most strongly of all by the area and coefficient of discharge of the inlet valves in their ports: the valve throat is normally the smallest aperture through which the mixture will pass in the latter condition. Incidental factors influencing the degree of depression in various parts of the induction system include wear of parts such as pistons, rings, valve stems, their guides, throttle valve spindles and their bearings. Leakages may occur, too, as a result of loose induction manifold joints or defective gaskets.

In general, it can be said that the velocity of flow attained is dependent upon the degree of opening of the throttle valve. The maximum is determined by the size of the inlet valve apertures. In other words, control over engine speed at any given load can be said to be effected by use of the throttle to regulate the volumetric efficiency, as defined in Section 6.4. This is why the specific fuel consumption (rate of fuel consumption per unit of power produced) of an engine deteriorates as the throttle opening is reduced below that at which maximum torque is developed. An overall view of the variations in pressure through the induction system is illustrated in Fig. 6.4 and explained in Section 6.6.

A simpler way of expressing the control philosophy, however, is to say

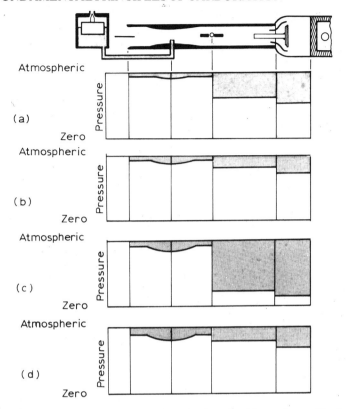

Approximate consumptions for a 2 litre engine at the above throttle openings and loads indicated in the caption

	(a)	(b)	(c)	(d)
Engine speed, rev/min	500	800	2000	2000
Air consumed at the pressures in the cylinders, litre/min	250	400	1000	1000
Pressures in cylinders, kN/m², given that atmospheric pressure is 103.4kN/m²	34.5	86.18	17.24	68.95
Above volumes consumed converted to atmospheric pressure, litre/min	83	333	166	666

Fig. 6.4   Top: diagrammatic representation of an engine induction system, from carburettor to cylinder. Middle, plots of the depressions, assuming no parasitic losses, at the various stages of transit from the air intake into the cylinder: at (a) with the engine idling at 500 rev/min; at (b) 800 rev/min with a large throttle opening, (c) 2000 rev/min with a small throttle opening; (d) 2000 rev/min with a large throttle opening. Bottom, Table showing air consumptions for a 2 litre engine

that, if at any given load the driver wants to reduce the speed, he must reduce the quantity of mixture entering the engine, by closing the throttle by the appropriate amount. Incidentally, the fall-off in overall efficiency from the throttle opening for maximum torque to that for maximum power is due mainly to the throttling effect of the constriction offered by the inlet valve throat as the piston speed, and therefore power consumed in pumping the gas into the cylinder, increases.

6.4 Volumetric efficiency

Consider a hypothetical 2 litre engine in which the clearance between the crown of the piston and the cylinder head (the *clearance volume*) is zero. If the crankshaft is rotating so slowly that the pressure inside the cylinder can rise to equal the ambient pressure before the inlet valve closes which, in this hypothetical case, is bottom (or outer) dead centre, it will consume 1 litre of gas per revolution. However, it will not consume 3 litres at, say, 3000 rev/min, since the pressure inside the cylinder will not have had time to equal that ouside before the inlet valve has closed. The ratio of the actual volume of gas consumed to that which would be consumed if the gas in the cylinder at the end of the combustion stroke were at atmospheric temperature and pressure is termed the *volumetric efficiency* of the engine. It is rarely much above about 80% at maximum power output. In practice, of course, the inlet valves neither open at top dead centre nor close at bottom dead centre since, in setting their timing, it is necessary to take into account the inertias of both the incoming and outcoming gases. Further explanation is to be found in Section 9.7.

In a 2-stroke engine, with an induction stroke every revolution, the rate of consumption of gas might be thought to be twice as much as that of a 4-stroke unit, but is not. This is because the burnt gas of the former is cleared out much less efficiently during the scavenge stroke and so there is not so much space available for receiving the fresh charge which, moreover, is heated by the burnt gas remaining from the previous combustion stroke and is therefore reduced in density.

The effect of the essential clearance volume above the piston crown is mainly that, because it contains very hot residual gas at the end of each power stroke, it will expand into the remainder of the cylinder during the induction stroke and some of its heat will be transferred to the incoming gas. This increases the volume and decreases the density of the incoming charge, and thus its weight and therefore energy content.

METERING IN PRACTICE AND THEORY

6.5 Basis of metering fuel and air

Since the density of the air passing through the carburettor to the engine varies considerably with its temperature, the only reliable way to meter the quantity of fuel to be mixed with it is on the basis of weight. With some modern injection systems this is actually done.

With simple carburettors, however, the weight of the air passing through is assessed on a basis of its velocity, and therefore on its volume at its prevailing temperature. Variations in temperature of course translate into variations in mass for any given volume of air drawn into the engine. However, except possibly occasionally by accident, they never translate into corresponding proportional variations in the mass of the fuel metered into the air by the carburettor. This is one reason why simple carburation is inherently less accurate than injection, in which metering can be, though not always is, effected on the basis of mass flow of air.

Compensation can be made for changes in temperature by electronic control over carburation. However this tends to offset the main advantage of carburation, which is simplicity. On the other hand, injection has several significant advantages, especially for controlling exhaust emissions, to be explained in Chapter 13, so it is likely eventually to render carburettors obsolete for road vehicles. Even so, the relatively low cost of carburation still leaves it attractive for cars produced for the bottom end of the market, and it is not beyond the bounds of possibility that, with electronic closed loop control, it might make a come-back.

6.6 Essential elements of a carburation system

All carburettors have a float chamber to keep the level of fuel supplied to the jets a little lower than the outlet for the fuel into the air stream. Without such

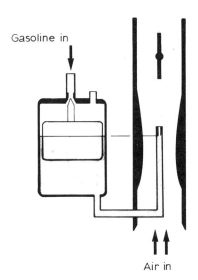

Fig. 6.5   A simple carburettor with a single jet

a device, fuel would flow through the jets continuously, even when the engine was stationary.

In Fig. 6.5 we see a very much simplified carburation and induction system. The fuel is being fed through a jet into a venturi, the function of which is to increase the speed of flow of air locally. According to Bernouilli's theorem, if we ignore the effects of drag on the walls, and assume absence of turbulence, the sum of the energies in a stream of gas or liquid in a pipe, or any other parallel constraint, remains constant throughout its length. Therefore, if its velocity is increased, its pressure must fall in proportion to the increase in speed. It is this speed-proportional drop in pressure that is used to draw fuel off from the jet in proportion to the volume of air entering the engine.

The diagram shows the complete system from the air intake, through the venturi, past the throttle valve, into the induction manifold and thence past the inlet valve into the cylinder. Below are diagrams showing the pressures at each stage. Note that the top line in each case represents atmospheric pressure and that, through all the stations beyond the air intake, the pressure is below atmospheric. As previously mentioned, the driving force inducing the air to flow into the engine is atmospheric pressure.

6.7 The gas flow

When the throttle is closed for idling, the rate of flow is very small, so the pressures between the air intake and throttle are not much lower than atmospheric. On the other hand, since virtually all the power being developed by the engine is directed to drawing air in against the resistance offered by the closed throttle, the depression between the throttle valve and cylinder is considerable. The slight constrictions due to the narrowing of the passage through the venturi and valve throat, reduce the pressures locally. That across the venturi first falls and then rises slightly as the diameter increases again. It falls further at the valve throat but, because the cylinder is the ultimate source of the pressure differential, or the driving force inducing the flow, it does not rise again inside.

The principal effect of opening the throttle slightly is to relieve the depression throughout the passages downstream of it. Since the rate of flow through the venturi is only slightly increased, the increase in depression at even its narrowest section is correspondingly small. At a wider throttle opening and relatively light load, a significant proportion of the power output is again devoted to drawing air in against the resistance offered by the throttle valve, so the depression downstream of the throttle is once more high.

With a wide open throttle, at constant speed at full load, the drop in pressure in the venturi is of necessity relatively large, to draw in the quantity of fuel required. In contrast, the increment of depression at the throttle valve is fairly small and entirely parasitic, as also is that at the valve throat except in so far as it is necessary for the generation of swirl in the combustion chamber for completeness of combustion.

The pressure diagrams are based on an assumption of steady rates of flow. However, since, in a single cylinder engine, the inlet valve is open for only about a quarter of each cycle, the flow is in fact pulsating. The pulsations are of course damped to a certain extent by the various restrictions along the induction tract and especially by that offered by the throttle valve. Obviously, the larger the number of cylinders the less pronounced are the pulsations relative to the total flow.

6.8 Fuel flow

Owing to the greater weight, relative incompressibility and greater viscosity and damping of the gasoline, the corresponding pulsations in its flow will tend to lag behind and be smaller than those of the low viscosity and relatively elastic air. The outcome is a high frequency fluctuation in the accuracy of metering, but the sizes of the jets specified for matching the requirements of an engine are normally such that the average, or overall, air:fuel ratio will be correct.

The rate of flow of fuel through a jet is determined by the pressure differential across it. This differential can arise from two causes: the depression and head of fuel, the latter usually negative, above the jet. The head of fuel is fixed primarily by the level of fuel in the float chamber. On the other hand, the depression, above the jet, in the venturi ranges from zero when the engine is stationary to perhaps as high as 4 kN/m^2 at wide open throttle, depending on the type of engine.

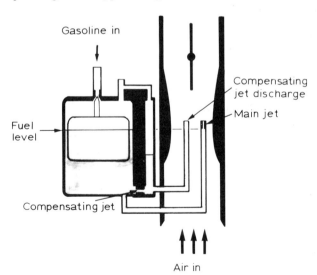

Fig. 6.6   Simple carburettor with main and compensating jets

Some carburettors, to be described later, have at least one jet in the bottom of a well, the level of fuel in which is progressively lowered as the depression increases, so that the effective head correspondingly reduces as speed increases. This is termed a *compensating jet*. As the speed is reduced and the level of the top of the well therefore again approached, the head must always remain negative, Fig. 6.6, otherwise the fuel would continue to flow after the engine was switched off.

One merit of the submerged jet arrangement accrues from the fact that, because the flow from the float chamber has to pass through against the head of fuel in the well into which it delivers, its orifice has to be of larger diameter. Consequently, it is less likely to be blocked by foreign matter in the fuel. Another advantage is that, by virtue of the larger orifice, the manufacturing tolerances are not so critical. Furthermore, the flow characteristics of a jet in the fully submerged condition are more favourable for contributing to mixture correction than if it has to deliver into air.

6.9   Velocity of flow

It should be noted that the rates of flow of both air and fuel are directly related to the pressure drops across and sizes of their orifices, respectively the venturi and jet. The float chamber is vented to atmosphere and the air intake is open to atmosphere. Therefore atmospheric pressure and the depression in the venturi are factors common to the pressure differentials across both the jet through which the air flows (the venturi) and that through which the fuel flows. The velocities of both flows are determined by the same law, so the volumes of flow per unit of time might be thought to be identical. They are not, however, owing to differences in the properties, mainly mass, viscosity and elasticity, of the different fluids, and the different flow coefficients of the orifices.

The fundamental formula for the velocity flow of a fluid, liquid or gaseous, through an orifice is comparable to that for the velocity of a body falling freely in a vacuum under the influence of gravity:

$$v = \sqrt{(2gh)} \tag{6.1}$$

where v is the velocity, h the head and g the gravitational constant.

Any units, metric, SI or Imperial, may be used provided they are applied consistently throughout and it is borne in mind that the SI unit, the Newton, contains the g element. In Table 6.1, in which the pressure heads are calculated from $P = \sqrt{Dgh}$, the density D of air is taken to be that at 0°C and a pressure of 101.3 kN/m^2. In these calculations no account is taken of viscosity, turbulence, reduction in the effective diameter of the throat owing to the necking of the flow, coefficient of discharge etc, so only the figure for the velocity of air is close to reality. In normal running conditions, the velocities of flow through fixed diameter chokes in a carburettor generally range from between about 40 to 85 m/s. The velocities of flow of gasoline through jets are of course much lower.

Table 6.1: VELOCITIES OF FLUID FLOW

Fluid	Density (kg/m³)	Pressure head (m)	Velocity = √2gh
Water	1000	10.33	14.23
Gasoline	753	13.72	16.4
Air	1.298	7955	395

In the equations that follow, the suffixes 1, 2 and 3 after the symbols relate those symbols to the stations 1, 2 and 3 in Fig. 6.7. If we want to express the velocity in terms of the pressure difference $P_1 - P_2$ and density D_1 of the air in the carburettor air intake (ambient), equation (6.1) becomes considerably more complex, as follows:

$$v_2 = \frac{\sqrt{2g(P_2 - P_1)/D_1}}{\sqrt{\{1 - (A_2/A_1)^2\}}} \qquad (6.2)$$

where, as shown in Fig. 6.7, P_1 is the absolute pressure at the entrance to the jet, P_2 is that at the section at which the velocity v_2 is to be ascertained, and A_1 and A_2 are the corresponding cross sectional areas.

6.10 Mass flow

Since the mass associated with any given volume of flow varies with both the temperatures and coefficients of thermal expansion, and those of gasoline and air differ considerably, mass flow is the more significant parameter. For fuel flow, we can calculate either the volume from $V = A \times \sqrt{(2gh)}$, where A is the cross sectional area of the orifice, or we can calculate the mass, from $M = A \times \sqrt{(2gh)} \times D$, where D is the density, which is dependent on the temperature.

For convenience, $(P_1 - P_2)/D$ is sometimes substituted for h, so that the formula for the mass flow becomes:

$$M = A \times \sqrt{\{(2g) \times (P_1 - P_2) \times D\}} \qquad (6.3)$$

6.11 The flow constants

Gasoline weighs about 753 kg/cm³ and air about 1.298 kg/m³, so the ratio of their densities is about 587:1. Since the ratio by weight of air to gasoline for complete combustion is about 14.4:1, the relative areas of choke and jet should be 14.4/1 × √587/1 = 14.4 × 24.228 = 348.88. Consequently, the ratio of the diameter of the choke to that of the jet should be √348.88 = 18.68:1.

However, neither air nor gasoline are perfect fluids without friction and other properties that influence their flows. Consequently, a more accurate expression for mass flow is derived by the inclusion of a constant K, which

Station

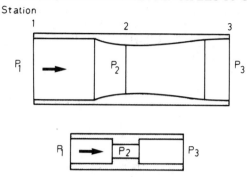

Fig. 6.7　Top, air intake and restriction (venturi). Bottom, fuel intake and restriction (jet)

combines the expression $\sqrt{(2g)}$, the viscosity, and the coefficients of discharge and flow. Equation (6.3) then simplifies to:

$$M = K \times A\sqrt{\{(P_1 - P_2) \times D\}} \tag{6.4}$$

Inserting the individual constants and again referring to Fig. 6.7, the equations for the mass M_a of air become:

$$M_a = C_c A_2 V_2 D_2 \text{ (constant} \times \text{area} \times \text{velocity} \times \text{density)} \tag{6.5}$$

or

$$M_a = C_d A_2 \frac{\sqrt{\{2g(P_1 - P_2)D_1\}}}{\sqrt{\{1 - (A_2/A_1)^2\}}} \{1 - 0.625(P_1 - P_2)/P_1\} \tag{6.6}$$

Where C_c and C_d are respectively the coefficients of contraction of flow and of discharge, the latter taking into account both the contraction and the frictional drag in the venturi. The coefficient C_d varies with the shape, surface finish and velocity.

Incidentally, for a carburettor venturi, the coefficient of contraction (the reduction in area due to necking of the flow at maximum rate) is of the order of 0.95. It should be noted that above the value of $(P_1 - P_2)/P_1 = 0.47$, the velocity of air equals that of sound (approx. 334 m/s) and cannot further increase. Similarly, at that value and above, P_2 is 0.53 P_1.

It can be more convenient to make calculations in terms of pressure heads and, with the relatively low pressures involved in carburation, heads of water rather than mercury are used. A head of 1 mm of water is the equivalent of a pressure of 1 kg/mu22 or, in SI units 98.03 N/m². Substituting head h in mm of water for $(P_1 - P_2)$ in equation (6.6) the mass of air in metric units therefore becomes:

$$M_a = C_d A_2 \frac{\sqrt{\{2gD_1(h_2 - h_1)\}}}{\sqrt{\{1 - (A_1/A_2)\}}} \{1 - 0.625(h_2 - h_1)/h_1\} \tag{6.7}$$

For the mass flow of fuel, the conditions are different, in that the viscosity is higher and, because fuel is virtually incompressible, there is no necking of the flow at the velocities with which we are concerned. Additionally, because A_1 is so much larger relative to A_2, we can omit it from the equation. Consequently, we have to use different constants, and the equations become:

$$M_f = A_2 V_2 D \tag{6.8}$$

or

$$M_f = C_y A_2 \sqrt{2gD(h_1 - h_2)} \tag{6.9}$$

where C_y is the coefficient of discharge for fuel, replacing C_d for air.

For carburettor jets, the discharge coefficient generally ranges from about 0.6 to 0.8 and, for a given jet, does not change much with size of orifice. Similarly, the coefficient of viscosity does not vary greatly with changes in temperature within the range likely to be experienced in a carburettor. On the other hand, variations in air temperature could result in enrichment of the mixture owing to reduced density on a warm day or at high altitude, and *vice versa*. If the variables are ignored, only two factors, pressure difference and area of orifice, influence mass flow.

Values for mass flow are needed by the chemists and combustion engineers for calculating the stoichiometric (chemically correct) mixture for complete oxidation of all the hydrocarbons. More on the latter subject is to be found in Chapters 12 and 13. Calculations of the volume flow, on the other hand, are required for the calibration of carburettor jets, since it is usual practice to stamp on each jet the figure for its flow in cm^3/min under a standard head of 500 mm of fuel. This is for the guidance of automotive engineers when they are selecting jets of different sizes for fitting in their carburettors during the process of developing an engine for optimum performance.

Chapter 7

Elements of carburettors

Prior to entering into detail on elements, it is necessary to have some idea of the general layouts of carburettors. There are three basic types: downdraught, updraught and sidedraught, as shown in Fig. 7.1. The prefix semi- in front of any of these is sometimes used to indicate that the axis of the venturi is not horizontal or vertical, but at some intermediate angle, usually not very large.

Which layout is adopted depends on the space available for the engine and its carburettor. Sidedraught carburettors enable a low bonnet line to be obtained, but are not always practicable if there are other large items, such as suspension struts, to be accommodated alongside the engine, or if the installation is confined within a narrow space.

Updraught carburettors, even though they tended to be inferior as regards accessibility, were originally used mainly with side valve engines. They were particularly suitable where the fuel was gravity fed to a carburettor below a simple induction manifold. In those days, carburation systems were fairly crude and it was deemed that an advantage of the updraught layout was that it tended to impede the entry of neat fuel into the engine, and thus to obviate flooding, especially when starting from cold. On the other hand, because the heavy fuel droplets had to be lifted up to the engine, starting in very cold conditions could be difficult.

With overhead valve layouts, however, the upwardly incoming air would have to be turned downwards again, and this would impair volumetric efficiency. Therefore, downdraft carburettors are by far the most widely preferred for modern engines. Not only are they accessible, but also the entry fuel vapour and droplets is assisted by gravity, instead of their having to be forced upwards by air pumped in at high velocity by the engine. Consequently, the venturi of a downdraft carburettor can be of larger diameter than if an updraught one were to be used, and this reduces the pumping losses. To keep bonnet lines low, combined air intake filters and silencers of flat or pancake forms are mostly used with carburettors of this type.

It is of interest to recall that downdraft carburettors were introduced first for marine engines, in the 1920s owing to the fire risk with the then widely used updraught types if the engine backfired and flames shot into the bilges, where leaked fuel and other inflammable substances tended to collect. The first car to have a updraught carburettor (a Stromberg DX) was the 1929 Chrysler Six in the USA, and the first in the UK were Humber-Hillman 1932 models.

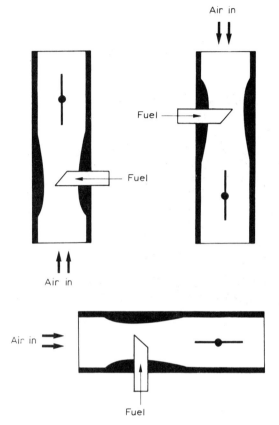

Fig. 7.1   Illustrating at (a) the updraught, (b) downdraught and (c) the side draught carburettor

THE COMPONENTS

7.1   The float chamber

Common to all carburettors is a float chamber, which has two main functions. One is to ensure that the head of fuel over the jets is constant and the other is to prevent fuel from continuing to flow into the engine when it has stopped rotating. It must be as close as practicable to one side of the venturi, or even actually surround or partially surround it, otherwise if the vehicle were to be parked on a steep incline, the float chamber might become higher than the orifices through which the fuel is drawn from the jets and delivered into the airstream. Then the fuel would run out of the float chamber through those orifices and, possibly, on into the engine.

In the majority of simple carburettors, an approximately cylindrical float with an upwardly pointing conical ended rod, or needle is employed mounted on the centre of its upper face. As the fuel rises to the required level, this needle is carried upwards by the float, ultimately to seat in the fuel inlet port immediately above it. After this, only when some of the fuel has been drawn off, either by natural evaporation or into the engine, can more enter. The conical end of the needle valve may or may not be tipped with a Viton cap. Viton is a material that has good dimensional stability and does not deteriorate in automotive fuels; it is wear resistant and has a low compression set, and therefore does not tend to distort in service.

Where a float assembly of exceptionally low height is required, other needle valve layouts have been employed. One is the use of a bell crank lever with one arm bearing down on the top of the float and the other actuating an inclined needle valve seating in a port in the side of the float chamber. More common is a pivoted lever which actuates a vertical needle valve seating in a port in its roof or floor but to one side of the float, Fig. 7.2. Toggle mechanisms have even been used to draw a valve down on its seat, Fig. 7.3, so that the head of fuel above it can help to keep the valve seated until the movement of the float causes it to open. This is not widely favoured, however, because of both its complexity and possible difficulties in service owing to the mechanism's sticking.

If the float chamber partially or wholly surrounds the venturi, either an approximately semi-circular or horse shoe shape float is used, or two floats, one each side of the venturi, are joined by a yoke to form a similar configuration, Fig. 7.4. Such a float assembly has, mid-way between the ends of the semi-circles, a small bracket pivoted about a pin carried in the body casting. The needle valve is actuated by a lever-like extension of the bracket. Four-barrel carburettors almost invariably have two independent float chambers.

The earliest floats were of cork, and some still are, usually varnished or

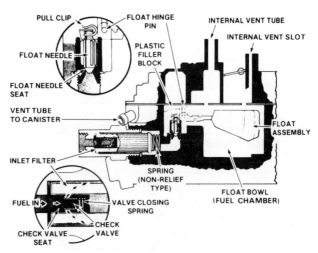

Fig. 7.2   The float chamber of the Rochester Varijet II carburettor with, inset to a larger scale, its needle and check valve assemblies

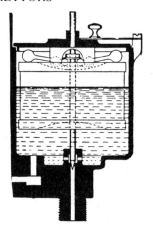

Fig. 7.3   Toggle type float valve mechanism on 1913 Zenith Standard carburettor. Later, similar mechanisms were used to pull overhead valves down on to their seats

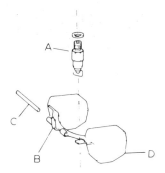

Fig. 7.4   Float mechanism on the Weber DFTH 4A carburettor
A: Needle valve, B, Yoke, C: Pivot pin, D: Floats

plastic coated for extra protection. Later, copper or other alloys were pressed and soldered to form robust hollow floats. Nowadays, however, plastics floats have been substituted, because they are extremely unlikely to either corrode, leak, absorb fuel, or fail owing to fracture. They have comprised variously of injection moulded polyamides bonded with formic acid, extrusion blow moulded polyacetal resins such as Delrin, or solid mouldings of expanded elastomers. The recent trend towards alcohol additives, notably methanol, in fuels has led to increasing use of acetal copolymers. Hollow plastics floats are now made from two parts either bonded or welded ultrasonically or thermally, radiant heat being preferred for the avoidance of a bead around the joint.

Float chambers must be vented to atmosphere, because it is the differential between the ambient pressure and that in the venturi that forces the fuel through the jets. Formerly this vent was simply a small hole in the top cover of the float chamber. However, with the introduction of regulations limiting the level of evaporative emissions, direct venting to atmosphere had to be abandoned and venting into the air intake upstream of the carburettor substituted. This extension of the carburettor is sometimes termed the *air horn*.

Venting into the air horn, however, can present a problem: if the engine is stopped whcn very hot, and the heat is conducted through the metal components to the float chamber, the fuel in it will evaporate into the horn; consequently, if the engine is restarted while still hot, the mixture drawn into the cylinders can be extremely rich and actually inhibit starting. On the other hand, if the float chamber is vented upstream of the air intake filter, it can wet it and contribute significantly to the blocking of the filter and, by increasing the depression over the jet, again enrich the mixture. To overcome these problems, some manufacturers incorporate a two-way valve in the venting system to switch the venting from one point to another as the throttle is opened from and closed on to its idling stop.

7.2   The venturi

All carburettors have a venturi, or choke, the function of which has been explained in Chapter 6. Generally it is of fixed diameter, though some have a variable diameter venturi. The latter are sometimes termed *constant depression*, or *constant vacuum*, carburettors. These and their basic principles will be described in Sections 8.3 to 8.10.

The engine designer has to decide what diameter venturi is best suited for the purpose for which his engine is intended. This is not easy since, if it is of large enough diameter to allow the air to enter with a minimum of losses at high speeds of engine operation, it will be too large to provide an adequate depression over the fuel jets at low speeds. He therefore has either to adopt a compromise aimed at optimum performance in the cruising range, which mostly means accepting something less than ideal for both ends of the speed range, or he must have a multi-venturi carburettor, which is more costly. In practice, the ratios of barrel to venturi diameter range from as low as 1.2:1 to as high as 3.0:1, the higher ratios being adopted where flexibility at low speeds is much less important than high power output.

Weber have produced some charts as an aid to the selection of venturi diameters. That in Fig. 7.5 is for in-line engines having up to six cylinders, for installation in family saloon cars. It can be seen that a 1 litre engine for this purpose would require a choke between about 19 and 22 mm diameter, and a single carburettor. Note however that, for a single or twin cylinder engine, the diameter should be taken generally as that indicated for an engine of approximately twice that size, which would be between 27 and 32 mm. This is because the induction manifold will be shorter and straighter and the area, and therefore viscous drag, of its walls smaller than that of a multi-cylinder engine, so more air will be drawn in at any given speed.

The curve in Fig. 7.6 is for a sports engine having one carburettor per cylinder. A single curve is drawn for each of three engine speeds, and the

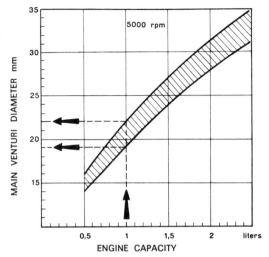

Fig. 7.5   Weber curves for selection of venturi diameters for 4- to 6-cylinder engines delivering maximum power at about 5000 rev/min. For a 2-cylinder engine, select a venturi corresponding to that of an engine of twice the cubic capacity (i.e. a 1 litre engine calls for 27-32 mm instead of 19-22 mm diameter venturi)

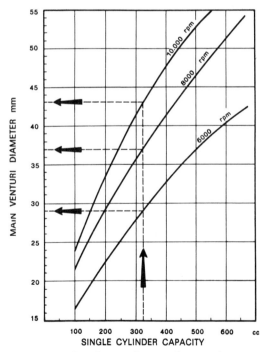

Fig. 7.6   The Weber curves for selection of venturi diameters for unsupercharged sports engines having one carburettor per cylinder

diameter of choke required is plotted against the capacity of a single cylinder. This curve is appropriate for obtaining maximum performance at the top end of the speed range, which is where it is needed for racing. Drivers of such cars are sufficiently skilled to be able, simply by slipping the clutch, to keep the engine speed up and thus avoid the problem that arises at low speeds. Because of the wide speed range of racing engines, it is impracticable to cater adequately for both ends.

7.3   The multiple venturi

Over the years, the speed ranges of engines for saloon cars have been increasing, and it is now common for two or three venturis to be installed in tandem, as illustrated in Fig. 7.7. This is sometimes termed a *double* or *triple diffuser* layout. For the large American engines in particular, even three venturis have been used because the induction tract is so large.

In principle, the first venturi delivers the air that passes through it into the low pressure area in the throat of the second, and so on. The main jet discharges into the upstream, or smaller, venturi. This arrangement has the advantage of improving the rate of vaporisation of the fuel. Additionally, the sleeve of dry air passing through the annulus between the main and supplementary venturi assembly surrounds the core of evaporating mixture and tends to prevent wet fuel from depositing on the walls of the manifold at least until it reaches the warmer areas closer to the engine. The depression over the main jet is high even at relatively low engine speeds. In general, in engines having multiple venturis, acceleration, cold starting and running,

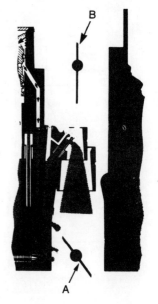

Fig. 7.7   A triple venturi assembly
A: Throttle, B: Strangler

and full throttle performance at low speed are enhanced. Note that, in all cases, the throttle must be downstream of the venturi, so that it can regulate the degree of manifold depression transmitted to the venturi. Moreover, in this position, it will not cause any turbulence in the flow over the fuel discharge orifices in the venturi.

7.4 A carburettor with simple compensation

The simple carburettor illustrated in Fig. 6.5 would be unsuitable, because the flow characteristics of air and gasoline, through a venturi and jet respectively, are not parallel and therefore cannot be made coincidental. In fact, as can be seen from Fig. 7.8, as the rate of flow of air through the venturi increases, and with it the depression, that of the gasoline through the jets increases more rapidly, so the mixture is said to become progressively *richer*.

In general, the percentage of time spent in any one speed range depends on the type of operation (urban or long distance etc). Idling to 5% power and from 75 to 100% full throttle may each account for 10% of the running time. The percentages between 5 and 45% and between 45 and 75% full throttle depend more on the style of driving.

The relative diameters of the venturi and main jets have to be such as to provide a chemically correct mixture at the most suitable part of the speed range, generally the most popular cruising speed. Compensatory measures

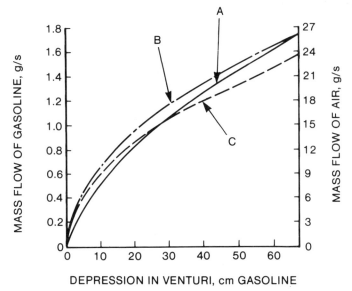

Fig. 7.8   Curves showing air and fuel flow characteristics
A: Fuel, B: Air with large venturi, C: Air with small venturi

must then be taken to either enrich or to weaken (as appropriate) the mixture as the speed of rotation rises above or falls below this design level. Three ways have been used to do this. One is by regulating the air flow, for example with a slide-valve to vary the size of the throat of the venturi. This device, actuated by a manual control lever and bowden cable has been common in carburettors for motorcycles. The slide valve is opened when the depression in the venturi is large, to correct for excessive enrichment of the mixture.

Another method of compensation is to have two jets, Fig. 7.9, and also illustrated in Fig. 6.6. This is sometimes called the *Bavery compound jet system*. The main jet feeds directly into the venturi, but the compensating jet is in the base of the float chamber and feeds fuel into a well which, like the float chamber, is vented to atmosphere. The fuel for compensation is drawn from the base of the well. Under all conditions of operation, fuel is drawn from both the jets. However, when the rate of fuel consumption is low and the well is full, the proportion of the fuel supply that is drawn from the base of the well is at its highest, because it is assisted by a relatively large head.

As the velocity of flow of air through the venturi, and therefore the depression, increases, fuel begins to be drawn out of the well faster than it can be replaced through the compensation jet. This reduces the head of fuel above the base of the well, and therefore also the rate of flow from the well to the venturi until, at maximum speed and load, fuel can be drawn from the well only at the rate at which it can pass through the compensation jet. At this stage, therefore, some air may be drawn from the well to mix with the fuel delivered through the compensation system.

The third method of compensation is the air bleed device, with which only

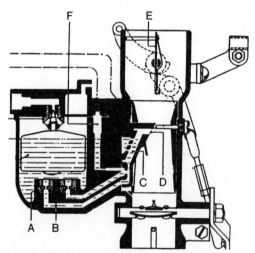

Fig. 7.9   Main and compensating jet system in the Zenith 30 VIG carburettor
A: Main jet, B: Compensating jet, C: Emulsion passage in spray tube, D: Discharge orifice, E: Strangler, F: Compensating jet well vented to float chamber

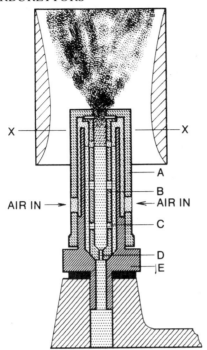

Fig. 7.10   An early Solex air bleed system
A: Jet cap, B: Jet tube, C: Atmospheric vents, D: Jet orifice, E: Jet carrier, XX: Static fuel level

one fuel jet is needed. An early Solex example, on an updraught carburettor, Fig. 7.10, serves well to illustrate the principle. The main jet is submerged below the fuel, in the lower end of a tube, the flanged upper of end of which is open to the depression in the throat of the venturi. In other applications, this type of tube is termed the *emulsion* or *diffuser tube*, but here it is called the *jet tube*. Air bleed holes are drilled radially into the jet tube: there can be as many as necessary for performing the compensation function. A thimble shape cap, with a central hole in its blind end, is passed over the jet tube to bear down on the flange at its upper end, and thus retain it. The lower end of this cap is screwed on to the jet carrier which in turn, is screwed into the body of the carburettor.

Interposed concentrically between the cap and jet tube is a tubular extension of the jet carrier, forming a well around the jet tube. Its upper end is clear of the inner face of the end of the cap, and therefore open to atmosphere through two diametrically opposite air holes, near the lower end of the cap, which are situated in the air intake upstream of the venturi.

As the throttle is opened and the well empties, air bleeds into the jet tube. This weakens the depression over the jet and thus reduces the flow of fuel through it, to offset the tendency towards enrichment of the mixture. There are numerous variants on this theme, one of which, on a Weber downdraft

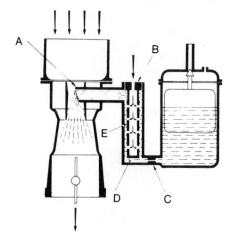

Fig. 7.11   A Weber air bleed correction system
A: Spray tube discharge nozzle, B: Air bleed jet, C: Main jet, D: Well, E: Emulsion tube

carburettor, is shown in Fig. 7.11. A similar Weber system, Fig. 7.24, has a rotary valve on the throttle spindle to close off part of the air supply to the emulsion tube when the throttle is wide open and thus to increase the depression in it to lift the level of the fuel in the well for power enrichment. Others are illustrated in *The Motor Vehicle*, by Newton, Steeds and Garrett (Butterworths). Incidentially, *The Motor Vehicle*, with its 880 pages, is among the most comprehensive treatises available on road vehicle design.

7.5   The spray tube

In most carburettors, the emulsified mixture of fuel and air is ultimately delivered through what is termed a *spray tube* or *spray nozzle* into the venturi. In Figs. 7.9 and 7.11, among others, this tube is set with its chamfered delivery end facing downstream, so that the air flow tends to increase the depression in it. In many instances, the spray tube is cast integrally with the main body of the carburettor or choke tube.

Several other arrangements have been used however. The alternatives range from simply a hole in the wall of the venturi to more complex systems. In some carburettors, the emulsion tube assembly is arranged coaxially with, and pointing upstream in, the venturi so that, as the depression draws the emulsified mixture out through holes near its upstream end, the airflow carries it downstream as the mixing process continues. Examples include the Solex B32-PBI-5 carburettor.

In the Zenith W type downdraught carburettor, Fig. 7.12, the emulsion tube is inclined at slightly less than 45° from the vertical, so that its lower end is in direct communication with the float chamber and its upper end projecting upstream into the venturi. The upper end is chamfered so that it is

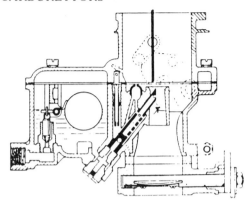

Fig. 7.12   In the Zenith W downdraught carburettor, the emulsion tube is inclined to bring its lower end into direct communication with the float chamber

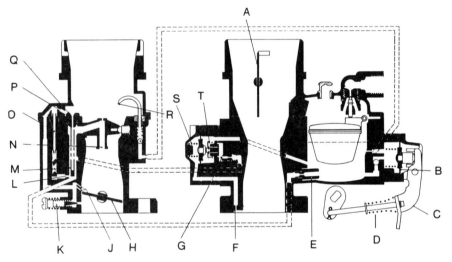

Fig. 7.13   In the Zenith IZ carburettor, the discharge nozzle of the spray tube is turned down parallel to the air flow and has an air bleed hole in its upper end
A: Strangler, B: Diaphragm type acceleration pump, C: Pump actuation lever, D: Lost motion device, E: Main jet, F: Calibrated restriction in depression duct to economy device, G: Supplementary fuel jet, H: Throttle valve, J: Idling progression holes, K: Idling mixture volume adjustment screw, L: Slow-running fuel flow restrictor, M: Main well, N: Spray tube discharge orifice, O: Slow-running tube, P: Air bleed orifice, Q: Air metering orifice, R: Acceleration pump delivery orifice, S: Depression-actuated economy device diaphragm return spring, T: Economy valve seating spring

parallel with the air stream, into which the emulsified mixture discharges. In the Zenith IZ carburettor, Fig. 7.13, the discharge tube is inclined about 20° upstream into the venturi but its upper end, instead of being chamfered, joins a tube coaxial with the venturi. The upstream end of the latter tube is closed except for a relatively small hole in it, through which air flows in quantities that increase with the velocity of flow, to assist in the emulsification process, and it discharges at its lower end.

7.6   Evaporation of fuel into the air stream

It should not be thought that all the fuel leaving the spray tube evaporates immediately, especially at wide throttle openings and only mild depressions, of perhaps no more than about 25 to 75 mm of mercury. The lighter fractions do, but the spray tube is usually designed to spread the fuel droplets as uniformly as practicable over the whole of the cross section of the venturi, and this may entail the heavier fractions tending to be flung against its wall. These fractions, dragged along by the incoming air, flow along the walls of the induction tract towards the inlet ports, evaporating as they go. Any liquid fuel remaining passes through the inlet valves and is evaporated by the heat of compression and the turbulence in the cylinder and combustion chamber. Naturally, the warmer the engine, the smaller the quantity of neat fuel remaining to be thus evaporated.

If the throttle is suddenly closed from full throttle operation, and therefore the pressure in the manifold lowered, the fuel flowing along its walls rapidly evaporates, giving an over-rich mixture. Indeed it may be so rich as to cause the lumpy and unsteady idling often observed following such an action. Once the conditions in the manifold have stabilised, its walls will become dry because the small quantities of fuel being metered into the manifold evaporate more rapidly in the severe depression then existing.

SPECIFIC REQUIREMENTS

7.7   Requirements for starting, idling and acceleration

Even with compensation, a simple carburettor, as described in Section 7.4, has no provision of starting and idling, in which conditions the flow of air through the venturi is inadequate to produce a depression large enough to draw fuel out of the jets. Nor does it incorporate any means for enrichment of the mixture when the throttle is suddenly opened to accelerate the vehicle. In the latter circumstance, although the air flow is suddenly increased, the fuel flow, owing to interia, lags behind the needs of the engine. Such a lag can even cause the engine to cut out because the mixture supplied to the cylinders is too weak to ignite.

Some lag in supplying adequate mixture, as distinct from adequate fuel, cannot be avoided since the inflow has not only to accelerate up to that required to supply the engine under its new steady state condition of operation, but also to increase the pressure in the manifold to its new level. The various devices for catering for starting, idling and acceleration will be described in the following Sections.

7.8 Idling and slow running devices

When the throttle is closed on to its stop, there is a venturi effect between its edge and the inner face of the wall of the throttle housing. Consequently, even though the volume of air entering the engine is too small to generate a significant depression in the venturi, it can create a strong local depression adjacent to the edge of the throttle. This depression is one of the two phenomena utilised for drawing gasoline from a slow running jet. The other is the fact that, as was explained in Section 6.6, the depression downstream (in the induction manifold) is much stronger than that upstream of the throttle valve. Advantage of both these factors is taken by positioning the discharge orifice for the slow running and idling system either directly opposite or slightly downstream of the edge of the butterfly when the throttle is closed on to its stop.

From Fig. 7.14, in which a simple idling and slow running system has been added to the air bleed system of the carburettor in Fig. 7.11, it can be seen that there are two adjustment screws. One has a taper end which projects into the hole below the edge of the throttle. This is used for setting the quantity of fuel delivered into the air, for adjusting the mixture for idling and the supply of emulsion for making the slow running mixture. The second screw is an adjustable stop, on to which the throttle valve closes. Without it, the throttle would close too tightly, and not only totally shut off the supply of air and fuel to the engine but also tend to jam shut, perhaps owing to contraction of the housing on to the throttle as the engine cools. Moreover, fine adjustment of the idling speed would be difficult.

From Fig. 7.14, it can be seen that the slow running jet is near the base of a vertical duct at the top the of which is an air corrector jet. It draws its fuel

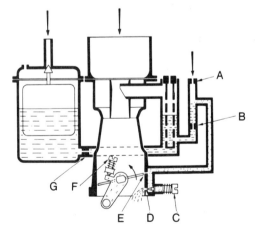

Fig. 7.14   A simple Weber idling system
A: Idling air jet, B: Idling fuel jet, C: Idle mixture adjustment screw, D: Idling fuel and progression emulsion delivery orifice, E: Progression orifice, F: Throttle stop adjustment screw, G: Main jet

from the main jet, but through a duct taken from the level of the lowest hole in the emulsion tube in the air bleed well into which the main jet discharges. Since the main jet is designed for much larger rates of flow of fuel than is the slow running jet, it does not offer any restriction to the flow for either idling or slow running.

As the throttle is opened, and fuel is drawn at an increasing rate from the well formed by the vertical duct containing the slow running and idling jet, the fuel level in it falls until air entering from the air corrector jet is mixed with the fuel passing into the idling and slow running system. This opening of the upper end of the slow running well to atmosphere through the air corrector jet offers the incidental benefit of preventing any tendency to syphoning, which otherwise might occur not only when the engine was stopped but also when the rate of flow of fuel required was very low.

An advantage of drawing the fuel from the main jet air bleed well is that when the throttle is wide open, and therefore the level of fuel in the well is below that of the air bleed holes in the emulsion tube, the supply of fuel to the slow running system is automatically cut off completely.

Indeed, at maximum power output (high speed with wide open throttle and heavy load) when the depression in the venturi approaches very high values and the manifold depression is virtually non-existent, the air flow in the idling and slow running duct is reversed, thus feeding extra air into the main jet air bleed system. This further helps to compensate for the tendency towards enrichment with increasing rate of air flow through the venturi. On the other hand, for high performance engines for racing, extra enrichment may be required to obtain maximum power, in which case the slow running and idling mixture may be taken directly from the float chamber.

Turning our attention now to the fuel supply for the idling system in Fig. 7.14, we see that a duct takes the fuel or air-fuel mixture from the vertical tube between the idling and slow running jet B and its air jet A down to a duct interconnecting two holes, one above the other, in the wall of the throttle housing, adjacent to the edge of the throttle when it is closed. In a carburettor in which the edge of the throttle comes very close to the adjacent wall of the throttle housing, it may virtually block off the upper hole, the main flow of fuel being delivered initially through the lower one the rate of flow from which is set by means of a taper ended screw for setting the idling mixture. Then, as the throttle is opened, the overall rate of flow increases because fuel is then delivered through both holes.

In some other systems, to obtain a progressive rate of increase of flow as the throttle is opened, the edge of the throttle in the closed position is either slightly upstream of or directly opposite to the upper hole. In such a case, when the throttle is closed on to its idling stop, fuel is delivered through the lower hole only, and air bleeds through the upper one into the duct interconnecting the two and is thus adding to that already mixed with the fuel being delivered through the lower one.

Alternatively, there may be one or more extra holes upstream of the throttle edge, or in some instances a vertical slot may replace all except the lowest hole. There may also be a taper ended screw for regulating an air supply through an air bleed orifice leading, in some instances, directly into the passage interconnecting the idle and slow running mixture discharge holes. The latter arrangement is sometimes termed *mixture control* over the idling and slow running system, to distinguish it from the *volume control* system, in which the taper ended screw varies the total quantity of mixture admitted. In all these systems, as the throttle is progressively opened, the quantity of fuel drawn off from the slow running discharge orifices decreases as that from the main jet increases.

7.9   Cold starting, manual chokes or stranglers

For starting from cold, when starter motors generally turn the engine at no more than between about 70 and 150 rev/min, a richer mixture is required than that provided by the idling and slow running system. In such conditions (of both cold and low velocities of flow) a high proportion of the fuel metered into and mixed with the air condenses out again, to be deposited on the cold walls of the induction manifold, and therefore does not reach the cylinders. Consequently the mixture in the cylinders is too weak to be ignited. Also, the lubricating oil, owing to its high viscosity when cold, exercises on the moving parts of the engine mechanism a drag that is too great for the power unit to overcome with its throttle closed down for warm idling.

The solution to this problem is twofold. First, what is termed a choke, or strangler, is introduced upstream of the venturi, as at A in Fig. 7.13, where the strangler valve is installed with its axis normal, instead of parallel, to that of the throttle valve. This is to avoid too much distortion of the flow into the manifold. Stranglers are generally butterfly valves. When closed, they increase the depression over all the jets, so that extra fuel is drawn from them. Secondly, a fast idle mechanism is introduced, to increase the engine

Fig. 7.15   Strangler with offset pivot and the spiral return spring that tends to hold it shut against the moment on the valve arising from the air flow and consequent differential pressure across it

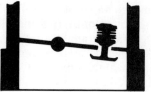

*Fig. 7.16   Anti-flooding
device, or depression relief valve*

speed under cold conditions, thus enabling it to develop enough power to overcome the extra drag.

A problem arises because drivers frequently forget to re-open the strangler once the engine has warmed up, thus causing waste of fuel, carbon deposition on the spark plugs, and dilution of the lubricating oil with fuel. This is in many instances partially overcome by offsetting the strangler spindle relative to the valve, and interposing a spiral spring between it and the linkage from the manual control, Fig. 7.15, in a manner such that the imbalance in loading on the areas of the butterfly on each side of the spindle, tend to open the strangler as the depression downstream of it, and therefore the volume flow of air past it, increases.

Even on strangler valves having offset spindles, what is sometimes termed an anti-flooding device is incorporated, as shown in Fig. 7.16. This is simply a poppet valve installed in a manner such that the depression downstream of the strangler opens it against the resistance offered by its return spring. The size of the valve and the strength of the spring are such that the air supply through it is adequate to prevent too much fuel from being drawn off from the jets.

With manually operated chokes, even those incorporating anti-flooding devices, a fast idle system is needed for the reasons already explained. It is generally a linkage between the lever that rotates the strangler valve and another that rotates a cam. The cam varies the position of the adjustment screw that limits the movement of the throttle towards the fully closed position, as described in the second paragraph of Section 7.8. This screw may be carried on one end of a lever, the other end of which is pivoted on the carburettor body and which is spring loaded on to the cam. The linkage is such that, as the strangler is closed, it progressively rotates the cam and thus causes it to lift the throttle stop adjustment screw, opening the throttle sufficiently for the engine to run smoothly and freely immediately after it has fired. Without such a fast idle system, the driver would have to exercise a degree of skill, which he or she might not possess, for holding the throttle pedal down to keep the throttle open just the right amount.

7.10 Automatic chokes

Automatic actuation generally entails control over the strangler valve by a bimetal coil, one end of which is attached to the spindle on which the valve is mounted and the other to some part of the carburettor body. This bimetal coil is subjected to either exhaust or water coolant temperature or is heated by an electric element switched on by the ignition key. Consequently, as the engine becomes cold, deflection of the bimetal coil closes the strangler valve, and *vice versa* or, if electrically heated, it is opened by the switching on of the heater element by the ignition key. An alternative to the bimetal spring is a capsule which, as its temperature increases, expands and actuates the lever on the end of the spindle that carries the strangler valve.

Originally, the bimetal coil was placed on the exhaust manifold, but reliability was difficult to achieve. A better way was found to be to draw hot air from over the manifold and to pass it through a jacket containing the coil. With the exhaust manifold close by, as described in Section 9.5, this is generally relatively easy. As an alternative, water heating is sometimes used but it entails a longer wait before the water becomes hot enough to cause the strangler to open. Electric heating is simpler but, operating on the basis of elapsed time instead of engine temperature, can be less satisfactory in some situations.

With automatic control, a fast idle cam having a lobe of continuous contour would present problems as regards calibration, adjustment and the effects of varying friction, which might prevent it from returning to its fully closed position when the engine was hot. Consequently, stepped cams with spring return mechanisms are generally used. Any number of steps can be incorporated, but there are mostly two or three. Under normal running conditions, the spring rotates the cam to set the throttle stop to its lowest position. As the engine cools, the temperature sensitive bimetal coil or capsule rotates the cam which, if its profile were a continuous curve, would lift the follower and thus progressively open the throttle. With a stepped cam, however, when the engine is started from cold, the first step comes up against the follower and further rotation is thus blocked. Consequently, before starting from cold, the driver has to depress his accelerate pedal momentarily, to open the throttle until it is clear of the stop. Then, when he releases the pedal, the throttle will close down on to the higher step that has been selected by the temperature sensitive element. A stepped cam device is described in detail in Section 7.12.

Many drivers prefer a manual control, because they can actually see whether the strangler is open or closed, but others prefer to trust in an automatic mechanism. With manual control, however, exhaust emission control goes by the board during warm-up, and can continue to do so if the driver subsequently forgets to open the strangler again. On the other hand, as compared with the starter carburettor, to be described in the next section, starting is quicker and the power output from the engine when cold is generally higher.

As soon as the engine has started, it needs more air to enable it to pick up speed. Consequently, devices are sometimes incorporated to obtain a more positive action than that afforded by an offset spindle on the strangler valve. Such a device, which has been used by Weber, is illustrated diagrammatically in Fig. 7.17. As previously described, the manual control compresses a coil spring (not shown in the illustration) which, in turn, bears

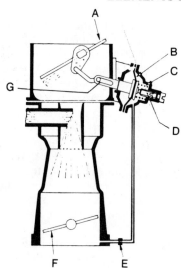

Fig. 7.17   This depression regulated strangler valve can be closed by a manually controlled lever but only within the limits of the lost motion slot in the diaphragm actuated rod
A: Strangler valve, B: Diaphragm, C: Diaphragm return spring, D: Adjustment screw, E: Depression restrictor, F: Throttle valve, G: Lost motion slot

on the strangler valve to close it. However, a lever at the opposite end of the strangler valve spindle is connected by a link to a lost-motion slot in the end of the actuating rod of a pneumatic control. The slot allows the strangler valve to be closed on to its stop provided the pneumatic control is not in operation.

When the engine starts, the depression in the manifold suddenly increases. This depression is communicated through the pipe taken from below the throttle valve to a chamber above the diaphraghm of the pneumatic control. As a result, the diaphragm is drawn upwards, compressing its return spring and retracting the slotted actuation rod attached to its centre. This takes up all the lost motion in the slot and opens the strangler valve by an amount that is determined by the adjustable screw stop above the centre of the diaphragm assembly. As a result, although the air flow can cause a moment to be applied about its offset pivot, and thus to open the strangler valve further within the limits of the lost motion slot, it cannot close beyond the limit set by the diaphraghm stop.

7.11   Auxiliary starting carburettor

An alternative way of enriching the mixture for starting is the use of an auxiliary starting carburettor. Originally, this was a separate unit, which could be mounted on or adjacent to the main carburettor, but later these devices were generally integrated into the body of the latter. Some were

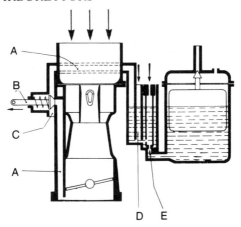

Fig. 7.18   Weber starting enrichment valve actuated manually by the control normally associated with a strangler valve
A: Starting mixture duct, B: Starting valve, C: Starting air jet, D: Starting reserve well, E: Starting fuel jet

brought manually into operation, while others were automatic. Mostly, separate passages were used to convey the starting mixture to the manifold, but with the tendency towards integration into the main carburettor, the idling ducts of the latter came to be more generally utilised for this purpose. When emissions control legislation was introduced, however, more sophisticated devices became necessary.

A very simple manually controlled auxiliary starting device is illustrated in Fig. 7.18. For starting from hot or cold, the throttle is closed right down on to a fixed stop, and bypassed by a separate air and fuel supply from the starting carburettor. When the valve B is pulled off its seat, by a cable connected to the strangler control lever on the dash, the depression downstream of the throttle valve is communicated through duct A to the fuel reserve well D, into which the fuel is fed through jet E. Fuel down from the well is mixed with air entering through orifice C. The mixture thus supplied is rich enough to compensate for condensation on the walls of the induction manifold and for starting the engine and allowing it to run up to a speed such that the power it develops is adequate to overcome the drag of the very viscous cold oil. Such a system can be refined by providing for progressive operation by interconnecting it with the throttle valve so that, as the starter control lever is returned, the butterly opens appropriately for the main to take over from the starter carburettor.

7.12   Zenith Auto-Starter

A typical example of a cold start device incorporating a thermostatically controlled stepped cam is the Zenith Auto-Starter used on the Zenith Stromberg CD4T and CD5T constant depression carburettors described in

Section 8.5. Its functions are to open the throttle slightly for cranking and idling during warm-up, and to supply extra fuel for these operating conditions and also for acceleration when the engine is cold.

In the Zenith Auto-Starter, the extra fuel is drawn from the main float chamber and supplied through the jet G in Fig 7.19 to the chamber between the throttle valve and the air slide. The flow through this jet is regulated by the tapered metering needle F linked to the bell-crank lever C, the position of which is determined by a coiled bimetal strip. This strip is secured at its outer end to its housing and at its inner end to the spindle that carries the bell-crank lever. It is housed in a dished cover over the cam and lever assembly. Cored in the outer face of this cast aluminium alloy cover is an internally finned jacket through which water is circulated from the engine coolant system.

As the engine warms up, the bimetal spring rotates the spindle anti-clockwise and thus plunges the needle deeper into the jet orifice to reduce the rate of flow of the fuel through it. As the engine temperature ultimately rises to that for normal operation, an elastomeric sealing ring around the shoulder of the needle totally cuts off the flow.

The stepped cam is not directly secured to its spindle, but is connected to it through the medium of a spiral spring. For this reason, before starting the engine from cold, the driver must first open the throttle and allow it to close again. This action rotates the lever L, to release the pin J, which is then lifted by its return spring clear of the cam, thus releasing the cam to allow the

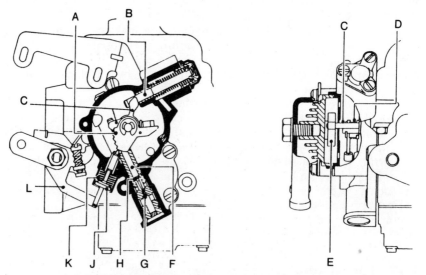

Fig. 7.19   The Zenith Auto-Starter, showing its depression actuator at the top and the tapered needle valve and fast idle pin respectively at approximately 5 and 7 o'clock
A: Stepped cam, B: Spring-actuated piston with depression retraction, C: Bell crank lever spindle, D: Torsion spring, E: Bimetal coil, F: Tapered metering needle, G: Starter fuel jet, H: O-ring seal, J: Fast idle pin, K: Return spring, L: Throttle stop lever

bimetal coil to rotate it to the position determined by its temperature. Thus, when the throttle is closed again, the lever L pushes the pin J down on the cam step appropriate for the temperature of the engine. As previously explained, this procedure is necessary because, whereas as the engine warms up, the pin can slide in turn from one step down on to the next, it cannot move successively back up the steps as it cools down again, unless the throttle is open.

To leave the device solely under the control of the bimetal spring, however, would not satisfy all requirements. Even a warm engine needs an enriched mixture for cranking and, with the carburettors for which this device is designed, if the vehicle were then to be accelerated away from rest, the engine would stall unless the mixture were once more momentarily enriched.

So, to provide an enriched mixture while the engine is bein cranked, the plunger B is retracted by its coil spring, pulling lever C to the right to rotate the cam so that the pin seats on the lowest cam. As soon as the engine fires, manifold depression communicated to the side of the plunger against which the spring bears, moves it out of its cylinder against the pressure exerted by its return spring, so that the end of lever C is then free to rotate within the confines of the lost motion slot in the end of the plunger rod. The length of this slot is adequate to allow the cam to rotate through the whole of the arc occupied by the steps on the cam. Should the throttle then be immediately opened, to accelerate the vehicle away from rest, the loss of manifold depression would release the plunger, again rotating the stepped cam to its richest setting.

ACCELERATION AND POWER ENRICHMENT DEVICES AND ELECTRONIC CONTROL

7.13   Enrichment for acceleration

Having got the engine started, we next want to accelerate the vehicle away. Acceleration calls for more power from the engine which, because of its inertia, will not respond instantly to the opening of the throttle. Moreover, the more sudden the opening, the more rapid will be the increase in pressure (reduction in the depression) in the induction manifold and this sets in train a whole series of reactions.

The high pressure in the manifold cuts the slow running jet out of operation. Reduction in pressure differential across the venturi, owing to the sudden rise in pressure downstream of it, reduces the rates of both the flow of fuel from the jets and its subsequent evaporation. Because the engine is still rotating relatively slowly immediately after the opening of the throttle, the rate of increase in flow of air through the venturi will be slow, though initially there will have been a momentary surge to relieve the depression in the manifold.

The resultant sudden increase in pressure in the manifold can cause

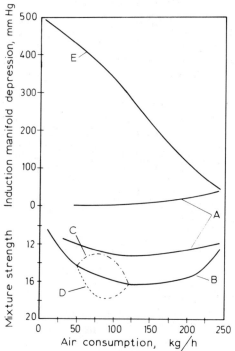

Fig. 7.20   During acceleration, the degree of enrichment of the mixture must not exceed that for full power
A: Curves relative to maximum power operation, B: Part throttle operation, C: Mixture strength that would be obtained without enrichment, D: Mixture strength required for good acceleration, E: Manifold depression

deposition of fuel on its walls, and hence a weakening of the mixture as described in the introduction to Chapter 9. Additionally because of the inertia of the fuel and its viscous friction in the jets, the supply of fuel will lag behind that of the air and the mixture become weaker. Indeed, in most instances, it will be so weak that the engine will misfire and its power output therefore fall.

To develop more power for accelerating both the engine and the vehicle, larger quantities of both air and fuel, in the appropriate proportions, are required. This is accomplished by spraying some extra fuel into the induction system so that, as the engine accelerates because the load arising from pumping the air through the throttle is reduced by its sudden opening, the power required can be obtained. The curves in Fig. 7.20 show typical airfuel ratio requirements and manifold depression levels as the throttle is opened. The departures from the part throttle curve are: at C, the lower air: fuel ratio needed for acceleration and at D, the air:fuel ratio that would be obtained without the introduction of the extra fuel. In general, for any given size of engine and a single carburettor, the larger the number of cylinders, the greater will be the quantity of the extra fuel needed for acceleration.

7.14   Static devices for acceleration enrichment

Several different methods have been used to supply the extra fuel precisely when required. The simplest is the drawing upon a reserve supply in a well. In many carburettors, for reasons that were described in Section 7.4, the main jet delivers into such a well, the top of which is open to the venturi, as in Fig. 7.21 among others. Since the rate at which fuel is drawn off from the reserve in this well is not restricted by any jet, the momentary increase in the flow of air through the venturi, owing to the opening of the throttle, will increase the depression in the venturi and will at least pick up some extra fuel from the well and provide some increased power, particularly when opening up from the lower end of the throttle range.

Although in some carburettors the main jet diffuser well is drawn upon for acceleration, others have a separate well for this purpose. An interesting supplementary device was used in some early Stromberg and Zenith carburettors. The air bleed into the well was restricted so that, at light throttle openings, the depression in the manifold drew the fuel in the well above its static level; then, when the throttle was then opened further, the level dropped and reserve of fuel thus made available discharged through the acceleration jet.

This, however, while adequate for some industrial engine applications, is not so for most automotive power units. Indeed, a more positive means of supplying the extra fuel can be regarded as essential in three circumstances:

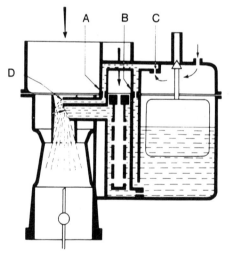

Fig. 7.21   Weber overfeeding system (jets and orifices A to D) for mixture enrichment, or compensation, as the throttle is opened. Some extra fuel will be drawn from the well up through the spray orifice S when the throttle is opened for acceleration from light throttle openings, but this will be inadequate for automotive applications, so an extra acceleration enrichment device is needed

A: Compensation mixture jet, B: Compensation fuel jet, C: Compensation air bleed, D: Compensation mixture delivery nozzle, S: Spray tube orifice in a multi-cylinder engine supplied by a single carburettor, for power units for sporting vehicles, and in any automotive engine in which the venturi is more than 22 to 24 mm diameter.

7.15   Acceleration pumps

In many instances, therefore, resort is made to interconnecting a simple plunger type pump mechanism with the throttle control in a manner such that, when the throttle is opened, the pump plunger is actuated to deliver fuel into the venturi. Generally, however, the interconnecting link and lever mechanism bears down not directly on the pump plunger but on a spring that it compresses against the plunger. With this arrangement, the plunger will be pushed down by the spring, but only as fast as the fuel will flow through the acceleration jet.

To avoid waste of fuel due to accelerator pump action when the throttle is opened only slowly, there is usually a restricted bypass duct or, more often, a small clearance between the periphery of the plunger and the cylinder in which it operates. The cross sectional dimensions of the bypass are such that it can accommodate the total flow from the pump up to a certain maximum value, which of course is that representing the speed of throttle opening at which extra fuel begins to be needed for acceleration.

The acceleration jet is calibrated to provide fuel at the rate required to provide the appropriate air:fuel ratio, which is higher than stoichiometric in order to provide the maximum obtainable increase in power. Even so, the acceleration pump jet or jets are selected to provide the extra fuel so far as practicable without detriment to economy. If too little is supplied, the acceleration will falter, or even stop, and there will be popping back in the carburettor. On the other hand, with too much fuel, the acceleration will again falter but, in addition, black smoke will issue from the exhaust. The position and direction in which the fuel spray is directed from the jet or delivery tube into the air flow may also be an important factor. In some instances, the best results are obtained by delivering the extra fuel from an aperture into the venturi on the side opposite to that on which, further downstream, the slow running mixture is discharged through the orifices into the air flow. The plunger type pump has the advantage that it is positive in action and its performance is consistent throughout the throttle range whereas, as explained in the next two paragraphs, that of the diaphragm type is not.

An obvious advantage of the diaphragm type, however, is that it does not require a precision-machined plunger and bore. Additionally, because it is actuated by manifold depression instead of a mechanical linkage, a series of points at which mechanical wear can take place are obviated. On the other hand, diaphragms too can be vulnerable to both wear and other forms of degradation and deterioration.

The effectiveness of such a pump is dependent on the degree of depression existing in the manifold before the throttle is suddenly opened, and so tends to be reduced at wide open throttle settings for cruising. It may be adequate

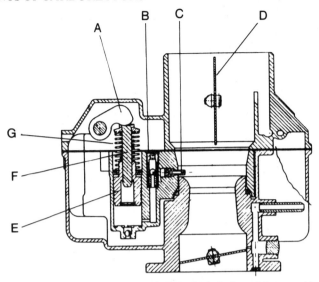

Fig. 7.22   On the Zenith IV carburettor, the shaft to which the lever A is secured is connected to the linkage controlling the throttle, the opening of which therefore actuates the acceleration pump A: Rocker connected to throttle control, B: Vent to allow thermally expanded fuel to pass into float chamber, C: Acceleration pump jet, D: Strangler valve, E: pump piston, F: Sliding connecting rod, G: Spring to delay action of pump

however if, at wide open throttle, the mixture is in any case amply rich to provide maximum power, and therefore the temporary weakening is less likely to cause the engine to actually hesitate.

At lighter loads, on the other hand, the throttle motion may start from only perhaps about 15° open, so the depression is adequate to compress the diaphragm return spring virtually instantly, leaving it pumping the fuel through the acceleration jet after the throttle has been opened and the depression consequently collapsed.

Mechanically actuated systems are illustrated in Fig. 7.22, and a diaphragm actuated system in Fig. 7.13. In the latter illustration, the function of the small bleed hole between the diaphragm chamber and the float chamber is to allow thermally expanded fuel to escape instead of being forced out through the acceleration discharge tube into the venturi. Each of the pumps illustrated has a non-return valve in its inlet and outlet. As the plunger or diaphragm is depressed, fuel is forced out through the outlet, though the delivery passages into the venturi. On its return stroke, the plunger or diaphragm draws fuel into the pump chamber through the inlet valve, ready for delivery again next time acceleration is demanded by the driver. Various ways have been used to actuate the pump by manifold depression. The simplest is to apply the depression to one side of the diaphragm, the fuel being in the pump chamber on the opposite side: the alternative of a diaphragm type actuator linked to the pump plunger is more complex and therefore is not now used.

7.16   Enrichment for maximum power

As was explained in the previous chapter, whereas for fuel economy it is necessary to provide extra air to burn all the fuel supplied, for maximum power, it is necessary to burn all the fuel, so a rich mixture is needed. Another consideration is that, at wide open thottle, a rich mixture will tend to obviate detonation, and thus increase engine life.

For engines with a single carburettor and only one or two cylinders, the increasing pulsation in the air flow rate as engine speed is reduced may be enough to weaken adequately the mixture from its maximum power value for economical cruising. Mostly, however, it is necessary on all automotive engines to make special provision, additional to using one of the flow correction devices mentioned in Section 7.4, either to weaken the mixture on pulling back the throttle from, or to enrich on its approach to the uppermost end of, its range. The overall effect of such enrichment is illustrated in Fig. 8.3 and described in the penultimate paragraph of Section 8.2.

The ideal carburettor, so far as reliability and freedom from maintenance are concerned, is one in which the only moving part is the throttle valve and choke control. Consequently, enrichment devices that are entirely automatic in operation and which have no moving parts are to be commended. One such device used in Weber carburettors, and called by them the *overfeeding device*, can be seen in Fig. 7.21. This was used in Section 7.14 as an illustration of a system capable of providing extra enrichment, through the main spray tube, for acceleration. The power system is entirely separate: it takes extra fuel from the float chamber and delivers it into the venturi, immediately upstream of the spray tube through which the fuel from the main jet is discharged. Fuel from the float chamber enters at the lower end of a vertical duct between the float chamber and the emulsion tube and well assembly. Three quarters of the distance up this duct is jet, which is widely termed the *power jet*. At its upper end it forms a T-junction with a horizontal duct. At the right hand end of the head of the T, as viewed in the illustration, is an air orifice open to the top of the float chamber. Air flows from the float chamber to the left to emulsify the fuel issuing from the power jet, and the emulsified mixture passes to the left-hand end of the head of the T, where it joins another duct that takes it down, through a calibrated bush and then parallel to the upper edge of the spray tube to discharge into the venturi. This system, activated by the depression in the venturi, is in operation over only the upper range of the throttle opening.

A similar arrangement is shown in Fig. 7.23. This however has no air orifice and emulsification system, so the delivery tube is extended to discharge at a point upstream of the venturi, and thus make extra provision for mixing after discharge of the fuel into the air stream. Not only is it in the air stream longer and evaporation encouraged by the progressive decrease in pressure during its subsequent passage through the venturi, but also it is subjected to additional turbulence as it passes over the mouth of the spray

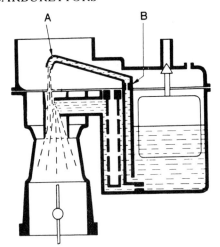

Fig. 7.23   This enrichment compensation system is similar to that illustrated in Fig. 7.21, except in that it has no air bleed for emulsification of the extra supply of mixture, which is why the fuel is delivered further upstream
A: Enrichment spray tube, B: Enrichment jet

tube and around its periphery. Indeed, in some carburettors the periphery of this tube has been designed specifically to generate micro-turbulence in the flow.

Among the devices for weakening the mixture as the throttle is closed from its maximum power range, instead of enriching it as it enters that range is one that has been used by Weber, Fig. 7.24. Air is taken from upstream of the venturi, through a duct down to a rotary valve at one end of the throttle spindle, whence another duct takes it up again, to supplement the supply to the emulsion tube. The valve is actuated by rotation of the throttle spindle, closing it as wide the open position is approached and opening it over the whole or only part of the remainder of the range as the throttle is closed, as necessary to compensate for the relative flow characteristics of the jets and venturi.

In other systems, a mechanical connection such as a lost motion linkage or a cam interconnects the throttle control and a lever opening or closing a poppet valve in the air bleed or fuel supply system or, alternatively, a depression actuated diaphragm, Fig. 7.25, performs this function. Tapered needle valves have also been used, the taper providing a progressive rate of increase and decrease of the extra fuel or air supply. Another arrangement used in some modern carburettors, notably Solex and Rochester, is simply to place the discharge orifice for the extra fuel from the power jet system upstream of the venturi, so that it will be subjected to a depression great enough to draw fuel from it only when the throttle is very wide open. Obviously, the simpler the system the less likely is it that difficulties will be experienced as regards calibration or maintenance, and the lower will be the cost.

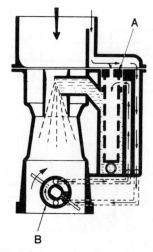

Fig. 7.24   When the throttle is wide open, the rotary valve at one end of its spindle closes the
supplementary air supply to the emulsifier well
A: Main air bleed correction jet, B: Rotary valve on end of throttle spindle

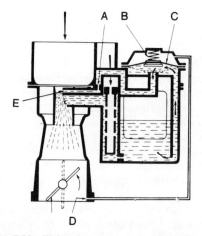

Fig. 7.25   Weber depression-actuated enrichment device
A: Enrichment jet, B: Diaphragm return spring, C: Diaphragm, D: Manifold depression connection, E: Enrichment delivery orifice

7.17   Electronically controlled carburation

With the increasing stringency of emission control regulations and the
upward trend in fuel costs from about 1973 onwards, there arose a need for
much closer control over mixture strength and combustion efficiency.
Moreoever, where catalytic converters are employed to oxidise any
unburned hydrocarbons remaining in the exhaust, a mixture that is too rich

will cause the catalyst to overheat and even self-destruct. It therefore became necessary to operate the fuel-air mixing system on the closed loop principle, using electric signals from an oxygen sensor in the exhaust. The only way to operate such a system is by electronic control.

Total electronic control of carburettors is a very complex task, which renders extremely complicated and costly what is otherwise an automatic system for mixing the air and fuel, the attraction of which has hitherto been its extreme simplicity and relative freedom from components liable to wear. Moreover, by adding electronics to what is, in effect, a hydro-pneumatic control, we are duplicating the control function. Therefore, it would appear to be almost inescapably easier to abandon the slightly imprecise hydro-pneumatic control in favour of the potentially very flexible and precise totally electronic system. In other words, metering can be performed more economically and reliably by gasoline injection, so there is little point in this chapter in going into detail on the basic principles of electronic control of carburation as practised so far.

However, it is not impossible that some manufacturer will eventually come up with a simpler system. For example, it does not seem unreasonable to envisage a carburation system that supplies over the whole operating range a slightly weaker mixture than is required, but which is trimmed continuously to bring the mixture precisely up to the strength appropriate to the instantaneous conditions of operation. The trimming might be done with an electronically regulated supplementary supply of fuel through either a jet or an injector, under closed loop control based on a lambda sensor in the exhaust. On the other hand, adding even the simplest of electronic equipment must add significantly to the total cost. After all, the basic advantage of the carburettor can be said metaphorically to be that it thinks for itself, whereas an injection system is totally unintelligent and therefore calls for the addition of an electronic brain to think for it.

Chapter 8

Constant Depression and Fixed Venturi Carburettors in Practice

So far, we have covered only the fixed venturi type carburettor and its components and sub-systems. Now, the theory of an entirely different type of carburettor, namely the *variable venturi*, or *constant depression* type will be covered. Subsequently, some actual carburettors of both the variable and fixed venturi type will be described, so that the reader may gain a better overall picture of the arrangement and working of a carburettor in practice. The fixed venturi carburettors of course comprise various combinations of the different components and sub-systems described in Chapter 7.

CONSTANT DEPRESSION TYPES

8.1   The constant depression type carburettor

The main disadvantage of the fixed diameter venturi is, as has been previously noted, that the flows of air and gasoline through a venturi and jet respectively are not equally proportional to the velocity of the air, and therefore to the depression, in the venturi. To overcome this, the variable venturi, or constant depression, carburettor was invented. In this type of carburettor, the flow through the venturi is constant over most of the speed and load range, and it also has the advantage of requiring only one jet, instead of all the compensation jets and other devices of the fixed choke carburettor.

The rate of flow of air into the engine is varied by means of a conventional throttle valve. A constant depression over the one and only jet is maintained by an automatically actuated *air valve*, in the form of a slide-valve, usually cylindrical, moving vertically in the venturi in response to changes in manifold depression with varying degrees of throttle opening, Fig. 8.1. At the same time, a calibrated tapered needle, hanging vertically downwards from the bottom of the slide valve, extends into the jet below, to vary its effective size. The taper on the needle is designed to maintain continuously the correct air:fuel ratio, regardless of variations in the volume of air flowing through the venturi owing to movements of the slide valve.

128

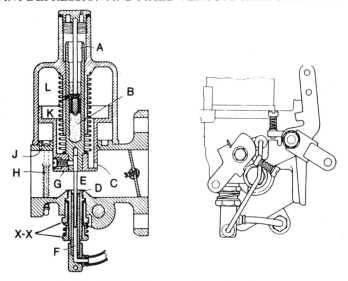

Fig. 8.1   The SU HS constant depression carburettor
A: Piston rod, B: Oil well, C: Vent from constant depression chamber to chamber above piston,
D: Flanged bush carrying jet in bridge, E: Jet needle, F: Jet sleeve, G: Air valve, H: Pin for lifting
piston manually, J: Atmospheric vent to underside of piston, K: Piston, L: Cylinder

As with the fixed venturi carburettor, the variable venturi is upstream of the throttle valve but, as previously mentioned, the depression that draws the fuel through the space of varying size around the needle in the jet orifice is virtually constant. This depression is usually of the order of 230 mm head of water, which is adequate for good vaporisation and atomisation of the fuel, yet without significantly impeding the filling of the cylinders.

Automatic operation of the assembly comprising the air valve and jet needle is effected by manifold depression, acting on either a piston or a diaphragm at the upper end of the air valve. The lower end of this valve is flat and, when the engine stops, closes on to a *bridge*, in which the jet is housed.

8.2   Mixture strength characteristics—fixed and variable venturis

At this point, it will be of interest to compare the mixture strength characteristics of the fixed and variable venturi carburettors. In Fig. 8.2, the full line curve shows air:fuel ratio characteristics for a constant depression carburettor. The fitting of a needle the diameter of which has been increased slightly over the middle of its length, gives a weak mixture over the cruising range, with enrichment for both maximum power and light load and idling. Since the air:fuel ratio is a function of both air and fuel flows, not of throttle opening, and these are regulated respectively by the air and needle valves, manual enrichment for cold starting, indicated by the dotted curve, is

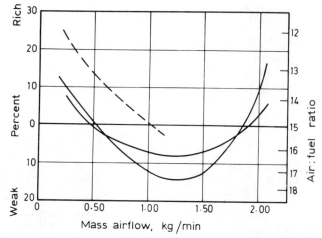

Fig. 8.2   *Characteristic mixture curves for constant depression carburettors. The broken line shows the enrichment curve for cold starting; the full line curve, part of which is parallel to it, is characteristic of a carburettor fitted with a needle of larger diameter over its mid portion but more steeply tapered at both ends than that represented by the third, flatter, curve*

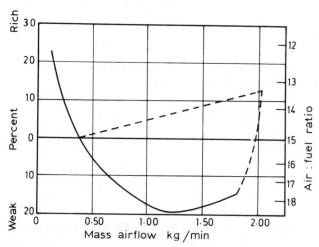

Fig. 8.3   *Characteristic curve for a fixed diameter venturi carburettor. The curved broken continuation line indicates the range over which the power jet is in operation, while the straight portion shows how the mixture strength falls as the load is increased from the point at which maximum power is developed and the engine speed is therefore falling*

obtainable only by lowering the jet. This is generally done by a means of a cable control similar to that for the strangler, or choke, of a fixed choke carburettor.

With a fixed venturi, on the other hand, the power jet gives what is termed a *dual characteristic*, Fig. 8.3. Here the full line shows the enrichment obtained as the throttle is opened beyond the cruising range to increase the power up to maximum output. The broken line continuation curve shows the effect of the power jet coming into operation. The straight portion takes the end of the latter to the point at which the full line curve meets the line showing the chemically correct mixture and illustrates the effect on mixture strength of further increases in load which, because the rotational speed is falling, is causing the engine to inhale the mixture at a progressively reducing rate (hence the simultaneous falling power output). At the low end of the speed range, the enrichment indicated by the rise of the full line is necessary to compensate for the dilution of the charge by exhaust gas which, incidentally, is aggravated in engines having a large valve overlap.

The first constant depression carburettor was invented by George Skinner as early as 1905, shortly before he founded the SU Carburettor Company to produce it. It had a leather bellows to actuate the piston, though subsequently the SU company has consistently used a piston type while Stromberg has favoured the diaphragm type actuator. Mechanical actuation of the slide valve, by means of a linkage connecting it with the throttle control, is practicable, but not for automotive engines. The most recent radical new development was the early 1980s, when Ford introduced their VV (variable venturi) carburettor, which had a horizontally moving air valve on an arm mounted on one end of a pivot pin. On the other end of this pin is a second arm approximately parallel to the first, but connected to a diaphragm type actuator, Fig. 8.12.

8.3   The SU carburettors

Features of the SU HS carburettor illustrated in Fig. 8.1 are as follows. The piston and air valve are integral and have a piston rod A, which slides in a precision ground bore B in a long boss machined coaxially with bore of the suction chamber. Depression from the constant depression chamber (between the throttle and air valve) is communicated, through a pair of vent holes C, to the portion L of the suction chamber above the piston, while the chamber beneath the piston is vented to atmosphere through the hole J. The lifting of the piston by the depression is opposed by its weight plus the force exerted by a return spring. This spring is of very low rate so that, over the whole of the piston stroke, the return force is preponderantly that of gravity on the mass of the piston and is therefore virtually constant. Consequently, the deflection of this piston is a function of the mass of air passing through the variable venturi beneath it.

As can be seen from the illustration, the fuel enters from the float chamber, through a connection at the bottom end of the jet sleeve F. For cold starting, this jet sleeve can be raised or lowered to override the basic setting, for instance by cam and link connections to the manual strangler control lever on the dash and to the throttle, to open it slightly for fast idling. In this particular design, the float chamber can be bolted to either side of the carburettor, to suit individual engine installations and layouts.

The jet sleeve is a close fit in the flanged bush D, which is a clearance fit in the bridge. On assembly, the jet sleeve and bush are together centred relative to the bore of the suction chamber, and thus to the piston and needle. Then the upper of the two nuts X-X is tightened to secure the whole assembly by clamping the flange of the bush against the shoulder on which it seats in the bridge. The lower nut is used subsequently, after loosening the upper one, for mixture adjustment.

A counterbore in the upper end of the piston rod forms a well, which is filled with oil. The top of this well is closed by a screw cap integral with which is a pendant rod with, at its lower end, a damper head which is beneath the surface of the oil and a fairly close fit in the counterbore. Vertical displacement of the depression-actuated piston forces oil through vertical holes in the head. On the upward stroke of the piston (relatively equivalent to a downward stroke of the damper), a plate-valve closes over the vertical holes.

It follows that, when the throttle valve is suddenly opened, the motion of the air valve lags behind it, so the depression over the jet is temporarily intensified to enable the flow through the fuel jet to increase in line with the rate of increase of the air flow. This obviates the need for an acceleration pump. On closure of the throttle, the plate valve opens to offer only minimal resistance to the associated downward motion of the slide valve.

8.4 Reduction of exhaust emissions

With the imposition of emission control regulations, certain modifications were introduced, which were subsequently incorporated in a new design, Fig. 8.4, called the HIF (Horizontal, with Integral Float Chamber). This is a compact unit having its float and float chamber concentric with the jet, from which it follows that the level of the fuel in the float chamber hardly varies at all with changes in inclination of the vehicle or acceleration, including that due to braking or cornering. A linear ball-bearing is interposed between the piston rod and its housing, to reduce friction and thus increase the accuracy of metering.

The jet needle is spring-loaded against one side of the jet, so that its orifice coefficient does not vary, as it would if it were centrally disposed but intermittently deflected off centre. To obtain this bias to one side, a spring, axially in line with, and bearing on a collar around the upper end of the needle, pushes it down against a peg beneath one side of the collar. This tilts the needle, causing its lower end to bear against one side of the jet orifice. Because the needle and jet no longer have to be centred relative to each other, the jet can be a close fit in its housing in the bridge. In fact, the jet is pressed into an aluminium tube, the lower end of which is pressed into a plastics moulding called the *jet head*.

At small throttle openings, a bypass emulsion system, Fig. 8.5, comes automatically into operation. Mixture flowing out of the jet is deflected into a slot downstream of it, and thence through ducts to a point just downstream

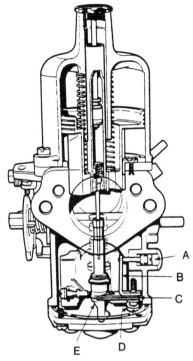

Fig. 8.4   The SU HIF carburettor with its float arranged concentrically around the jet assembly
A: Jet adjustment screw, B: Bell crank lever, C: Bimetal strip, D: Pivot screw for bimetal
assembly, E: Jet head

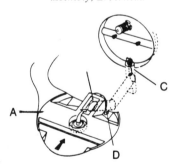

Fig. 8.5   SU HIF part-throttle emulsion bypass system
A: Bridge, B: Slot downstream of jet, C: Delivery port in line with edge of partly open throttle,
D: Bypass duct

of, or in line with the edge of the throttle valve, when it is closed or slightly open. The intense depression at this point draws the fuel from the jet into the idling system, and the high velocity of the air flow atomises the fuel and mixes it thoroughly with the air.

For cold starting, the mixture is enriched by the device illustrated in Fig.

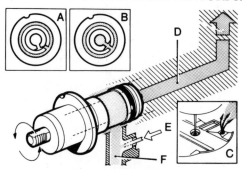

Fig. 8.6   SU HIF cold starting enrichment device. The scrap views A, B and show respectively two positions of the rotary valve spool, and the fuel discharge port in a slot to one side of the part throttle bypass slot in bridge
D: Delivery duct to bridge, E: Air bleed, F: Fuel from float chamber

8.6. Extra fuel is drawn directly from the float chamber, upwards past an air-bleed hole to emulsify it, and into the sleeve of a rotary spool-valve. The emulsion then passes on through a radial hole in the spool into a counterbore in one end, out of which it then flows into the passage from which it is discharged downstream of the bridge, into the constant depression chamber. It is of course the depression over the discharge hole that draws the fuel up from the float chamber.

The spool is rotated in the stationary sleeve by a lever type cam-follower actuated by what would, with a conventional carburettor, be described as the strangler or choke, which simultaneously actuates a fast idle mechanism. Rotation until its radial holes do not line up with those in the sleeve, cuts off the flow. However, as can be seen at A and B in Fig. 8.6, a groove is machined tangentially across the spindle where the radial hole breaks out of it, so that the flow starts and stops progressively.

To prevent irregular firing and explosions in the exhaust during overrun, there is a small, spring-loaded poppet valve in a hole in the butterfly valve, similar to that in Fig. 7.16. The intense depression in the manifold when the throttle is closed pulls this valve open and thus allows a small quantity of the air-fuel mixture to pass through to maintain regular combustion.

Compensation for variations in the viscosity of the gasoline with changes in temperature is provided by a bimetal strip regulating the height of the jet tube assembly relative to the needle, Fig. 8.4. The bimetal spring assembly is in the form of a bell crank lever. Around the pivot screw is a coil spring that causes the lever to rotate until the upper end of the bell crank is stopped against the end of an adjustment screw in the side of the float chamber. Clockwise rotation of the adjustment screw of course enriches the mixture and *vice versa*. The setting is effected on assembly and then, to discourage subsequent tampering, a plug is inserted into the countersink containing the head of the screw.

To draw off the crankcase emissions and burn them in the engine cylinders, a tube is taken from the constant depression chamber to the

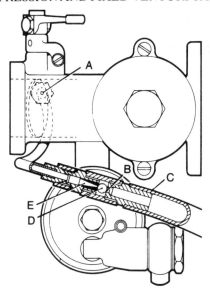

Fig. 8.7   SU device for weakening the mixture for economical cruising
A: Connection to induction passage, in line with edge of throttle when slightly open, B: Calibrated
orifice, C: Connection to air intake, D: Vent to float chamber, E: Small calibrated venturi

crankcase. A vent, usually in the oil filler cap, allows fresh air to enter the
rocker or cam box and to pass on down into the crankcase to replace the
fumes as they are drawn out. Because the emissions are discharged into the
constant depression chamber, the venting does not interfere with the slow
running mixture supply, nor is there any risk of excessive depression from
the manifold being transmitted to the crankcase. On cars equipped for
evaporative emission control, Sections 13.22-25, venting may be done
through the carbon canisters, to help to purge them.

A device that has been used on some SU carburettors to weaken the
mixture for cruising is illustrated in Fig. 8.7. It is a system for venting the
float chamber two ways, through a T-connection. The leg of the T is the vent
from the float chamber, one arm communicates with atmospheric pressure
in the air intake while the other is connected to a port adjacent to the edge of
the throttle valve. This port is positioned so that, when the throttle is closed
or slightly open, it is in the constant depression chamber; but, as the throttle
is opened further, for cruising, its edge sweeps past the port, exposing it to
manifold depression.

The connection communicating with the constant depression chamber
contains a venturi, and the flow through it is further restricted by a calibrated
orifice. Consequently, at full throttle, when the depression throughout the
manifold and constant depression chamber is minimal, the float chamber is
virtually at atmospheric pressure. Over the medium throttle range, the
depression transmitted to the float chamber is high because the flow across
the arms of the T is limited by the restriction, through which the velocity of

the air cannot exceed that of sound. At light load, the pressure in the float chamber is again almost atmospheric, because the hole is open to the constant depression chamber in which, with the throttle almost closed, the depression is small.

8.5   The Zenith Stromberg constant depression carburettors

As can be seen from Fig. 8.8, the principal difference between the SU and Stromberg constant depression carburettors is the use in the latter of a diaphragm instead of piston actuated slide valve. The provisions for cold starting also differ: on the Stromberg CD, a semi-cylindrical bar seats in a groove across the bridge, the flat side of the bar forming a continuation of the profile of that part of the venturi. When the strangler control is actuated however, it rotates the bar so that one edge of its circular section lifts the slide-valve, thus partially blocking the choke aperture and restricting the air flow through it, while also lifting the needle to increase the flow of fuel through the jet. A link and cam mechanism connected to the strangler control simultaneously opens the throttle slightly to increase the idling speed.

The CD model was superseded by the CDS, CDSE, CD4 and CD5 units which were introduced to meet progressively increasing demands for tighter emission control. If an Auto-Starter, described in Section 7.12, was fitted, the letter T was added so that they became CDSET, CD4T etc. All have, instead of the bar, a rotary disc valve for supplying additional fuel for cold starting.

This disc is illustrated in the scrap view in the illustration of the CDSE, Fig. 8.8(b). When the strangler control is operated, the disc rotates until the series of small holes near its periphery, which had been previously blanked off, progressively open into a slot into which fuel flows from the float chamber. Passing through these holes to the far side of the disc, the fuel then flows back again, through a larger hole diametrically opposite the previously mentioned series, into a second slot from which it passes into the *mixing chamber*, which is the term Stromberg use to describe what SU call the *constant depression chamber*.

The main jet is fixed and adjustment for idling is effected by means of a

---

Fig. 8.8   Zenith-Stromberg CDSE constant depression carburettor: (a) section; (b) left hand side, as viewed from the engine, with scrap section of rotary disc valve for enrichment for cold starting; (c) right hand side, with scrap view in which on the right is the throttle bypass and, on the left, the bridge bypass containing bimetal automatic mixture control and idling trimming screw A: Diaphragm, B: Air valve, C: Jet needle retainer assembly in base of damper tube, D: Jet (in bridge), E: Float, F: Duct from constant depression chamber to chamber above diaphragm, G: Damper well, H: Screw for flow calibration by adjusting depression above diaphragm, J: Damper head, K: Diaphragm return spring, L: Rotary disc valve, M: Throttle bypass cover, N: Bimetal strip, O: Automatically controlled valve, P: Adjustment for idling emission control, Q: Depression-actuated throttle bypass valve, R: Diaphragm

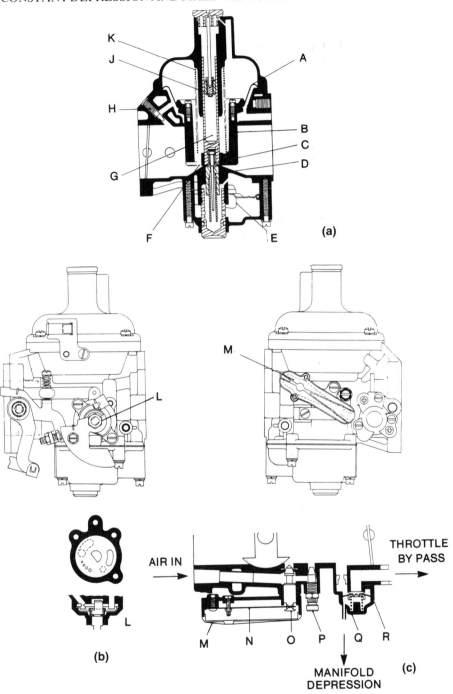

(a)

(b)   (c)

screw, the end of which forms a needle-valve for limiting a supply of air bypassing the air valve, through a duct from the air intake to the mixing chamber, shown in the scrap section in Fig. 8.8(c). Since this chamber communicates with that above the diaphragm for actuating the slide valve and jet needle, an adjustment increasing the rate of air bleed into it lowers the needle and *vice versa*. The adjustment is carried out, during dynamometer tests, to reduce the quantities of carbon monoxide in the exhaust gas. A similar system for bleeding air into the mixing chamber, but controlled automatically by a bimetal strip, is used to adjust the mixture as the engine warms up. This is shown in the same scrap section.

On the CD4, however, adjustment to the mixture is made by raising and lowering the needle relative to the jet. A special tool is inserted down the damper tube to turn the adjustment screw, B in Fig. 8.9, at the upper end of the needle. The needle is biased to one side of the jet orifice in a manner similar to that in the SU carburettors, except in that the needle is spring loaded in a carrier housed in the piston, the head of the needle being tilted by either a peg or a swaged tag. This device is used also in the CDSE.

On the CD4 and CD5, a two-way float chamber venting system is used, as shown also in Fig. 8.9. Under normal running conditions, actuated by a linkage connected to the throttle control, the valve B is moved to the left to close vent A and open the duct C venting to a point upstream of the air valve. When the throttle is closed, however, the linkage closes C and opens A. The latter is connected to a point upstream of the air cleaner so that, if heat soak causes fuel to boil out of the float chamber, it will not collect in the horn of the carburettor and inhibit restarting.

Another feature of these two carburettor models is the incorporation of the overrun valve in the body of the carburettor, instead of in the butterfly, though a few examples were made with the latter arrangement. It is a depression-actuated valve in a duct bypassing the throttle butterfly, Fig. 8.8(c), to allow some mixture to get through to the cylinders to maintain regular firing when the throttle is closed.

Further to improve the quality of mixture control under idling conditions is what is termed the *downstream discharge circuit with idle regulator,* Fig. 8.10. Manifold depression draws a proportion of the fuel issuing from the jet through the calibrated orifice C to a point D downstream of the throttle butterfly. As the throttle is opened and the edge of the butterfly passes downstream of the point of discharge, the system ceases to operate.

Air enters the downstream discharge circuit past the tapered end of the adjustment screw A, by means of which the idling mixture can be regulated. This screw is in fact two, one inside the other. The outer screw has a coarse thread, and its adjustment is made in the factory and locked. In contrast, the inner screw has a fine thread and can be adjusted in service, to alter the idling mixture strength by about ± half an air:fuel ratio. Idling speed is adjusted by the throttle stop, F, in Fig. 8.9.

In the CDSE, a very simple temperature compensation device is employed to correct for changes in fuel viscosity with temperature. A set of four radial emulsion holes is drilled fanwise around the side opposite that

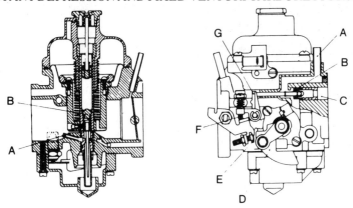

Fig. 8.9   Zenith-Stromberg CD4 constant depression carburettor. Left, section showing needle jet arrangement;
A: Air jet for temperature compensation device, B: Jet needle adjustment screw
Right, two-way venting system;
A: Vent to atmosphere, B: Vent valve, C: Internal vent, D: Fast idle cam, E: Fast idle adjustment screw, F: Throttle stop, G: Throttle control lever

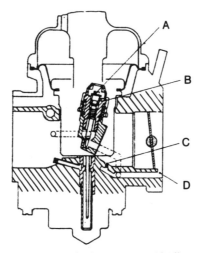

Fig. 8.10   CD4 downstream discharge circuit with idle regulator
A: Adjustment screw, the fine thread, B: Adjustment nut, coarse thread, C: Calibrated orifice in bridge, D: Downstream discharge hole

against which the biased needle bears in the jet, but downstream of the section that is narrowed by that needle. Air is metered to them through a duct with a calibrated orifice in its outer end, which is in the ramp leading up to the bridge from the air intake. This emulsifies the fuel passing up to the narrowed section of the jet. Its effect in the avoidance of unstable idling owing to over-enrichment is especially noticeable.

A SIDEDRAUGHT CONSTANT DEPRESSION CARBURETTOR

8.6   The Ford VV carburettor

A shortcoming of both the SU and Stromberg types of carburettor is that they are suitable only for sidedraught or semi-sidedraught installations, so they cannot be accommodated in some vehicles, especially those powered by V-engines. The Ford VV (Variable Venturi) unit was introduced for use where downdraught carburettors are needed. It has a separate idling system, which although adding to complexity and cost, gives tight control over emissions.

In the Ford VV carburettor, the slide valve is pivoted on a pin in the upper end of one arm of a vertical lever, the lower end of which is clamped to a pivot pin, Fig. 8.11, so that it slides horizontally, thus opening away from or closing on to the metering block, or bridge, in a vertical variable venturi. At light load, the gas speed, at about 90 m/s through the variable venturi of this carburettor, is about 7-10 times that through a comparable fixed venturi at small throttle openings. This, Ford claim, approximately halves the CO output during operation on the EEC 15 urban cycle.

As in the other constant vacuum carburettors, the jet needle is carried in the end of the slide valve, but of course horizontally disposed. Again, the needle is biased to one side of the jet orifice. This is done by means of a coil spring in tension, one end being connected to the lower end of the swinging arm and the other to the end of the slide valve, to swing it about its pin in the upper end.

The lower end of this arm is clamped to a spindle on which, side-by-side with it, is a second arm the upper end of which is connected to the centre of a rolling diaphragm, Fig. 8.12. This diaphragm moves the lever and therefore also the slide valve. As in the SU and Stromberg constant depression carburettors, it is subjected on one side to the depression in the *control chamber*, which is the term Ford use to describe the mixing, or constant

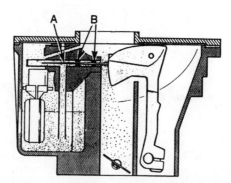

Fig. 8.11   Ford VV carburettor, showing the needle in the tandem main jets and, above them, the float chamber vent
A: Jet needle, B: Two jets, the inner one for fuel and the outer for emulsion

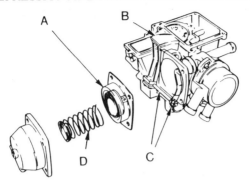

*Fig. 8.12   Constant depression control, showing how the needle carrier arm and diaphragm arm
are mounted on a common spindle
A: Diaphragm assembly, B: Jet needle arm, C: Assembly comprising the pivot and jet needle and
diaphragm arms, D: Diaphragm return spring*

depression, chamber. The other side of the diaphragm is vented to atmosphere.

The throttle valve is rotated by lever carrying on its outer end a roller follower running in a cam slot in one arm of a bell-crank lever, the other arm of which is connected to the throttle pedal. By virtue of the shape of the cam slot, the throttle is opened relatively slowly over the initial portion of its travel and more rapidly over the last portion. This gives good control when starting from rest and during gear changes. Normally, control movements in excess of about half throttle are not required, except for short bursts of acceleration, which of course is when rapid opening is required.

8.7   Float chamber and main jet

Features of the float chamber, Fig. 8.13, include a Viton tip on the needle valve, for good sealing. To avoid wear due to chattering of the valve, which could occur for instance when driving over pavé, a spring loaded pad is housed in its end that bears on the end of the lever carrying the float. Venting is effected through a duct to the constant depression chamber, immediately downstream of the carburettor air valve, so that the pressure over the fuel in the float chamber is sensibly constant regardless of the state of the air cleaner, but higher than that in the throat of the venturi.

As in the other constant depression carburettors, any variation in depression in the control chamber, due to the opening or closing of the throttle, is communicated through a duct to the face of the diaphragm appropriate for opening the slide valve, against its return spring, to the degree required for bringing the depression in the control chamber back immediately to its constant value. The rate of supply of fuel is of course determined by the corresponding axial movement of the needle in the jet.

In detail, the jet is of especial interest since, as can be seen in Fig. 8.11, it

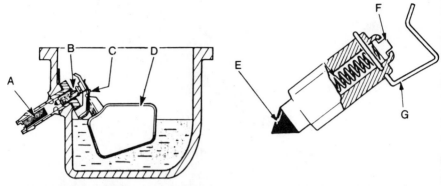

Fig. 8.13   The float and its needle valve assembly with, right, an enlarged view of needle valve
A: Filter thimble, B: Needle valve, C: Float pivot, D: Float, E: Viton tip, F: Spring-loaded pad,
G: Spring clip

actually comprises two jets in tandem. That nearest the float chamber is for metering the fuel, while that nearest the venturi is for controlling the depression transmitted to the fuel jet. An advantage is that, as the shoulder of the needle closes towards the depression jet, it has no effect on the discharge coefficient of the fuel jet orifice. The position of this main jet assembly is not adjustable in service. Instead, that of the needle together with its threaded holder is adjusted by rotating it in the carrier, while checking the CO content of the exhaust gas.

8.8   Idling system

For idling, the throttle is stopped in the slightly open condition, to allow for adjustment of idling speed and so that it will not be gripped as the throttle barrel cools after the engine has been switched off. About 30% of the fuel for idling is drawn through the main jet, 70% passing through a separate idling system, Fig. 8.14. This, as previously mentioned, allows much closer control over the idling air:fuel ratio to be obtained than would otherwise be possible.

Essentially, the idling system is a duct taking fuel from that serving the main jet. After the air is drawn through a bleed hole, it bypasses the throttle valve, to discharge an emulsified mixture just downstream of it into the induction manifold. Both the fuel and air bleed jets for the idle system are in a Delrin insert in the metering block, or bridge. They are of very small diameter for two reasons: first, with the throttle closed on to its stop for idling, the depression is high; and, secondly, the rate of flow of fuel required for idling is small. This is fortunate since the bleed back of air into the main jet system during operation between light and full load is therefore negligible. Three other features of the idling system are of interest.

First, just before the duct breaks out into a channel adjacent to the point at which it is discharged into the induction tract, the tapered end of a screw,

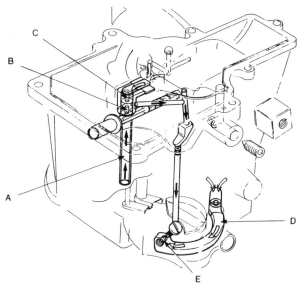

Fig. 8.14   Ford VV idling system
A: Main fuel pick up tube, B: Idle fuel jet, C: Idle air jet, D: Bypass gallery, E: Sonic discharge
tube

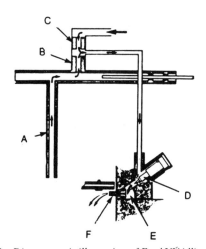

Fig. 8.15   Diagrammatic illustration of Ford VV idling system
A: Main fuel pick up tube, B: Idle fuel jet, C: Idle air bleed jet, D: Mixture adjustment screw, E:
Air bypass channel, F: Sonic discharge tube

for adjustment of the idling mixture supply, projects into it, Fig. 8.15. After
the initial setting has been done in the factory, the head of this screw is sealed
with a plastics plug to discourage subsequent adjustment except by a
qualified mechanic using an exhaust gas analyser to check the results.

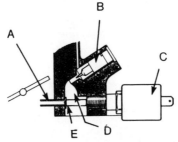

Fig. 8.16   Ford VV anti-dieselling valve
A: Sonic discharge tube, B: Idle mixture adjustment screw, C: Solenoid valve, D: Bypass air channel, E: Viton coated tip

Secondly, from the bypass channel, the idle mixture is discharged through a sonic jet into the induction manifold. A sonic jet is a feature used also in the idling systems of some Ford fixed venturi carburettors. It is simply a jet the orifice of which is so small that, as described in Section 6.11, the flow through it attains sonic speed, the shock wave ensuring that the droplets of fuel are thoroughly broken up as they are discharged into the manifold.

Thirdly, it incorporates a shut-off valve, Fig. 8.16, which is opened by a solenoid, and returned by a spring on to the inner end of the sonic discharge tube when the solenoid is de-energised. A Viton tip on the seating end of the armature ensures good sealing. The solenoid is wired in series with the ignition switch, so that the idle system is operative when the engine is switched on but closed when it is off. As the throttle is opened, a cam-actuated switch breaks the circuit to the solenoid to cut it out of operation. Ford call this an *anti-dieselling* valve and, again, it is used also in some of the Ford fixed venturi carburettors.

8.9   Acceleration

The function of the accelerator pump is, as usual, to prevent lean stall but without over-enriching the mixture. It is depression-actuated, so there is no mechanical linkage with the throttle valve. Under normal running conditions, the depression communicated to it from the induction manifold holds the diaphragm down, against its return spring. If, however, the throttle is opened suddenly, the collapse of the depression in the manifold allows the spring to push the diaphragm up, forcing the fuel above it past a non-return valve into the venturi, Fig. 8.17. A restrictor in the duct from the manifold to the diaphragm slows down the movement, to prevent momentary over-enrichment.

As the depression in the diaphragm chamber builds up again, it pulls the diaphragm down, drawing fuel from the float chamber in past another non-return valve, to replace that which has just been used. An orifice in the duct from the pump to the jet not only bleeds some air into the fuel as it is delivered to the venturi, but also serves as a vacuum break to prevent fuel

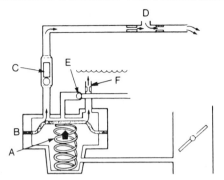

Fig. 8.17   Acceleration pump in delivery mode of operation
A: Diaphragm return spring, B: Diaphragm, C: Delivery valve, open, D: Vacuum break air
hole, E: Fuel inlet valve from float chamber (closed), F: Back bleed orifice

from being drawn from the pump by the depression in the venturi under
steady-state operation.

During idling, or short-term parking, heat soaking from the engine into
the diaphragm chamber might cause vapour to form in it and this, together
with the thermal expansion of the fuel within the chamber, could damage the
diaphragm. To prevent this, a back-bleed vent containing a restrictor allows
the excess expanding fuel and vapour to return to the float chamber.

8.10   Cold start and warm-up

By virtue of the incorporation of an automatic system, starting is equally
easy at all temperatures, and emissions are kept under better control than
where the devices for manipulating the air slide and main jet needle are
employed. Moreover, there is no demand on the driver to exercise fine
judgement in the pre-setting of the throttle and a strangler. Enrichment of

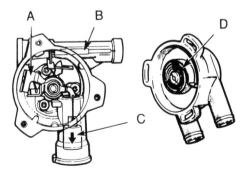

Fig. 8.18   Automatic choke actuation mechanism and its bimetal strip in the housing cap
A: Pick up arm for bimetal strip, B: Jet needle, C: Pull-down piston, D: Bimetal strip

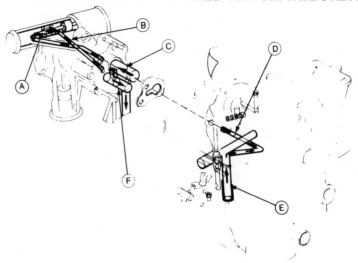

Fig. 8.19   Air and fuel flows in the Ford VV cold starting and idling enrichment system
A: Jet needle, B: Idling fuel delivery gallery, C: Mixing chamber, D: Fuel gallery in main jet
housing, E: Main fuel pick up tube, F: Mixture delivery duct

the fuel supply for cold starting is effected by a bimetal coil sensitive to engine temperature and, for subsequent light load operation, a depression-actuated override device reduces it progressively to its normal level during warm-up.

As can be seen from Fig. 8.18, there is a cup shape cover over what is, in effect, a three-arm bell-crank lever with arms at approximately 3, 9 and 1 o'clock, and engine coolant circulates through a water jacket cored in the outer wall of that cover. The arms at 9 and 3 o'clock are on the outer and that at 1 o'clock on the inner end of the spindle. Between the water jacket and the bell-crank lever is the bimetal coil, its outer end being secured to the cover and its other end registers in a slot in the end of the arm at 9 o'clock. Therefore, with changes in temperature, it will rotate the spindle and therefore the other two arms. A choice of four slots is provided for setting the device to cater for both manufacturing tolerances and subsequent wear or relaxation of the bimetal coil in service.

In Fig. 8.19 can be seen details of the air and fuel ducts associated with the needle jet B in Fig. 8.18, which is actuated by the arm at 1 o'clock. The similar, but vertical, tubular extension below houses a depression-actuated pull-down device secured to the arm at 3 o'clock. Fuel supply is of course regulated by the tapered needle in the jet orifice. Regulation of the air supply, on the other hand, is effected by a brass rotary sleeve valve pinned to and extending inwards from the spindle on which the bell crank lever is mounted.

Fuel enters the needle jet at its end remote from its actuating lever and issues from the other end. From here, it passes through a duct to a tiny mixing chamber. The air supply to the mixing chamber comes through a duct from a control port in the chamber between the air and throttle valves, but only just upstream of the latter. Before entering the mixing chamber, however, it passes through the brass sleeve valve extension of the throttle spindle. The air and fuel mixture is delivered into the induction tract at a point downstream of the throttle valve.

When the engine is cold, a radial hole in the brass sleeve is in line with the port to the mixing chamber and manifold. As it warms up, however, the rising temperature of the coolant in the water jacket, acting on the bimetal strip, rotates the bell-crank lever spindle and its sleeve extension, thus progressively turning the radial hole out of alignment and ultimately closing it completely. Simultanteously, the other arm of the bell-crank progressively moves the needle in the jet until finally its shoulder seats on the jet orifice, closing it too.

In the meantime, as the throttle is opened and the edge of the butterfly valve passes over the control port, the increasing depression pulls down the horizontal arm of the bell-crank lever. Thus both the fuel jet and the air duct are positively closed against the influence of the bimetal coil. This arrangement is needed because the rich mixture previously provided is not required for light-load steady-state cruising. If the throttle is opened for acceleration, the reduced depression releases the pull down device, and thus ceases to cancel out the cold start enrichment until a steady-state mode of operation is re-established.

FIXED CHOKE CARBURETTORS

8.11   Weber TL Series, single-barrel fixed-choke carburettors

To conform with continually tightening emissions regulations, many of the devices described in Chapter 7 had to be modified, making them more complex. For example, major proportions of the HC and CO emitted over the urban cycles are generated during idling and slow running, so the relatively simple idling and progression systems so far described have tended to become more elaborate, as for instance in the case of the Weber TL series of carburettors to be described in the succeeding paragraphs.

Zenith and Solex carburettors have been described in detail in the book *The Motor Vehicle*, by Newton, Steeds and myself, and published by Butterworths. To illustrate the practical application of the principles, I shall therefore confine the descriptions in this chapter mainly to some Weber and a Rochester carburettor.

Weber carburettors have for many years been preferred for applications where high power output coupled with good fuel economy is a priority. In their TL series, two floats are mounted on a common pivot pin, one each side of the block carrying the main jets. This arrangement has the advantage that the central disposition of the jets in the float chamber renders them

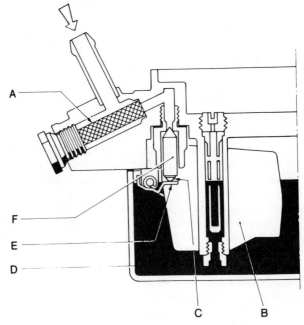

Fig. 8.20   Weber TL float chamber assembly, including main jet well
A: Filter, B: Float, C: Spring-loaded ball, D: Float chamber, E: Float-actuated lever, F: Needle valve

relatively unaffected by movements of the fuel in the chamber owing to either tilting or longitudinal or lateral accelerations of the vehicle. As can be seen from Fig. 8.20, a lever attached to the pivot pin actuates the needle valve, through the medium of a spring-loaded ball housed in a counterbore in the needle. The spring and ball device is interposed between the end of the lever arm and the needle valve to damp out vibrations that might affect the flow of fuel into the chamber, including any that might be caused by either surge or surface ripples.

8.12   Idling system

The idling system, Fig. 8.21, comprises two parts, one for supplying the basic lean mixture and an auxiliary system for providing extra fuel, as required, for progressing to the point of take-over by the main jet. The fuel supply for the basic idling system is drawn, by manifold depression, from the base of the diffuser tube, immediately above the main jet, into a vertical duct J to the left of the diffuser tube assembly. After passing up this duct, at the upper end of which is the basic idling jet A, it is mixed with air bled in at atmospheric pressure and then passes down to an orifice into which the tapered end of the basic idling mixture adjustment screw G projects. The

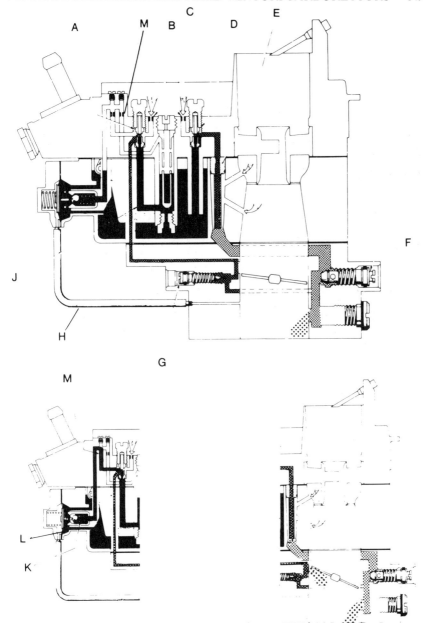

Fig. 8.21   Idling and progression circuits of Weber TL carburettor
A: Basic idling jet, B: Air bleed for basic idling jet, C: Air bleed for auxiliary idling jet, D:
Auxiliary idling jet, E: Tube with calibrated orifice at top, F: Auxiliary mixture adjustment screw,
G: Basic idling mixture adjustment screw, H: Manifold depression tube, J: Basic idling fuel
supply duct, K: Spring loaded ball-valve, L: Power augmentation diaphragm, M: Progression jet

setting of this screw is effected in the factory, after which it is sealed. From this orifice, the emulsified mixture goes on through a duct to a point below the auxiliary mixture adjustment screw, which is on the opposite side of the throttle barrel, at F, and out through a discharge orifice downstream of the throttle valve. For starting, the throttle valve is closed on to its stop, so the driver is not called upon to exercise any special skill in positioning it.

As the throttle is opened, the auxiliary system comes into operation. First, extra fuel is drawn up a pipe shown on the right of the diffuser tube, in the illustration. This tube dips well below the level of the fuel in the float chamber. The auxiliary fuel flows up it and through the auxiliary idling jet D, where, again, air is bled into it. From here it is taken down a tube, through a calibrated orifice E, and out into a larger diameter duct where more air is drawn into it through two bleed ducts from stations before and after the throat of the main venturi where there is a depression, but not as strong as that in the throat or of course in the secondary venturi.

It follows that the air can bleed through these ducts into the system only as long as the depression over them is not so great as that over the idling mixture discharge port. Therefore, as the throttle is progressively opened, and the velocity of flow through the venturi increases and the depression in the manifold declines, the air bleed ceases, thus increasing the rate of flow of fuel to the idling discharge orifice, and maintaining the correct air:fuel ratio until the throttle is opened so far that the main jet can take over. In this carburettor, the take-over point is higher up the range of throttle opening than in most others. In other words, the outputs from the main and idling systems are skilfully balanced to provide an accurately regulated air:fuel ratio for steady operation over much of the throttle opening range, the upper end of the range being catered for by supplying extra fuel through a power jet.

If the throttle is closed right down on to its stop, the supply of emulsion passing through the basic idling system is slightly lower than that needed, because it is supplemented from the auxiliary mixture system. Consequently, the total quantity of emulsion passing out through the previously mentioned discharge port is regulated by the auxiliary mixture adjustment screw. This can be adjusted in service, to set the idling speed with the throttle closed down on to its stop.

As the throttle is opened slightly for driving away from rest, its edge swings past a progression port, on the left of the induction passage in the diagram, exposing it to manifold depression and thus increasing the flow of emulsion from the basic idling system, as shown in the scrap view on the right in Fig. 8.21. Emulsion cannot flow out of this port at an earlier stage since, until the edge of the throttle has been moved beyond it, the pressure over it is too high.

A further stage in the progression occurs if the engine speed, and therefore the rate of consumption of air, rises at light load. As the pressure in the manifold, and therefore that over the diaphragm L on the left in the left-hand scrap view increases, the diaphragm is forced to the right by its return spring, thus opening the spring-loaded ball-valve, K, termed the power augmentation valve (not to be confused with any part of the power jet system, Section 8.14). This allows the depression over the basic idling jet to draw extra fuel from the float chamber through a series of passages, the diaphragm chamber, ball-valve, the progression jet M and on to supplement that already passing down the basic idling fuel supply duct. The thus augmented supply is discharged through the ports on both sides of the main tract downstream of the throttle valve.

8.13 Main jet

If the throttle is opened further, and the velocity of the air flowing through the two coaxial venturis increases, the depression in the secondary venturi rises to the point at which it starts to draw fuel off from the main jet system, Fig. 8.22. This fuel passes from the main jet into the base of the main well, up around the outside of the diffuser tube, and past the emulsion holes. Here, air entering the emulsion tube through an orifice drilled axially in the centre of the plug that closes its upper end, is bled into it. The emulsion thus formed is then discharged through the spray tube into the centre of the secondary diffuser.

As the vehicle accelerates and the engine speed therefore increases, the falling depression in the induction manifold allows the diaphragm on the left to be deflected to the right by its spring, opening the ball-valve. This once more brings the power augmentation system into operation, Fig. 8.23, delivering extra fuel through the idle discharge ports, which remain in

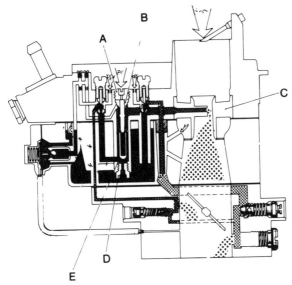

Fig. 8.22   Weber TL main jet system
A: Air bleed orifice, B: Emulsion tube, C: Secondary venturi, D: Main jet, E: Main well

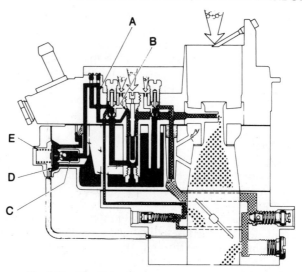

Fig. 8.23   The Weber TL power augmentation system
A: Power augmentation jet, B: Power augmentation fuel delivery duct, C: Power augmentation
valve, D: Diaphragm, E: Diaphragm return spring

operation, though at rates of delivery that otherwise fall as the throttle is opened. As the throttle is opened still further, the depression in the main jet spray tube becomes strong enough to draw some extra fuel through a jet in the vertical duct parallel and to the right of that for the basic idling fuel supply and to the left of the main well, whence it is taken on straight through the top of the emulsion well, where air is introduced into it, and on into the spray tube discharging into the secondary venturi. Thus, while a weak air:fuel ratio is obtained over the cruising range, extra fuel is supplied as the wide open throttle condition is approached.

8.14   Power jet and acceleration pump

Over the last few degrees of throttle opening, the depression in the manifold has fallen so low that no fuel is being drawn off from the idle system. On the other hand, the velocity of flow through the air horn is high enough to generate a depression there. This brings the power jet system, Fig. 8.24, into operation.

Fuel is drawn directly from the float chamber and passes through the power jet, which is a bush housed in counterbores in the abutting ends of the vertical duct where it passes across the joint face between the upper and lower halves of the carburettor casting. This duct delivers it up into a small spray tube and out through its open end into the centre of the air horn, a calibrated orifice in the plug that closes the other end bleeding air into the fuel as it enters the spray tube.

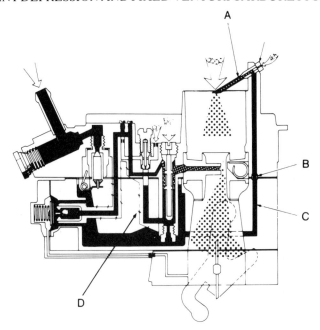

Fig. 8.24   Weber TL carburettor power jet system
A: Power jet spray tube, B: Power jet air bleed, C: Delivery duct to power jet, D: Float

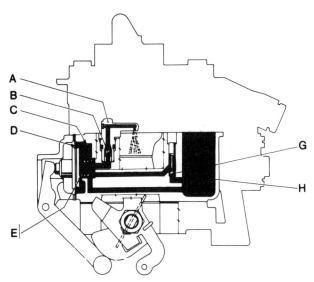

Fig. 8.25   Acceleration system of the Weber TL carburettor
A: Delivery tube, B: Delive·y valve, C: Pump jet, D: Diaphragm, E: Delay action spring, G: Pump inlet valve, H: Float chamber

The acceleration pump, Fig. 8.25, is actuated by cam on the throttle valve spindle. As the throttle is opened, the lever type cam follower depresses a spring-loaded plunger type progressive action device, to deflect the pump membrane to the right, as viewed in the illustration, against its return spring. This displaces fuel from the membrane chamber, opening the delivery valve, and discharging it through the delivery tube into the upstream end of the primary venturi. As the throttle is closed again, the delivery valve closes and the pump inlet valve opens, allowing fuel to enter through a duct from the float chamber, to replace that which was delivered to the engine when the throttle was opened. As usual, there is a back-bleed orifice to allow fuel and vapour to vent into the float chamber if its temperature subsequently rises.

8.15 Cold starting

When the choke control is actuated, it closes the offset-pivoted plate-valve upstream of the throttle valve and venturi. At the same time, a cam rotating with the valve lifts the throttle stop to open the butterfly valve to its fast idle position, Fig. 8.26. If the engine is then cranked, the differential pressure on the offset strangler valve opens it sufficiently to allow an appropriate quantity of air to pass. Since the depression downstream of the strangler valve is high, it draws fuel from all the jets, except that for power enrichment.

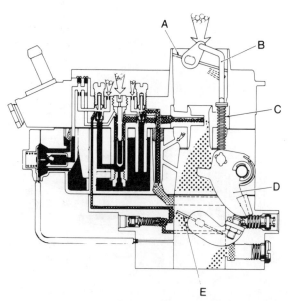

Fig. 8.26   Weber TL strangler control and cold starting system
A: Strangler valve, B: Strangler control rod, C: Sprung telescopic element, D: Strangler control rod and fast idle cam, E: Throttle valve

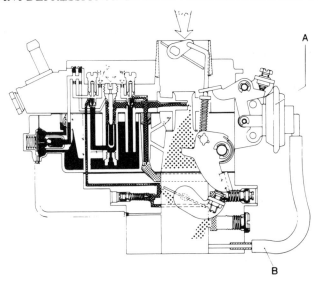

Fig. 8.27   Automatic control for progressively opening the strangler as the throttle opens and the depression in the manifold therefore decreases
A: Diaphragm type actuator, B: Rubber tube transmitting manifold depression to actuator

As the engine fires, the sudden increase in depression downstream of the throttle valve is transmitted to a diaphragm type actuator that rotates a lever carrying a stop, which is depressed to prevent the strangler valve from closing too far and thus causing over-enrichment, Fig. 8.27. Further opening of the throttle increases the differential pressure on the strangler valve and thus opens it, against the force exerted by a spring-loaded telescopic element in the rod linking it to its control lever, increasing progressively the rate of flow of air while continuing to draw off from the jets the extra quantity of fuel appropriate for maintaining the necessary enrichment of the mixture.

MULTIPLE AND MULTI-BARREL CARBURETTORS

8.16   Carburettor installations for larger engines

The larger the capacity of the engine, the greater is the difficulty of supplying it with the correct air:fuel ratio throughout the whole of its speed range. For maximum speed, a large diameter venturi is necessary to supply the air needed. At low speed, on the other hand, the velocity of the air flow through such a large choke is so low that it will not generate a depression high enough to draw off sufficient fuel. Solutions to the problem include having either one carburettor per cylinder, or for each pair of cylinders, or even for each set of three adjacent cylinders.

An even better arrangement, described in Section 8.17, is to fit a single carburettor incorporating either one or two pairs of throttle barrels, one venturi in each pair being smaller and its associated smaller throttle opening earlier than the other. Carburettors in which the larger throttle valve opens only after the smaller one is fully open, are said to have *sequentially opening* throttles. Medium size engines usually have two venturis, while the large V-eight units may need four.

Where low cost is the prime consideration for remaining competitive in the car market, engines of medium to large capacity may nevertheless have only a single barrel carburettor. In this case, the designer has to decide on a compromise between good performance at the upper end of its speed range and ease of starting and driveability at the lower end.

Incidentally the term *twin carburettor* means what it says, which is two separate carburettors, which may or may not be joined together. The term *twin barrel* carburettor means a device having a single float chamber but bolted to, or integrated with, two venturis or chokes and throttle barrels. A twin barrel carburettor can be likened to a single carburettor with duplicated main jet systems. Similarly, a four barrel carburettor is like a twin barrel one but with duplicated pair of venturis and corresponding jet systems. Consequently, we do not need to go on to describe in detail a range of multiple and multi-barrel carburettors, but can confine ourselves to the means of coupling their throttle valves. The Rochester Quadrajet 4-barrel carburettor, described in Sections 8.18 to the end, can be regarded almost as two Rochester Varajet twin barrel units joined together.

In most instances, a synchronised twin barrel carburettor is adequate for delivering into a single manifold on even a fairly large automotive engine. Such a carburettor may be used also for delivering into two separate manifolds, each barrel supplying the mixture to a group comprising half the total number of cylinders. In either case, the throttles open simultaneously. However, both must at all times and under all conditions of operation supply precisely identical quantities of mixture at precisely the same air:fuel ratio. With delivery into separate manifolds, the initial setting and maintenance of such synchronisation throughout the life of the vehicle may present difficulties. Failure can result in uneven running, loss of power, high fuel consumption, and impairment of both starting and idling.

For synchronised twin- and multi-carburettor installations, the throttles may be mounted on common or separate spindles. For ease of synchronisation, however, they are generally in line and interconnected by means of an adjustable coupling. There are several methods of synchronisation of the throttles, the most common being equalisation of the depressions in the manifolds, using pressure gauges such as U-tube or dial reading manometers. In some installations, the manifolds are interconnected through a restricted orifice to help to equalise their depressions—more about this in Section 9.11. The orifices are sometimes described as *compensation orifices, ducts or passages*, and they may render synchronisation slightly less critical. Although accurate equalisation of manifold depressions in such cases, is impossible unless the interconnections are plugged, it is the overall state of synchronisation that is required to be checked, taking into account the effect of the compensation orifice.

8.17 Twin-barrel carburettors

As previously indicated, unless very high performance is the priority, a better alternative to twin carburettors, and therefore more commonly used, is a twin-barrel carburettor with sequentially opening throttle valves. The first to open supplies all the mixture required by the engine for starting and throughout the lower portion of its power range, after which the second begins to to open, to supplement the mixture supply throughout the remainder of the range. The first to open is termed the *primary throttle* and the other the *secondary throttle*. Generally, the primary venturi is smaller than the secondary, so that the flow through it is rapid enough to create, even at fairly low speeds and light loads, a depression large enough to draw fuel from its main jet system, which generally is capable of metering more accurately and efficiently than, for example, the idling system. The primary venturi and its jet systems, therefore, are designed for starting, idling and economical cruising, while the secondary venturis and their jet systems are for full power and, in some instances, acceleration. In other words, duplication of the power, idling and progression systems may be unnecesary.

For sequentially actuated twin-venturi carburettors, the throttle valves are mounted on separate spindles, the primary one being linked directly to the accelerator pedal and the secondary, through a lost motion mechanism, to the primary. Such a mechanism is illustrated diagrammatically in Fig. 8.28, which shows a system used by Weber.

A potentially more sensitive method of interconnection is the use of a depression-actuated diaphragm for both locking and actuating the

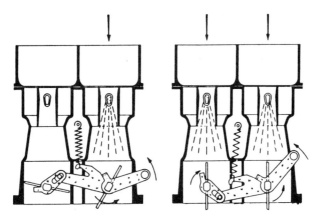

Fig. 8.28   Twin barrel carburettor with interlinked primary and secondary throttles, the secondary remaining locked closed until the primary is fully open

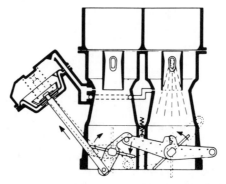

Fig. 8.29   Weber twin barrel carburettor with a diaphragm-actuated secondary throttle

secondary throttle. This is generally favoured for engines required to develop high power output over the upper end of the speed range, in which case, venturis of equal diameter may be, though not necessarily are, used. I Fig. 8.29, which again is a Weber system, a lever on the primary throttle actuation mechanism locks the secondary throttle in the closed position until that in the primary barrel is wide open, when it unlocks. As the accelerator pedal is lifted, after acceleration, first the secondary throttle closes down on its stop and is locked, and only then does the primary throttle begin to close.

The diaphragm of the secondary throttle actuator is subjected to, on side side, atmospheric pressure and, on the other, the depression in the primary venturi and a counter-force exerted by its return spring. This spring has a compression rate such as to allow the throttle to open gradually in proportion to the rate of flow of air into the engine. When the increasing depression in the primary venturi begins to open the secondary throttle, the total air induction capacity increases and so the velocity of flow through the primary venturi could drop. Consequently, both the timing and programming its opening, and therefore the balancing of the spring force against that exerted by the diaphragm, are fairly critical design and development operations.

ELECTRONIC CONTROL

8.18   An electronically controlled 4-barrel carburettor

To demonstrate that any attempt to control electronically a conventional carburettor inevitably makes it extremely complicated, we have only to look at the GM E4 M Quadrajet designed for the large American V8 engines. The 4 indicates that it has four venturis, and the E that it has been equipped with electronic control. An additional E at the end (E4ME), however, would indicate that it had an electrically heated thermostat to regulate the choke, while a C (E4MC) indicates that air is ducted to the thermostat from over the exhaust manifold.

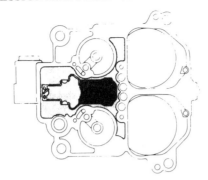

Fig. 8.30   Layout of the four barrels and float chamber of the GM Rochester Quadrajet electronically controlled carburettor

A feature of the E4M series is an electronic control module (ECM) exercising control, through a single solenoid, simultaneously over four vertical rods two stepped and projecting into the main fuel jets serving the primary venturis, and two with tapered ends projecting into the idle air bleed orifice. Signals from an oxygen sensor in the exhaust manifold enable the ECM to exercise closed loop control, but this can be modified by signals from open loop sensors, for indicating for example throttle position and engine temperature. Throttle position is indicated by a sensor adjacent to and actuated by the accelerator pump mechanism in the carburettor float chamber.

As can be seen from Fig. 8.30, the two large diameter secondary venturis are in front of the two significantly smaller primary venturis, the latter being spaced apart to accommodate the float chamber between them. Fuel enters the casting at the level of the base of the float chamber. It first passes through a Viton plunger type check-valve seated by a coil spring. This valve is accommodated in the open end of a pleated paper thimble type filter. Its function is to prevent escape of fuel from the float chamber in the event of a roll-over accident.

From the valve, the fuel passes radially outwards through the filter, the outer end of which is seated on a shoulder in the fuel inlet port by a coil spring, bearing against its inner end. Since it is never likely to become totally blocked, and bypassing therefore is unnecessary, the spring is strong enough to prevent it from doing so.

A single, closed-cell rigid foamed plastics float is integrally moulded on to a lever the pivot for which is near its other end. Attached by a spring clip to the end of the lever remote from the float is the needle valve, the lower conical end of which is Viton tipped. This valve closes down on to a brass seating, the face ground at two angles, the lower of which is the more obtuse, to encourage the entry of fuel under the pressure generated by the lift pump, and thus to facilitate the opening of the valve in the event of its tending to stick owing to deposits on it of sticky gums from the fuel.

The float chamber has a dual venting system. One, the main vent, is a small diameter duct taken to a point in the air horn, well downstream of the air filter. This is in operation until the engine stops, when another duct takes over automatically, by virtue of the fact that it is of much larger diameter. The latter vents the float chamber to atmosphere through a carbon canister filter, which prevents the hydrocarbons from escaping. When the engine is started again, the larger diameter vent is closed by a valve actuated by manifold depression. The valve can be made to open automatically for a brief period when the engine is started, to draw air through the carbon filter into the manifold, and thus to purge it of any fuel and vapour that might have collected in it.

8.19   Starting and idling

For starting and idling, the smaller primary throttle valves open first, the larger ones remaining locked against their stops, by the throttle control linkage. Each pair of barrels has its own mixture supply system, one for the larger and the other for the smaller barrels. The idling system, Fig. 8.31, is of course common to only the primary barrels. Automatic adjustment of the throttle position, by the electronic control, holds the idling speed constant regardless of variations in the load owing to, for example, switching on the saloon air conditioning system.

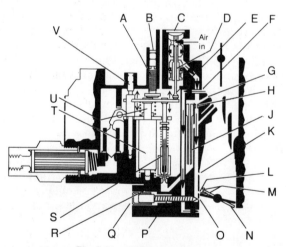

Fig. 8.31   Quadrajet idle system
A: Factory-adjusted rich mixture screw, B: Exhaust gas recirculation plug, C: Riveted cover, D: Factory adjusted idle air bleed valve, E: Valve stem, F: Fixed idle air bypass, G: Idle air bleed, H: Idle channel restriction, J: Idle tube, K: Lower idle air bleed, L: Off-idle port, M: EGR timed control ports, N: Throttle valve, off-idle position shown in outline, O: Idle discharge hole, P: Factory adjusted idle mixture needle, Q: Plug, R: Main metering jet, S: Main metering rod, T: Mixture control solenoid, U: Solenoid plunger in its upper position, V: Factory adjusted lean mixture screw

Engine designers using this carburettor are offered either of three methods of effecting the automatic control. One is an electronically adjusted throttle stop. The second, termed idle load control (ILC), is a manifold depression actuated movable stop, the actuator being a spring returned diaphragm. The third, an idle load compensator (ILC), is simply a solenoid that is wired through the ignition switch to prevent run-on when the engine is stopped or, alternatively, through the air conditioning switch to prevent the engine from stalling when that service is switched on.

When the throttles are closed or nearly so, there is of course a strong depression over the idle discharge port, downstream of the edge of the butterfly valve, in each primary barrel. Consequently, the atmospheric pressure over the fuel in the float chamber forces it through the idle system and out through that port. The fuel is drawn from the main well, into which it is fed through the main jet. Extending down into this well from its upper end is the idle tube, in the lower end of which is the idle fuel metering jet. Fuel passes up the idle tube and, at its upper end, is mixed with air entering through the air bleed orifice, which is regulated by the ECM through the medium of the solenoid-actuated tapered needle. It is then directed downwards again, first through a calibrated idle restriction and then further, picking up more air first from the small air bleed hole level with the top of the idle tube and, subsequently, lower down from the off-idle port above the throttle valve. Finally, it passes through the orifice into which the tapered end of the idle mixture adjustment needle projects, and out through the idle discharge port, into the manifold just downstream of the throttle valve. Adjustments of both the solenoid-controlled air bleed and idle mixture adjustment needles are effected in the factory, the sockets housing their screws being then sealed with hardened steel plugs to discourage tampering by untrained personnel in service.

As the throttle is opened, the edge of the butterfly moves past the off-idle discharge port, which is slotted to come into operation progressively. Thus, this port is exposed to the depression in the manifold and, as the edge of the throttle moves up past it, an increasing quantity of fuel is drawn through it. Further opening of the throttle increases the air flow sufficiently to draw fuel also through the lower idle air bleed hole further upstream. Indeed, fuel continues to be drawn through the idle system, supplementing that discharged through the main metering system, right up to wide open throttle.

For engine applications in which large quantities of air are needed to maintain the appropriate idling speed, a fixed idle air bypass duct is incorporated to deliver air from the air horn to a point below each primary throttle. This enables the throttle stop to be adjusted so that the butterfly valve closes further. The aim is at reducing the flow through the venturi during idling, and thus preventing the main jet system from supplying fuel through the discharge nozzles into the highly efficient triple-venturi.

8.20   Ports for ancillary functions

There are three or four more ports in the region of the butterfly valve, some being what are termed timed ports, because the timings of their coming into effect are determined by the movement of that valve. Two are vapour canister purge ports of which one, for continuous operation, may be downstream of the closed butterfly valve, purging the carbon canister that absorbs emissions of fuel vapour from the tank and carburettor float chamber, while the other, a timed port, is next to the off-idle discharge port. Manifold depression is transmitted through these ports to either the purge valve, described in Section 13.26, or directly into the canister. Either timed or continuous purge, or a combination of both, may be required: the continuous purge is restricted, to avoid over-enrichment of the idling mixture passing down the manifold, and thus adversely affecting idling quality, the timed port coming into operation subsequently to increase the purge rate as the throttle is opened for off-idle operation.

There may also be timed ports for exhaust gas recirculation (EGR) control. To prevent recirculated gas from adversely affecting the quality of idling or slow running, the EGR valve is actuated by the depression from the manifold transmitted through a timed port punched in the passage upstream of the butterfly valve, where it will not become effective until the throttle has been opened by a predetermined amount. Some automatic transmissions have a torque converter cut-out clutch that is actuated by manifold depression. This, again, calls for a timed port, in some instances slotted for progressive action, above the butterfly valve.

8.21   The solenoid control mechanism

As mentioned previously, a single solenoid controls the two main jet needles and idle air bleed valves for the pair of primary barrels. The upper end of the solenoid core is fixed to a yoke to which are also attached the upper ends of the main jet rods below it, and the lower end of the stems of the idle air bleed valves, which are above it. Energising the solenoid weakens the mixture and the return motion under the influence of the return springs enriches it, the two rods and air bleed valves being actuated simultaneously, regardless of whether the main or idle systems are in operation at the time. The vertical motion of the yoke is limited by two screw stops, Fig. 8.31, and there are more adjustment screws, one for setting the datum positions of the idle air bleed valve and the other that of the throttle position sensor. All are adjusted and sealed during manufacture.

8.22   The main metering system

The main metering system is identified for each of the two primary venturis. It discharges through a spray tube, which is what GM term a plain tube nozzle, into the centre of the triple-venturi. As the rate of flow of air increases and, therefore, the depression decreases in the venturi, the depression over the idle and off-idle discharge ports and, therefore, the fuel flow through them, decreases. The main metering system therefore comes into operation at off-idle and continues to full throttle.

A vertical rod the diameter of which is reduced in two steps projects into the main jet, through which the fuel passes into the main fuel well, Fig. 8.32. As previously mentioned, this rod is moved down into the weak position by a solenoid, and up by a return spring. The solenoid is energised by the ECM at a rate of about 10 pulses/s, the duration of the pulses being primarily dependent upon signals received from an oxygen sensor in the exhaust manifold. It is also influenced, however, by the open loop control sensors. For instance, signals from the throttle position indicator enable the ECM to determine what the air:fuel ratio should be when the throttle is closed, or partly or wide-open.

When the ECM receives a signal indicating that the position of the throttle valve has changed, it identifies the last remembered set of operating conditions that gave the ideal air:fuel ratio at the new position, and programs the solenoid operation accordingly. Then, if necessary, the

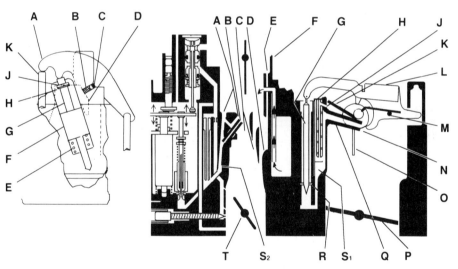

Fig. 8.32   Main metering system with, left, a scrap view showing the throttle position sensor Left; A: Accelerator pump lever, B: Factory adjusted screw, C: Plug, D: Adjustment lever, E: Sensor spring, F: Throttle position sensor, G: Actuator plunger, H: Retainer, J: Seal, K: Pump stem. Right; A: Main air bleeds, B: Main discharge nozzle, C: Boost venturi, D: Main Venturi, E: Internal vent slot, F: Baffle, G: Secondary metering rods (two), H: Accelerator wells and tubes, J: Accelerator well ports, K: Air valves (closed), L: Metering rod lever (down), M: Hing pin, N: Eccentric, O: Baffle, P: Secondary throttle valves, Q: Main discharge nozzles, R: Metering discs, S: Main fuel wells, T: Primary throttle valves (partly open)

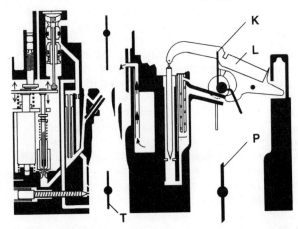

Fig. 8.33   Power system, key as for Fig. 8.32, except where noted here
K: Air valves (wide open), L: Metering rod lever (up), P: Secondary throttle valves (wide open),
T: Primary throttle valves (wide open)

oxygen sensor effects further adjustment. At wide open throttle, the throttle position sensor signals the ECM to actuate the solenoid in a pre-programmed rich mode of operation.

Some versions of this carburettor have a pull-over enrichment device. Just below the strangler valve in each bore is a calibrated hole in the outer end of a duct leading from the base of the float chamber. During high speed operation at light load, the rate of flow through the air horn is high enough to create a depression over this hole large enough to draw fuel from the float chamber through it. The flow, indicated by the four arrows in the centre of Figs. 8.32 and 33, supplements that flowing through the main metering system.

There is also a power system, Fig. 8.33, and this comes into operation at high speed and heavy load. It is effective in all four barrels, through the main metering systems. When the throttle approaches the wide open position, the acceleration pump lever continues to move the throttle position sensor plunger down, ultimately changing the output signal from the ECM to program the solenoid to provide a rich mixture from the primary systems, for the development of maximum power.

8.23   Secondary system

The secondary metering systems are entirely separate from those for the primary barrels, and they do not deliver into venturis. Instead, the fuel is drawn from the jets by manifold depression maintained over them by an air valve upstream of the throttle valve in each barrel. Thus, although control over the air flow is effected conventionally by the throttle valves, that over fuel metering is maintained by both the depression induced by the spring-loaded eccentrically pivoted air-flow control valves and a mechanical linkage between a plastics cam on their common spindle and the secondary metering rods, which project into metering orifices in discs serving as the main jets. Additional trimming of the fuel flow is effected by air bleed and changes in the levels in the secondary fuel wells and acceleration wells and tubes.

As the accelerator pedal is depressed to the point at which the primary barrels can no longer satisfy the engine demands for air and fuel, a lever on the primary throttle shaft begins to open the secondary throttle valves. It can do this, however, only if a thermostatic coil exposed to engine temperature has been warmed sufficiently to release a secondary throttle valve lock. This coil also actuates the automatic strangler valves upstream of the primary butterflies.

As the secondary throttles open, they expose the undersides of the air valves to manifold depression. These eccentrically pivoted valves are held shut by their return springs and are opened by the difference between the atmospheric pressure upstream and manifold depression downstream of them. To ensure a smooth transition from primary to secondary operation, a dashpot regulates the rate of opening of the air valves. This dashpot, linked to a slotted hole in the end of the lever controlling the air valve, Fig. 8.34, comprises essentially a diaphragm held down by manifold depression against a return spring. If the depression is lower than 127-152 mm of mercury, the diaphragm is in full control. As it rises above this value, however, the spring begins to take over, the rate of return of the diaphragm being limited by a calibrated orifice in the tube between it and the induction manifold. If the depression is small, the dashpot rod will be in the forward end of the slot, so that the air valve will be free to open rapidly when the accelerator pedal is depressed, otherwise its opening will be slightly delayed.

From this point on, since the secondary fuel metering systems are

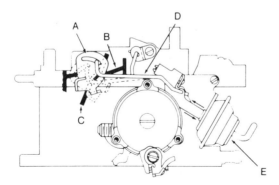

Fig. 8.34   Air valve dashpot for obtaining a smooth transition from operation on the primary to the secondary system
A: Air valve lever, B: Closed, C: Open, D: Air valve actuation rod, E: Diaphragm unit

identical for each barrel, we need consider only one barrel. To avoid a temporary lean mixture, or flat spot, before the fuel begins to feed through from the secondary discharge nozzle, fuel is in the first instance drawn from the acceleration pump well. In each bore, as the edge of the opening air valve springs upwards, it passes a port through which the depression thus communicated to the secondary acceleration well draws fuel up from it into the air stream. This fuel is drawn from the base of the well into the lower end of a tube that extends down into it, and passes up through a calibrated orifice to the discharge port.

Then, as the air valve opens further and the main secondary metering system comes into operation, the plastics cam lifts the taper ended secondary needle in its orifice in the metering disc, thus progressively increasing the rate of fuel flow into the secondary well, where it is mixed with air passing through the radial holes sin the emulsion tube. The emulsion thus formed then passes on up to the secondary discharge nozzle situated immediately below the air valve spindle. On some versions, a slot in the largest diameter shoulder on the rod prevents it from sealing off the metering orifice, so that a small quantity of fuel can leak through to replace any that might boil off from the well after the engine has been stopped when very hot.

The air flow capacity of the carburettor can be limited by a stop on the air valve. At low rates of flow, the fuel distribution to all cylinders is equalised by a baffle plate extending into each bore from immediately below the air valve and around the secondary discharge nozzles. For some engines, another may be fitted in the air horn and over the secondary air bleed holes leading into the emulsion tubes, to prevent the incoming air from driving down the level of the fuel in the well and thus causing secondary nozzle lag during rapid acceleration.

8.24 Acceleration pump

This pump, Fig. 8.35, is of conventional design housed in a fuel well in the float chamber, but one or two details are of interest. The plunger head has a limited degree of axial float on its rod so that, on its downward stroke, a shoulder on the rod seats on the piston. Therefore, fuel is forced out from beneath the piston, past a non-return valve, through the pump jets into the venturi. The downward force is applied by a lever connected to the throttle sensor, through a coil spring to the piston, to prolong the fuel supply for the avoidance of a flat spot after rapid opening of the throttle.

As the throttle is closed again, the plunger is pulled up by the linkage connecting it to the throttle position sensor, and the shoulder on the rod unseats from the hole through the piston, thus allowing fuel to pass through from the well into the cylinder, ready for the next call for acceleration. It is held in the unseated condition by a return spring, to allow vapour to vent from the well.

During high speed operation, the depression over the pump jets might

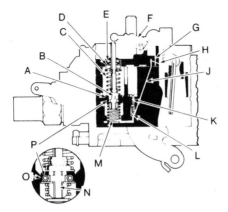

Fig. 8.35   Acceleration pump system
A: Cup seal, B: Pump plunger, C: Prolonged action spring, D: Retainer, E: Seal, F: Pump actuation lever, G: Pump jet suction vent, H: Pump jets, J: Pump delivery duct, K: Delivery valve retainer screw, L: Delivery valve, M: Pump return spring, N: Pump plunger, O: Cup seal, P: Expander spring

pull fuel continuously out of them. This is prevented by venting the pump delivery ducts, from a point just downstream of the jet, up to the air horns.

8.25 Automatic strangler control

For warm-up, only the primary barrels are in operation, the secondary throttle valves being locked in the closed position. Consequently, the two eccentrically pivoted strangler valves are sited in the primary barrels, upstream of the venturis. The eccentricity is of course set so that, with increasing engine speed, and therefore air flow, the strangler valves are progressively opened.

When the engine is started from cold, a coiled bimetal strip tends to rotate the strangler valves to close them. It tends also to rotate a stepped fast idle cam, mounted on their pivot pin, to the position in which the throttle stop would seat on the step appropriate to the temperature, to open it enough to prevent the engine from stalling. However, because rotation of the cam is obstructed by its steps coming up against the throttle stop, nothing can happen unless the driver, following the instructions in his manual, has first depressed his accelerator pedal down to the floor. This movement of the pedal will also have caused the accelerator pump to spray fuel into the region of the venturi, and thus prime the engine.

To avoid excessive emissions, the rich mixture stop for the primary jet rods is adjusted so that the bimetal coil enriches the mixture to the minimum degree necessary for obtaining a satisfactory start at the coldest temperatures likely to be experienced. So long as the crankshaft speed remains below 200 rev/min, the ECM keeps the solenoid switched out of operation, so the primary jet rods and the idle air-bleed plunger are held by their return springs in the maximum enrichment position. As the speed rises above this level, the ECM takes over control, setting the solenoid in a rich mixture (open loop) mode of operation.

Heating of the bimetal strip can be effected either by air from a jacket over the exhaust manifold or, on a timed basis, by an electric heating element. As the engine warms up, the bimetal strip progressively rotates the strangler valves, opening them and also allowing the throttle to be closed down step-by-step on to the fast-idle cam until, for hot idling, it can seat on its fully closed stop.

The control exercised by the bimetal strip alone after the engine has fired, however, would be too imprecise. Therefore, a depression-actuated diaphragm mechanism is added to regulate more accurately the rate of application and release of the choke with variations in throttle opening and manifold depression during starting and warm-up. This mechanism can be either of two types and, on some engines, both are fitted. Each is similar to that used for opening the secondary air valve.

One is the positive acting type, which responds immediately to applied depression: when the manifold depression is high because the throttle is closed and the flow through the strangler valve is small, it sets the choke valve correctly for cranking and then, immediately following firing, resets it. The other, the time delayed type, has either a simple restrictor in the atmospheric port to its diaphragm actuator or a check-valve with a small bleed hole in its centre in the depression port, the latter delaying the build-up of depression beneath the diaphragm. Delayed types generally respond more slowly to applied depression and, after a delay of a few seconds, allow the choke to open further. Their function is to prevent the engine from stalling owing to too sudden an opening of the choke and therefore weakening of the mixture. In some installations, a thermal switch is mounted in the air cleaner housing to prevent the manifold depression from reaching the diaphragm chamber, or chambers, until the carburettor inlet air temperature, regulated by a heated air intake valve for emission control, rises to an appropriate level.

For operation in very cold conditions, the characteristics of the depression-actuated diaphragm unit can be modified by interposing, either internally or externally, what is termed a bucking spring between the bimetal coil and the diaphragm return spring. In such extreme conditions, the force exerted by the bimetal coil against the bucking spring is very strong, deflecting the spring and pulling the choke further towards the fully closed position than in warmer conditions.

Chapter 9

Induction Manifold Design

For single cylinder engines, a short pipe can be used to take the mixture from the metering unit to the cylinder but, for multi-cylinder engines, what is termed an *induction manifold* is needed. An induction manifold is usually an aluminium or iron casting, though more recently plastics mouldings have been used to reduce weight and, in some instances, cost. Ford, for instance, have been using on their 1.8 litre diesel engine a polyester plastics induction manifold, cast in a mould with a fusible metal core, which is induction heated to melt it out of the finished product. Because the smooth finish of the metal core is reproduced in the passages of the manifold, high efficiency of flow is obtained and the weight saving is claimed to be 40%, as compared with a metal component.

Induction manifolds serve as brackets to carry the metering equipment (carburettor or injection unit). Their major function however can be defined as to receive the mixture from the metering equipment and deliver it, in both qualitatively and quantitatively equal proportions, to each cylinder in turn as inlet valves open. In the early days, the manifold ducting was sometimes cored in the cylinder head. This however, is most unsatisfactory—not only does it complicate the cylinder head casting but, more importantly, it presents no opportunity for regulating the temperature of the ingoing charge, either to keep it cool for good volumetric efficiency, or to warm it to aid evaporation when the engine is cold.

Pressures in manifolds influence the design of gaskets. They may range from about 150 mm Hg, when the vehicle is running down hill with the throttle closed, and up to about 720 mm Hg with wide open throttle at maximum rev/min. These figures are of course absolute values and correspond respectively to values of about 81 and 5.5 kN/m^2 (11.8 and 0.8 lb/in^2) below atmospheric pressure. Fluctuations in pressure of this order can adversely affect acceleration and, as explained in the next paragraph, are the major reason for the need for an acceleration pump in the carburettor. Higher pressures are of course experienced in manifolds of turbocharged engines but, whereas even slight leaks at pressures below atmospheric can have a seriously adverse effect on idling and light load mixture strength, leaks at pressures above atmospheric do not.

With a warm engine at idling, the air flowing at low pressure through the manifold is virtually saturated with fuel vapour, and the walls of the manifold are almost dry. If the throttle is suddenly opened, the pressure and density of the air rises. This, in effect, squeezes some of the vapour out and deposits it on the walls of the manifold, so the mixture passing through tends suddenly to weaken. It is this weakness that must be offset by the acceleration pump if smooth acceleration is required. With some automatic transmissions on the other hand, this problem either does not exist or is of minor significance, because the drive is not taken up until engine speed has risen to about 1800-1900 rev/min.

FUNDAMENTAL CONSIDERATIONS

9.1 Mixture distribution

Uniform distribution of the mixture from cylinder-to-cylinder is often extremely difficult to achieve. Incoming air flow can be biased to one side by some peculiarity of the air cleaner and silencer, the throttle valve or spray tubes in the carburettor, and the shape of the manifold. Without uniform distribution, the overall mixture strength has to be increased until the cylinders receiving the weakest mixtures will fire regularly, otherwise there will be a risk of popping back through the carburettor. Nor is this all: the consequent loss of efficiency is aggravated by that fact that optimum ignition timing varies with mixture strength and therefore inevitably the timing in some cylinders is inappropriate.

With one carburettor and induction pipe per cylinder, as in many racing car applications, distribution problems are obviated, and both power output and efficiency high. Not only individual induction pipes, but also manifolds and their branch pipes can be tuned, on the principle of the organ pipe, so that the pulsations arising from the resonant vibrations of the air columns in them tend at certain speeds to supercharge the cylinders. The force inputs exciting the vibration are those arising from the sudden changes in gas flow owing to the opening and closing of the inlet valves. A particularly good example of manifold tuning is the very ingenious Vauxhall/Open Dual Ram system, described in Section 9.14.

9.2 Some general design considerations

In addition to the prime requirement of distributing the mixture equally, the manifold must also offer minimum resistance to its flow and be of low cost, compact, light weight, and easy to manufacture. Cost is to a major extent dependent upon material and manufacturing technique. Cast iron is generally the cheapest material but heavy. Aluminium has the advantages of light weight, good thermal conductivity and therefore rapid warm-up, and it can be cast accurately. Plastics materials tend to be costly, but are light, can be produced to closer tolerances and used more economically than metals and tooling costs are much lower.

Minimum resistance to flow is obtained by keeping the ducts as straight as practicable and, where curves must be introduced, they must be of large radius. However, in some designs, especially the straight-rake and buffer types, tighter curves or even right angle bends are deliberately introduced, for reasons to be explained in Section 9.6.

Clearly the interior walls of the manifold should be as smooth as practicable to minimise viscous drag, though a rough surface does have the advantage of generating turbulence in the layers of mixture adjacent to it, and therefore of promoting evaporation. Indeed, for some special applications, in which early transition from cold to normal running is more important than a high maximum power output, a case could be made out for actually roughing the walls and floor of the manifold. Furthermore, because the flow round bends has to be such that the velocity at their inner is lower than that at the outer radii, rough surfaces on the former and smooth ones on the latter can result in freer flow and therefore better filling of the cylinders than if both are smooth. The degree of benefit obtainable depends, however, on the magnitude of the mean radius. Another important requirement is accuracy of alignment and continuity of the inner faces of the passages, at one end, between the manifold and the throttle barrel and, at the other, between the branch pipes and the ports in the cylinder head.

9.3   Manifolds as evaporation chambers

Since in cold conditions, the fuel obviously cannot evaporate instantaneously as it issues into the airstream passing through carburettor, the manifold has to serve also as a mixture preparation chamber. When the manifold is cold, some liquid fuel is deposited on to its walls and runs down on to its floor, ultimately evaporating out again into the air flowing over it. The rate of evaporation increases of course as the temperature of the manifold rises.

In former times, fear of fire due to backfiring of the engine into a manifold in which petrol was swilling about led to manifolds being sloped down from each end to the centre. From here a drain pipe was taken down to a level below the base of the sump. It generally contained a non-return valve, to avoid weakening the mixture owing to passage of air through it into the manifold. Such devices were needed as, for several reasons, starting was more difficult in those days so, because liberal choke application was required, considerable quantities of fuel could collect in the manifolds.

For modern four-cylinder engines, however, straight manifolds with branch pipes sloping down towards the cylinders tend to be preferred. With such engines, starting is generally easy, carburettor starting systems meter the fuel more accurately and fuel injection systems even more so. The argument in favour of downwardly sloping branch pipes is that the correct mixture for starting should be accurately supplied and all immediately transferred into the cylinders, where evaporation can be completed during the compression stroke. In any case, evaporation is greatly assisted by modern manifold heating devices.

9.4 Manifold heating

There are three basic methods of heating of induction manifolds: exhaust, engine coolant, and the use of an electric element. There is a fourth method of heating, but it is not applied to the manifold. Instead, the incoming air is heated by passing it through a shroud over the exhaust manifold before it enters the air intake. Such an arrangement usually includes a thermostatic control to switch from heated to cold air when the ambient temperature is high enough for the heating to be discontinued. This ensures that there is not any unnecessary loss of volumetric efficiency. It is used, however, mainly as a means of reducing exhaust gas emissions, and will be dealt with in Section 13.16.

Electric heating is perhaps the simplest, though not necessarily the most reliable or least costly. Mostly, it is based on the use of a thick disc with the electric terminals on its edge and a heating element inside. Heating is generally necessary with not only carburation but also single-point gasoline injection: the electronic control can be conveniently employed either to set the time that the heater element shall remain in operation, or to switch it off as the engine temperature rises to the appropriate level in relation to ambient temperature. With all systems, it is necessary to limit the heat supplied, otherwise the density of the charge will be reduced and the volumetric efficiency of the engine therefore lowered.

Water heating may be almost inescapable where the inlet and exhaust valves are on opposite sides of the cylinder head, though in a few instances the exhaust gases have been conducted through pipes over or around the engine from the exhaust to the inlet manifold. Following a cold start, a water jacket comes into effect later than exhaust heating, since the engine coolant temperature rises only slowly and never to such a high level. Consequently the water jacketing has to be spread around a larger area of the manifold, which means that it tends to be particularly effective in preventing ice from depositing on the throttle valve and the spray tube in the venturi.

On the other hand, coolant heating has several disadvantages. First, because the hot water cannot be so easily diverted as exhaust gas, the risk of lowering volumetric efficiency is greater, especially when the engine becomes very hot as the vehicle is driven up a long steep incline. Engine coolant temperature can vary widely, for example owing to the switching on, or off, of an interior heater blower, and this can detract from the consistency of water heating. Transferring the coolant from the engine to the manifold can complicate the installation, and increase the possibility of leakage.

Exhaust heating has the many advantages especially if the inlet manifold is close enough above to be bolted down on to that for the exhaust. It is simple, begins to become effective very soon after the engine has fired, and can be confined to the small area immediately below the carburettor riser, on to which wet fuel droplets tend to be flung because of their tendency to move in straight lines. The heating can also be easily deflected away from the manifold as the temperature rises, thereby avoiding loss of volumetric efficiency.

Furthermore, provided the size of the hot spot is limited, the device can be made to be approximately self-compensating. This is because, as engine speed and the rate of flow of exhaust gases increase, so also does the mass flow through of mixture through the induction manifold. Consequently, neither the rise in temperature of the ingoing mixture nor the fall in volumetric efficiency is so steep with increasing speed as might otherwise be expected. Additionally, as the load on the engine is increased beyond the point at which maximum power is developed and speed therefore falls off, the increasing rate of heat input to the mixture tends to compensate for the fall off in efficiency of atomisation owing to the reduction in the rate of flow of gas through the venturi.

A high velocity of air flow through the carburettor is conducive to good atomisation, and a wet mixture is the optimum for developing maximum power. Such a mixture will cool the ingoing charge, and thus increase volumetric efficiency and reduce the tendency towards detonation. However, at low speeds, distribution and therefore driveability may be poor.

9.5 Exhaust heated hot spots in practice

A good example of the early post World War II ideas on what an exhaust heating system should be is that used on the Vauxhall 1.5 and 2.75 litre 4 and 6 cylinder engines introduced in 1952. This had a flap valve, or deflector, that was both thermostatically and gravity actuated, to ensure that the heat was applied to the induction system only when the engine was cold. To prevent heat from being conducted up to the carburettor float chamber, a block of thermal insulation material separated the bolted joint faces between it and the riser.

As can be seen from Fig. 9.1, the exhaust manifold is bolted up directly below the centre of the inlet manifold riser. A deflector is eccentrically pivoted in the exhaust passage, just below its junction with the inlet manifold so that, when the engine is working hard and the exhaust gas flow is therefore considerable, it tends to blow open, bypassing the hot spot, and deflecting the gases directly into the downpipe.

Attached to one end of the spindle on which the deflector is mounted is a bimetal coil which, when cold, tends to rotate the spindle in the direction that causes the deflector to divert the exhaust gas upwards against the base of the riser and up through a jacket that surrounds it, from which it finally passes downwards again into the exhaust downpipe.

Fixed to the other end of the spindle is a bob-weight which, when it passes over tdc, assists the bimetal coil in opening the deflector. As the engine warms up, and the bimetal coil relaxes, rotating the deflector in the opposite direction, to bypass the hot spot, it swings the bob weight back over tdc, thus again assisting the bimetal coil, but this time in closing the deflector valve which thus, even after some deterioration of the bimetal strip and the pivots has occurred in service, moves reasonably smartly from fully open to fully

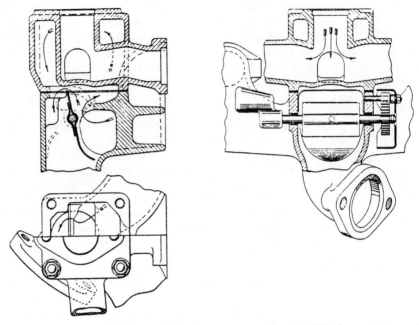

Fig. 9.1   Vauxhall's induction manifold heating system introduced in 1952 has yet to be bettered as regards exhaust heated hot-spot design practice. The arrows in the section on the right represent the flow of the induction, and those on the left the exhaust gases

closed. Moreover, the mechanism is fail-safe because the strip, if seriously defective, would not have enough strength to lift the bob-weight up over the tdc position as the engine becomes cold. Starting would then be difficult, but at least over-enrichment and dilution of the lubricant would be avoided.

On some engines in which the inlet manifold is bolted down on top of the exhaust manifold, the junction between the two is left open except in that it is closed by a thin stainless steel plate interposed between the joint faces. In such cases, a jacket around the base of the riser is dispensed with. The idea is to confine the heat to precisely where it is needed for evaporating droplets of fuel splashing down into the base of the riser. With such an arrangement, the induction manifold can be made of a lighter material than the exhaust manifold, which is almost invariably of cast iron.

9.6   Manifold shapes and sizes

The diameter of the passages in the manifold will be large for racing engines, to obtain good volumetric efficiency. However, this leads to poor driveability at low speeds, because the velocity of flow of the mixture through them is slow. High velocities of flow first tear the fuel away from the end of the spray tube and then, by virtue of the energy content of the flow, continue to assist atomisation and evaporation. For this reason, for family saloon cars much is to be gained by restricting the diameters of the passages through the manifold rather than those through the inlet valve ports and seats.

For acceptable volumetric efficiency coupled with good atomisation, evaporation and mixing, the maximum velocity of flow through the manifold should not be greater than about 70 m/sec. However, higher speeds can be tolerated if the manifold heating capacity is large enough. The diameter of the riser is normally the same as that of the carburettor barrel, which ranges from between about 1.2 and 3.0 times that of the venturi. For a 6-cylinder engine with a single carburettor, the cross sectional area of the manifold in in^2 is generally from 0.65 to 1.1 times the swept volume in in^3 and, for a 4-cylinder unit, the corresponding upper limit may be as high as 1.9.

Incidentally, when the engine is started from cold at very low ambient temperatures, only about 5% of the liquid fuel may vaporise, the remainder being deposited in the manifold, for subsequent evaporation. In other words, surface carburation occurs until the engine becomes warmer. In some instances, therefore, a well is formed beneath the riser so that, if the quantity of temporarily condensed fuel is greater than that which can be immediately evaporated in the manifold, it will be contained for subsequent evaporation.

Cross sectional shapes of both the main tract of the manifold and its branch pipes influence flow characteristics as well as rate of evaporation. For the main tract, a D-section is widely used, the flat of the D forming the floor of the passage so that liquid fuel can drain down from the curved walls into a shallow pool of large surface area, to facilitate subsequent evaporation. An alternative is a square or a rectangular section with its major axis horizontal. Both these shapes have the additional advantage of discouraging swirling of the gas around the axis of the tract which would, by its centrifugal action, tend to deposit more droplets of fuel on its walls.

Manifold shapes and sections are mostly a compromise. A good arrangement is as follows. Immediately below the riser, the main tract is of rectangular section, with its major axis horizontal, to present a large floor area for evaporation. From here it may first taper to a square section and then merge into circular section branch pipes. If the engine is installed longitudinally, with its major axis inclined, the manifold floor should be horizontal, otherwise all the liquid fuel will run down to one end.

On the other hand, a circular section is the more efficient, because it contains the maximum volume of air within walls of minimum surface area and resistance to flow too is a minimum. Moreover, circular sections can be easily aligned with and matched to the inlet valve ports. A method of ensuring accuracy of alignment is to insert, into counterbores in the ends of the ports in the head, location sleeves which, when the manifold is bolted on, register in similar counterbores in the ends of its branch pipes. The inner diameters of these sleeves are of course identical with those of the ports and branch pipes, to form an uninterrupted surface over each junction.

The question of the most suitable radius of curvature of passages is

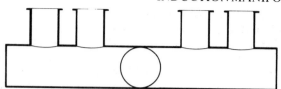

Fig. 9.2   Diagramatic representation of a buffer type induction manifold for a four cylinder engine

answered preferably at the development stage. There may be a tendency for the inertia of droplets of fuel to cause them to deposit on the outer wall in the bend. However, if the curvature is such that a low pressure is generated adjacent to the surface of inner wall, this is where fuel deposition may occur. On the other hand, many manifolds have right angle bends of very small radius between the branch pipes and the main tract. This is termed the *straight rake* type.

If the inlet valves of the end cylinders are close to the ends of the manifold, these ends may be extended to form what are termed *buffers*, Fig. 9.2. Buffer ends trap some of the heavy droplets of fuel, so that they can subsequently flow back along the manifold and evaporate after the adjacent valve has closed. This helps to avoid over-enrichment of the end cylinders when the engine is cold. Generally, however, the aim is at damping the pulsations caused by the opening and closing of the adjacent valves, so that they will not interfere with the filling of other cylinders. The lengths of the buffers can be critical so, for development purposes, telescopic ends are often used so that they can be varied to determine the length conducive to optimum performance.

With updraught carburettors long risers should be positively avoided because, in cold weather, fuel deposits on their walls and falls back down again. This can seriously impede starting. For downdraught or sidedraught carburettors, the other hand, they tend to deliver a smooth and uniform flow of mixture into the manifold and thus contribute to good distribution. However, for such installations, low bonnet lines generally dictate short risers, or even none at all.

9.7   Effect of inlet valve operation

As the velocity of movement of the piston up each cylinder first increases and then decreases sinusoidally, the pressure in the manifold of course tends to fluctuate correspondingly. The actual opening and closing of inlet valves, however, initiates pressure pulses of magnitudes that can have a profound effect on the power output obtainable from the engine. Inlet valves may open at approximately 10° before tdc and close some 50° after bdc, giving total open and closed periods of about one third and two thirds (240° and 480°) respectively of the 720° of the four-stroke cycle. During the closed periods, the mixture tends to stagnate in parts of the manifold and porting.

The effects in practice vary according to the number and layout of the cylinders and crankshaft. Crankshaft layout is determined primarily by dynamic balance and torsional vibration considerations, though the designer also takes into consideration the effects of inlet valve operation on induction manifold performance. The timing of valve opening is a function of parameters such as engine speed range, the speed at which maximum performance is required, the degree of flexibility needed and the rate of burning. Other factors being equal, the rate of burning will be determined by combustion chamber design and the degree and type of swirl and turbulence generated in the charge.

In a single cylinder engine, the gas velocity through the manifold fluctuates strongly from zero at first to a maximum just beyond the mid-point of the induction stroke. As the column of mixture flows into the cylinder, its inertia builds up considerably and tends to induce it to continue to do so even after the piston has passed bdc. Indeed, this supercharging tendency causes the flow to continue until the crank is perhaps 50° past bdc. On the sudden closing of the inlet valve, a pulse of high pressure is reflected back along the induction system, perhaps causing deposition of fuel in the port and manifold.

LAYOUTS

9.8 Twin-cylinder engines

In multi-cylinder engines, the pulses in pressure in the manifold due to valve opening and closing can affect, either beneficially or adversely, the filling of the cylinders. In some instances, to obviate problems arising from poor filling of individual cylinders owing to interference between inlet pulses, carburettors are mounted on plenum chambers, from which branch pipes are taken to the individual ports. Generally, however, it is better to arrange the valve opening and closing sequences and port branches in a manner such as to avoid such interference.

With two cylinders of a 4-stroke engine in line and crank throws at 360° (or two connecting rods on a common crankpin) the stagnant period is about 120°. Consequently, there is no overlap of inlet valve opening periods, and the inlet ports therefore can be siamesed. If, however, the cranks are set at 180°, the stagnation period is 300° and the induction strokes occur at intervals of 180° and 540°, overlapping each other by about 60°. Consequently, unless each cylinder is separately served, the first will have a smaller charge than the second and, moreover, little is available in the inertia of the inflowing mixture to help charge the second.

The V layout with a single throw crankshaft is commonly adopted for such engines, especially for motor cycles where it may fit naturally into the triangulated frame. With a 90° V, the interval between the induction strokes of Nos. 2 and 1 cylinders is 210°, and the stagnation periods are 210° between 1 and 2 cylinders, but only 30° between 2 and 1. During the long period of

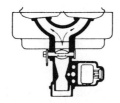 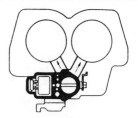

Fig. 9.3   On a twin-cylinder engine in which the gas stream from the carburettor divides directly into port branches set at an acute included angle, it is virtually impossible to obtain equal distribution. These two diagrams show how Weber have overcome the problem: left, with a sidedraught and, right, a downdraught carburettor

stagnation between the opening of the inlet valves of Nos. 1 and 2 cylinders, therefore, the volume of fuel deposited on the walls of the tract will be considerably greater than between 2 and 1. Consequently, No. 2 cylinder will tend to run on a significantly richer mixture than No. 1. This can be countered to a large extent by employing a short manifold to present a small cold area on to which fuel can condense.

In general, although designing a manifold shape for a twin-cylinder engine might appear to be simple, there are some pitfalls. For instance, a Y-shape other than, possibly, with a very obtuse angle between the arms of the Y is to be avoided since, even without the throttle valve pivoted in the same plane as the junction between the arms, it is virtually impossible to divert the gas stream equally down each branch of the Y at all speeds of operation. This difficulty arises partly owing to the need for manufacturing tolerances but also because of slight diversions of the main stream by spray tubes and other components either in the carburettor or further upstream. Some twin-cylinder induction systems are illustrated in Fig. 9.3

The horizontally opposed twin-cylinder arrangement presents a different set of problems, even though the stagnation periods are of course the same as those for twin side-by-side cylinders, having similar crankshaft layouts. Generally, a long pipe, with a riser mid way between its ends interconnects the two inlet ports, a downdraft carburettor being mounted on the riser. Because of the length of the induction pipe, which usually forms an arch spanning the engine between inlet valve ports, condensation in cold weather is severe and therefore starting is difficult. A generously proportioned exhaust heated hot-spot helps, but tends to reduce volumetric efficiency. One carburettor per cylinder is a better arrangement, but more costly.

9.9   Three cylinders

With crankpins at 120° intervals, the three cylinder engine is particularly attractive for 2-stroke operation since, with power strokes occurring at equal intervals, torque output is relatively smooth. However, we need not discuss the 2-stroke cycle here, since no such engine is used to power any car in production at the time of writing. Even so, with the demand for lighter,

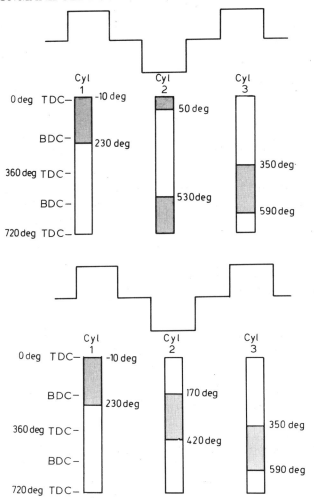

Fig. 9.4   *Charts showing how the inlet valve opening periods overlap with a 3-cylinder 4-stroke engine having a plane crankshaft and firing orders as follows: top, 1-3-2; bottom 1-2-3. The shaded areas represent the periods during which the valves remain open, assuming that the inlet valves open 10° before and close 50° after tdc*

more compact power units, and the advent of gasoline injection, with its potential for the use of blown scavenge without loss of fuel through the exhaust port, this cycle could make a come-back.

Three cylinder 4-stroke engines are not of much significance so far as the automotive industry is concerned. However, owing to their simplicity, they are useful as an example to illustrate the basic principles, for the beginner. With a plane crankshaft having three throws at 180° intervals the firing order can be either 1-3-2 or 1-2-3. In both cases, there is inlet valve overlap

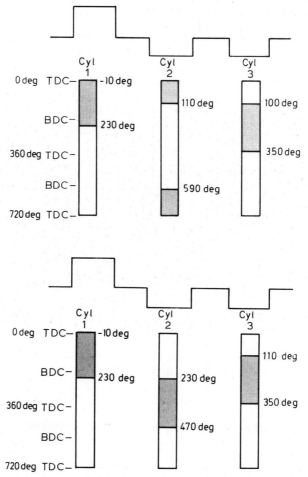

Fig. 9.5   Charts similar to those of Fig. 9.4, but for an engine with its cranks at 120° intervals. As before, the vertical bars each represent the 720° of the 4-stroke cycle, plus 10° to include the opening of the inlet valve in the first cylinder to fire. The firing orders are: top 1-2-3, bottom 1-3-2

between adjacent cylinders in turn, but not between cylinders 1 and 3 the cycles of which, as is demonstrated in Fig. 9.4, are separated by 360°. A satisfactory manifold arrangement is a single downdraught carburettor on a riser over the centre of a main tract having three branches, one to each cylinder. Alternatively, half of the six-cylinder layout, with 120° between each crank, giving the diagram shown in Fig. 9.5, could also be used. In this case, the valves would open in turn at 120° instead of 180° intervals, but the preferred timing is that in which the inlet valve in No. 2 cylinder opens during the second revolution of the four-stroke cycle. This gives more uniform firing intervals, though there is a little overlap between Nos. 1 and 3 and more between Nos. 2 and 1 cylinders.

9.10   Four-cylinder in-line engines

With four cylinders in line, the crankshaft has throws at 180° and the firing order is generally 1-3-4-2 though the alternative of 1-2-4-3 is sometimes used. With both, the induction impulses occur at 180° intervals. With the 1-3-4-2 order, these impulses are directed alternately outwards from the centre of the manifold, i.e. from 2-1, then 3-4. Examples of manifolding are shown in Figs. 9.2 and 9.6.

Adverse effects of the overlap of valve opening periods can be avoided by using a twin-tract manifold, one tract serving the outer and the other the inner pair of cylinders. The engine then becomes the equivalent of two twin-cylinder units with cranks at 360°. However, since the aim is at obtaining maximum performance, a better arrangement is two carburettors on risers situated one between each pair of cylinders, on a more conventional single-tract manifold. An alternative, neater arrangement with a Weber twin-barrel synchronised sidedraught carburettor is shown in Fig. 9.7. The restricted balance orifice between the two sets of two branch pipes, equalises the pressures in the two sections of the manifold. Two more Weber arrangements, but with two twin-barrel synchronised carburettors, in one case sidedraught and in the other downdraught, are illustrated in Fig. 9.8.

With the 1-2-4-3 timing, the inlet valve of No. 2 cylinder opens 60° before No. 1 closes, and Nos. 4 and 3 are similarly timed, so each end of the

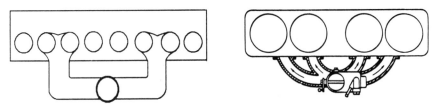

Fig. 9.6   Diagramatic representations of two possible manifold layouts for 4-cylinder engines with downdraught carburettors

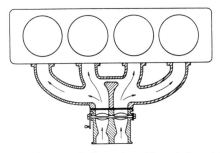

Fig. 9.7   Weber arrangement for a 4-cylinder engine with a twin barrel sidedraught carburettor. Note that, to ensure that the pressures in each half of the manifold are equal, there is balance orifice in the web that divides them

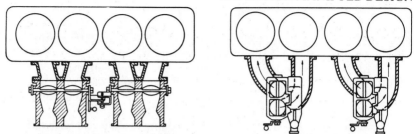

Fig. 9.8   Two more Weber layouts for twin-barrel carburettors, each barrel serving one cylinder, on a 4-cylinder engine: left, with sidedraught and, right, downdraught carburettors

manifold alternately will be subjected to depression for a period of 420°, followed by stagnation for 300°. The suction impulses in each half of the manifold progress towards the centre, and the reversal of flow from one to the other takes place at the port branches nearest the carburettor. Unless the pairs of ports are siamesed, so that the central ones are reasonably remote from the riser, the effect of this reversal on the flow at the junction between the riser and main tract is strongly disturbing and can cause uneven mixture distribution.

With two carburettors each serving an adjacent pair of cylinders, and without siamesed ports, the engine becomes, so far as carburation is concerned, two twin-cylinder units joined together, with 180° crank angles. The alternative arrangement, of the inner and outer pairs each having a separate induction tract, can be compared to two twin-cylinder engines each with 360° cranks. With the former, the induction strokes overlap but, with the latter, they do not since the suction pulses occur 360° apart.

9.11   Six-cylinder in-line engines

With the cranks at 120°, the six-cylinder engine is inherently balanced dynamically. Either of two 120° crank arrangements shown in Fig. 9.9 can be used. Although many different firing orders are possible, the best are 1-5-3-6-2-4 with the upper and 1-4-2-6-3-5 with the lower of the two crank arrangements illustrated. This is because the suction impulses occur at equal intervals alternately in each half of the manifold. In neither case can overlap

Fig. 9.9   Diagrammatic representation of alternative shafts, with 120° angles between cranks, for 6-cylinder engines

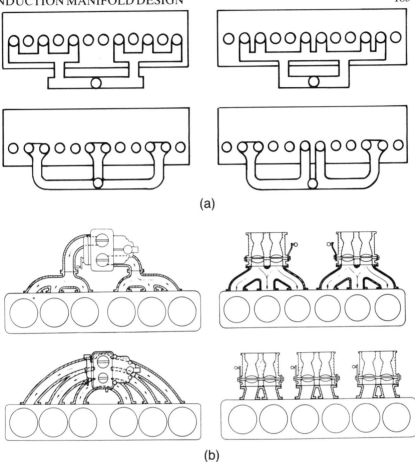

(a)

(b)

Fig. 9.10   Represented diagrammatically at (a) are four early induction manifold layouts for 6-cylinder engines with single barrel carburettors. Of these, the two lower ones risk uneven distribution owing to the close proximity of the riser to the branch pipes to the two cylinders opposite it. The two upper ones have been designed to avoid this problem but, with induction tracts cored into cylinder head castings, volumetric efficiency can be adversely affected by variations in engine temperature. Note the balance orifice in the right hand manifold. At (b) are some more modern Weber layouts for synchronised twin-barrel carburettor installations with, left, downdraught and, right, sidedraught carburettors

between the opening of the valves be avoided, and of course there is relatively little build up of pressure after the valves have closed.

For the latter reason, significantly better performance is obtainable with two carburettors, each serving a set of three cylinders at each end of the block. The result is, in effect, two three-cylinder engines joined together, but with cranks at 120°. Suction pulses occur at intervals of 240°, and there are no stagnation periods. It is usual to have a balance orifice communicating between the two manifolds, to equalise the mean pressures in them. Either of the previously mentioned two firing orders is satisfactory, though 1-5-3-6-2-4 is slightly better because it gives a more favourable sequence of suction impulses in the individual manifolds. Examples of manifolding for six cylinder engines are shown in Fig. 9.10. Fitting three carburettors to a six-cylinder engine is not recommended, as the valve opening intervals between adjacent cylinders are too irregular.

9.12 Eight cylinders

Some early straight-eight cylinders were, as regards crankshaft layout, basically two four-cylinder engines in tandem. These are known as the 4-4 type. Each set of four cranks is in a single plane, but the two planes are at 90° to each other. If the front set of four are in a vertical plane, the rear set can have its central pair of cranks to either the left or the right, each arrangement giving a different firing order. Alternatively, instead of having the outer two of the four cranks on the front section of the shaft directed upwards and its central pair downwards, the cranks can be set alternately up and down. The rear set of four will then be similarly arranged but, as previously, in a plane at right angles to that of the first set. Yet another possible arrangement is with the big ends of the connecting rods of the each adjacent pair of cylinders side-by-side on one crankpin, so that only four crankpins are needed for the eight cylinders. In this case, each end crankpin is at right angles to its neighbour, the two central ones being at 180°. Clearly the range of possible firing orders is enormous.

Most manufacturers, however, adopted one of the two crank arrangements illustrated in Fig. 9.11. A popular crankshaft arrangement has been that at the top, with a firing order of 1-5-2-6-4-8-3-7-5. This is analogous to the 1-2-4-3 order for a four-cylinder unit, but firing alternately in each set of four cylinders instead of in direct sequence. Another widely used arrangement has been that immediately below it with a firing order of 1-6-2-8-4-7-3-5.

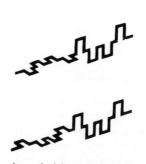

Fig. 9.11 *The two most commonly used of the several possible crankshaft layouts for straight-eight engines arranged as if those for two 4-cylinder engines had been joined end-to-end. The most suitable firing order with the top layout is 1-5-2-6-4-8-3-7, while that for the lower one is 1-6-2-8-4-3-7-5, though eight alternatives are possible with each*

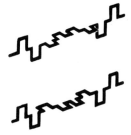

Fig. 9.12   *These two crankshaft layouts are the most popular of those possible for straight-eight engines constructed as if one 4-cylinder unit had been interposed between the front and rear halves of a second. Dynamic balance is easier to achieve with this layout than with that of Fig. 9.11. The best firing order is 1-6-2-5-8-3-7-4*

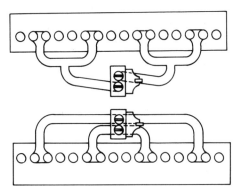

Fig. 9.13   *Two induction manifold layouts for straight eight engines with twin-barrel carburettors. By joining the manifolds at their centres, single barrel carburettors can be installed, but these are almost invariably inadequate for such large engines*

Because of dynamic balancing problems arising with the 4-4 arrangement, however, what is known as the 2-4-2 type was introduced and soon became the most popular. This is basically a 4-cylinder engine with an extra pair of cylinders added to each end. Of the two crankshaft arrangements shown in Fig. 9.12, the most popular has been the uppermost, with a firing order of 1-6-2-5-8-3-7-4.

With a single carburettor and suction impulses at 90° intervals, there is considerable overlap between two and, for short periods three valves, and a total absence of stagnant periods. Because of the consequent interference with three valves overlapping in the open condition, either two separate or a single twin-barrel carburettor is favoured. Either arrangement is mounted on what is in effect two 4-cylinder manifolds. With the 4-4 arrangement, one manifold serves the front four and another the rear four cylinders. The 2-4-2 layout is not so simple, the central four cylinders having one manifold and the outer four another, the latter inevitably with longer branch pipes. In practice, a wide range of different manifold layouts is practicable, but the most common for the 4-4 and 2-4-2 types are illustrated in Fig. 9.13. In both instances, twin-barrel carburettors are shown, one barrel serving each section of the manifold. The former type has long been virtually totally obsolete, while the latter is no longer installed in any production car.

9.13   The V layouts

The difficulty of installing a straight-eight in a private car arises, of course, out of its great length. Reduction in length, therefore, was the aim in the development first of V8 layouts and subsequently, for engines of smaller swept volume, the V6s and V4s. The last two were of course especially advantageous for transversly installed engines. These are often arranged with one bank of cylinders parallel to the dash, leaving the other inclined forwards.

For the V4, the firing order is normally the same as for a straight four, that is 1L-3R-4R-2L, cylinders 1 and 2 being in the left-hand and 3 and 4 in the right-hand bank. This, with a V angle of 60° and a crankshaft the throws of which are offset 30° from the 180° layout of a straight four engine, gives equally spaced firing intervals. A typical example of such an engine is the Ford V4, in which the inlet valves open 24° before tdc and close 52° after bdc. Manifolds for V4s are generally of X shape with the carburettor mounted on a riser in the centre of the X, and each arm serving one cylinder.

For the larger V engines, the cylinders are usually numbered from the front, first along one bank and then along the other. For example, on a V6, cylinders 1-3 would be on the right and 4-6 on the left, those in the right-hand bank being offset forward relative to those on the left. The angle between both the banks of cylinders and the crank throws is 60°, and the firing order is 1R-4L-2R-5L-3R-6L. Manifolds for V6 engines are generally similar to those of the V4s, but with an extra branch pipe on each side so that the whole casting is in the form of two Y-shapes superimposed, as shown in Fig. 9.14. Alternatives, of course, include one carburettor, either twin- or single-barrel, per bank or for each pair of cylinders across the banks or, as on

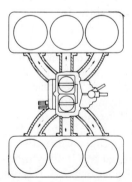

Fig. 9.14   A Weber twin barrel carburettor installation on a V-6 engine. V-4 manifold layouts are similar, but of course without the central branch pipes

some very high performance engines, even one single-barrel carburettor per cylinder.

For the V8 engine, the crankshaft layout used most is that shown in Fig. 9.15. The cranks are as shown in the illustration and the cylinder banks at 90°. This enables 180° intervals to be obtained between suction impulses, and stagnation periods of the same order as in four cylinder engines. A common system of numbering is 1, 3, 5 and 7 cylinders in the left-hand and 2, 4, 6 and 8 in the right-hand bank. The preferred firing orders are 1L-8R-7L-3L-6R-5L-4R-2R or 1L-8R-4R-3L-6R-5L-7L-2R though, as in the case of the straight eight, many more are practicable. In both instances the manifolding is in the form of two, two-legged Ys, crossing over as shown in Fig. 9.16, the two branches serving the outer cylinders in one bank and the inner ones in the other.

An alternative crankshaft arrangement is as shown in Fig. 9.17. In this case, the firing orders giving suction intervals of 180° are either

Fig. 9.15   Crankshaft layout for a 90° V-8 engine with manifolding as show in Fig. 9.16

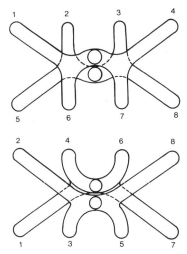

Fig. 9.16   Manifolding for a V-8 engine with cylinders numbered as shown and preferred firing orders, top 1-5-4-8-6-3-7-2; bottom 1-8-7-3-6-5-4-2. As with the straight-eight, other firing orders are practicable

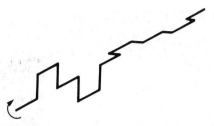

Fig. 9.17   Crankshaft for 90° V-8 engine with manifolding as shown in Fig. 9.18

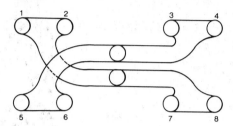

Fig. 9.18   These manifold layouts for V-8 engines are more clumsy and difficult to fit, and therefore not favoured for modern engines. Where they have been used, the best firing orders have been generally regarded as 1-3-7-4-8-5-2-6 and 1-3-2-4-8-5-7-6

1L-3L-7L-4R-8R-5L-2R-6R or 1L-3L-2R-4R-8R-5L-7L-6R. This calls for two S-shape manifolds, crossing one over the other, the ends of the S being bolted to the inlet ports of two pairs of cylinders in each bank, as shown in Fig. 9.18.

Finally we come to the V-12 engine, which almost invariably has 120° crank throws and 60° included angle between the banks of cylinders. This is simple because, having what is in effect a separate manifold or pair of manifolds for each bank, it is treated as two six-cylinder units. An arrangement commonly adopted is a twin downdraught carburettor between the banks, each barrel discharging into a tract serving one bank. An alternative is one or more carburettors on one or more manifolds on the outer face of each cylinder bank, again with manifolding as for a six-cylinder engine. The firing order is either 1-5-3-6-2-4 or 1-4-2-6-3-5 for each bank.

INDUCTION SYSTEM TUNING

9.14   A tuned manifold for an injected engine

The principles of design of manifolds for engines having gasoline injection systems are similar to those for carburettors. However, the riser may be replaced by a horizontal connection to the body of the throttle valve. A particularly good example, and the first of its kind, was that of the 6-cylinder 2969 cm^3 24-valve engines installed in the 1990 Vauxhall/Opel Senator CD 3.0i 24V and Carlton GSi 3000 24V models, Fig. 9.19. It was called the Dual

Fig. 9.19   The Carlton GSi 3000 24V engine installation, showing its Dual Ram induction system

Ram induction system. The Bosch Motronic M1.5 digital injection equipment was used.

Ram tuning of induction pipes is based on the resonance of the columns of air in the pipes, as is experienced in organ pipes, Fig. 9.20. It is effected by selecting lengths of induction pipes such that they resonate at a fundamental frequency equal, or nearly so, to that at which the inlet valves open, and in a manner such that the pressure wave, or pulse, helps to drive the charge into the cylinder. It has been described as supercharging without incurring the extra cost of a supercharger.

Ram tuning had been practised for many years but, prior to the introduction of the Dual Ram system, it had not been entirely satisfactory with 6-cylinder engines because the firing frequency is fairly high and therefore short induction pipes are needed for improving the torque at high speeds. Consequently, there is an undesirable fall-off in torque as the speed falls. In many instances, therefore, compromises were made, by bringing the benefit lower down the speed range.

On the other hand, the torque of a ram-tuned 3-cylinder engine tends to peak lower down the speed range, and therefore to fall off as maximum speed is approached. The new Vauxhall/Opel 3 litre engine, however, has been ingeniously tuned as a conventional 6-cylinder unit at high speeds but, lower down the range, it is switched over to what is, as regards manifolding, two 3-cylinder units the crankshafts of which are coupled.

In effect, therefore, the overall torque curve is a composite comprising that for two coupled 3-cylinder engines over the lower and one 6-cylinder unit at the upper end of the speed range. The principle is illustrated

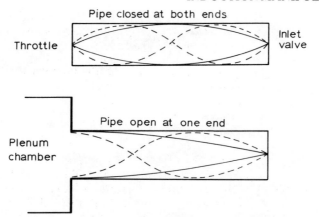

Fig. 9.20 *Standing waves in pipes with, top, both ends closed and, bottom, one end open and the other closed. The fundamental frequencies are those represented by full lines, while the first overtones are shown dotted*

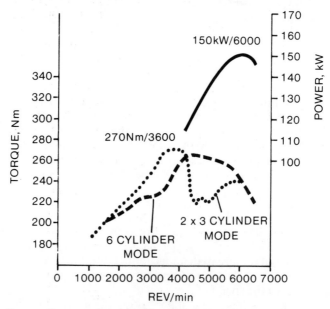

Fig. 9.21 *Power and torque curves of the Carlton GSi 300 24V engine. The former is indicated by the full line, and the latter are dotted for the 12 × 3 cylinder mode, and dashed for the 6-cylinder mode of operation*

diagrammatically in Fig. 9.21, from which it can be seen that the cross-over point of the two curves is set at 4000 rev/min, the peaks occurring at 3600 and 4400 rev/min. Since, on this engine, the maximum torque values at these speeds are respectively 270 Nm for the 2 × 3-cylinder and 265 Nm for the 6-cylinder modes, the overall curve is much flatter, though with a slight dip between the two maxima. As the speed falls from the maximum of 6600 rev/min, the back-up is considerably better than that of a typical ram-tuned 6-cylinder engine. In fact, between 3000 and 5800 rev/min, the torque does not fall more than 10% below maximum and, even at 1500 rev/min, it drops to no lower than 75% of maximum. Incidentally, the inlet valves open 14° before bdc and close 68° after bdc.

9.15   The Dual Ram concept in detail

Because the frequency of inlet valve opening, of a 3- is half that of a 6-cylinder engine, it requires induction ram pipes of approximately double the length. On the 3-litre engine, this is achieved by taking two induction pipes from the throttle valve to a plenum chamber approximately half way to the inlet ports, and then continuing with two sets of three pipes from the plenum chamber to the ports, Fig. 9.22.

The plenum chamber is divided into two parts, each maintaining the continuity of a set of four pipes. In this condition, the flow from each of the two pipes from the throttle valve passes directly into the corresponding group of three induction pipes. Consequently, as each inlet valve opens in turn, the column of air throughout the whole length between it and the right-angle junction with the throttle valve body vibrates at its resonant frequency.

The division between the two parts of the plenum chamber, however, is a flap valve, which can be opened to destroy the continuity of the four-pipe system associated with each half of the plenum chamber and doubling its volume. This makes it large enough to form an effective discontinuity between the two pipes from the throttle valve and the six to the induction valve ports, so that the air columns in only the latter can resonate, which

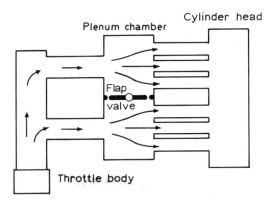

Fig. 9.22   *Diagrammatic representation of the principle of the Dual Ram induction system with the division in the plenum chamber closed, for operation in the 2 × 3 cylinder mode. When it is open, the plenum chamber effectively breaks the continuity of the induction tracts, so that only the six short pipes can resonate*

they do at the appropriate higher frequency. The flap valve is opened at the crossover point of the two torque curves in Fig. 9.21. It is actuated by manifold depression and controlled by the engine management system.

For this particular engine, calculations revealed that to obtain gas column resonance over a major part of the speed range would have entailed varying the pipe length between 300 and 840 mm. Incidentally, for the purpose of development testing, this is relatively easily done by using telescopic pipes. For the production engine, the actual resonance lengths chosen for the two conditions (3-cylinder and 6-cylinder) were 400 mm for the six short pipes from the valves to the plenum chamber and 400 plus 300 mm for the longer lengths between the valves and the throttle body. These lengths give resonance speeds of about 4400 rev/min and 3300 rev/min respectively. The diameters of the pipes influence the abruptness of the onset of resonance. In this instance, it was found that a diameter of 60 mm for the 300 mm pipes gave the required gentle progression of torque throughout the speed range.

9.16   Three-stage throttle for injection systems

As explained in Section 8.17, the sequential throttle arrangement associated with many twin-barrel carburettors has the advantage that the air velocity through the venturis is always high since, at the lower end of the speed range, the throttle valve in the larger of the two venturis is closed. On the 3-litre Dual Ram engine, the designers again displayed considerable ingenuity by obtaining a three-stage throttle opening with only two throttle valves and barrels. Because this is an injection system, however, there are no venturis. Therefore the advantage sought was simply a consistently high depression in the manifold throughout the speed and load range, to assist evaporation of the fuel injected and thus to optimise the torque characteristics, especially during transitions between primary and secondary throttle operation.

The diameter of the primary barrel, at 25 mm, is smaller than might be expected relative to that of the larger one, which is 64 mm. This is practicable only because there are three stages of opening.

Over the first 20 mm of pedal travel, which is the equivalent of 27° opening of the butterfly valve, the air enters only through the primary throttle. The second butterfly valve begins to open at 20 mm travel and continues to 30 mm, representing 27° to 46° throttle movement. Thirdly, as the pedal is further deflected from 30 mm to 55 mm, the second butterfly valve moves from 46° to 90°. This final movement, constituting the third stage, is obtained as follows:

To one side only of its pivot, the secondary throttle valve plate is of conventional section. On the other side, however, it is of wedge shape something like a segment of an orange with its thin end adjacent to the pivot, Fig. 9.23. Consequently, as one edge of the large diameter valve begins to open, the thick edge of the wedge section blanks off the gap between its other edge and the bore of the throttle barrel. Only when the secondary throttle has opened through 9° does the edge of the thicker half of the

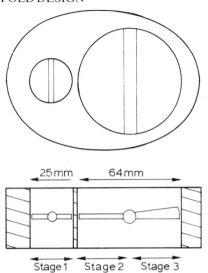

Fig. 9.23   The three-stage throttle arrangement. Only when the small primary throttle is almost fully open does the left-hand edge of the secondary throttle crack open, the right-hand edge, because of its greater thickness, not doing so until about 9° later

throttle plate crack open. At its perimeter, even the thickest part of the wedge section is thinner than the diameter of the boss surrounding the pivot pin, so it does not add significantly to the resistance to the flow through the valve.

The throttle actuation mechanism is conventional in that the primary throttle is opened directly by the control and the secondary throttle is interconnected with it by a lost motion linkage so that it does not begin to crack open until the primary throttle valve has opened up to 27°. Each throttle, however, has a separate spiral return-spring. Consequently, to open the large secondary valve, the driver has to overcome the extra resistance offered by the second spring, which he feels as a light kick-down effect. This is not a disadvantage: on the contrary, because the driver can feel the change-over point from the smaller to the larger throttle, he finds it helpful as an indication that he is running on only the smaller throttle, which he may wish to do either to obtain outstandingly good fuel economy or for safety on icy roads.

Chapter 10

LPG fuel and mixing systems

Since road vehicles are not generally designed for running on gaseous fuel, an LPG system has to be substituted for the existing gasoline one. In detail, a special fuel tank is installed, usually in addition to the original, and a combined evaporator and pressure regulating unit and a mixing unit is substituted for the carburettor or injection equipment. These changes are based on the fact that the gas has to be stored in liquid form in the vehicle. Consequently, after it has been delivered from the tank to the engine, it has to be evaporated and of course only then mixed with the incoming air.

ENGINE DESIGN CONSIDERATIONS

10.1 Engine modifications

Some modifications are required to the engine too. Because of the high octane number of LPG, Fig. 10.1, improved performance can be gained by advancing the ignition by approximately 10% at low speeds. However, since it burns more slowly than gasoline, the ignition must be retarded by about 15% at the upper end of the speed range, Fig. 10.2. Modifications to the cylinder head may be unnecessary if it has valve seat inserts from which heat can be easily conducted away through an aluminium or other locally well cooled casting, but the cast iron heads of engines designed before, or early in, the 1980s may have to be fitted with hard seat inserts to obviate rapid wear during prolonged operation at high speeds.

However, the fitting of inserts can often be avoided simply by running the engine for about 10-15% of the time on leaded fuel, the lead deposited on the valve seats then being sufficient to avoid local welding of the peaks of the surface roughness, and therefore rapid wear of the seats. The main requirement is of course good cooling to keep the temperatures of the seating faces below those at which local welding can occur. Many operators have run on LPG successfully simply by starting from cold on leaded gasoline and switching over to LPG after the engine has come up to its normal operating temperature. Such precautions are rarely required, however, with engines designed specifically for operation on unleaded fuel, since resistance to valve seat wear has been designed into them. In this case, the disadvantage of having to accommodate both a gasoline and an LPG tank is obviated.

194

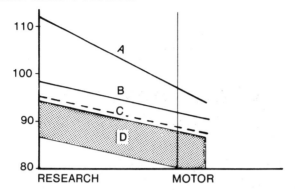

Fig. 10.1 Octane numbers of various fuels
A: LPG (Propane), B: Super grade gasoline, C: Butane, D: Normal grade gasoline

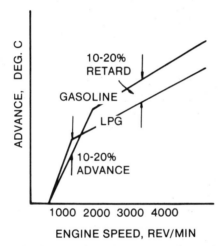

Fig. 10.2 Spark advance and retard requirements for gasoline and LPG

The spark plug voltage has to be increased by 30-40%, Fig. 10.3. This is because the gas is a dry fuel, as compared with gasoline vapour, and therefore has a higher electrical resistance. An outcome is that spark plugs may have to be changed more frequently, mainly to avoid difficulties in starting. On the other hand, whereas an engine can be run on LPG with its gasoline ignition settings, albeit not so satisfactorily, it cannot normally revert to gasoline with ignition settings for LPG.

Another modification is needed on engines having a thermostatically controlled hot and cold air intake system. Since hot air system is required only to evaporate the gasoline from the walls of the manifold when the engine is started from cold, whereas LPG is so much lighter that it does not condense on them, hot air is unnecessary. In any case, more power will be obtained if the air entering the engine is cold. A highly desirable addition to

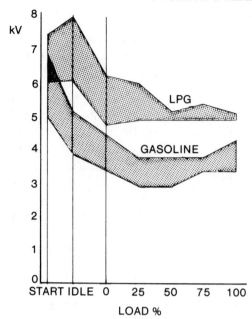

Fig. 10.3   Spark voltage requirements for gasoline and LPG

the fuel system is a shut-down valve actuated by the ignition key, so that the flow of gas is stopped automatically when the engine is switched off.

A longer period of running-in is required with LPG than with gasoline, because the dry gas does not wash any of the lubricant from the cylinder walls. Consequently, full power should not be used until the vehicle has covered about 1500 miles. Alternatively, it can of course be run-in on gasoline and only then the LPG used.

LPG EQUIPMENT

10.2   LPG systems

LPG equipment is produced mainly in Italy, Holland and the USA. The Landi-Hartog systems are fairly representative, so it is these that will be described here. For bulk storage, the liquid is pressurised to about 12 bar. When it is dispensed to the vehicle, however, its pressure is reduced to about 6.9 bar (100 lbf/in^2), but it will not evaporate until the pressure is reduced to about 0.5 bar. The volume of the gas delivered to the engine is 259 times greater than that of the liquid in the tank on the vehicle. An important consideration is that LPG will ignite at any air:fuel ratio between 1.5:1 and 10:1, and this means that even slight leaks could lead to dangerous accumulations of highly inflammable gas mixtures in, for example, service pits or closed garages. LPG is heavier than air.

10.3   The LPG tank

The tank, to contain the gas under a pressure of up to about 7 bar, has to be much heavier and stronger, and therefore more costly, than its equivalent for gasoline. It is generally a 3 mm thick steel cylinder, the ends of which are closed by welded-in domes of the same material, Fig. 10.4. However, ellipsoidal and doughnut sections (hole through the middle) have been produced. The welding has to comply with the regulations regarding the construction of pressure vessels. Even allowing for ambient temperature variations, the maximum working pressure is only about 7 bar, but tanks are rated at 18 bar and have to be tested at a pressure of 30 bar. In general, they range from about 30 to 120 litres capacity.

Interchangeable tanks, looking something like the calor gas containers used for instance for cooking fuel on caravans, are also available, Fig. 10.5. When empty, these tanks can be removed and replaced by full ones, thus avoiding the problems that could arise from a need to install a bulk storage tank in what is perhaps an extremely inconvenient, or perhaps even virtually impossible, location.

If any welding has to be done on adjacent structure or body panels, the

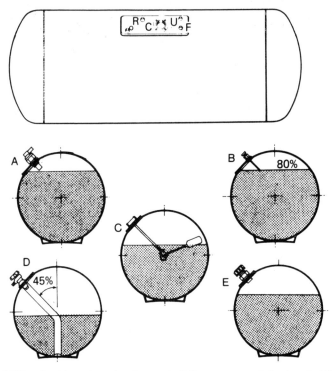

Fig. 10.4   LPG tank with sections showing, at A: Safety pressure-relief valve, B: Ullage-level valve, C: Fuel contents indicator, D: Service or delivery valve, E: Filler valve

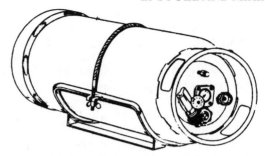

Fig. 10.5   Portable exchangeable tank

tank has to be removed and stored in conformity with Health and Safety regulations. Basically, this means preferably in an open space, and certainly well away from any electrical or other equipment that could generate a spark. Precautions must be taken, too, to ensure that it cannot be tampered with or accidentally damaged, for instance by passing vehicles.

To accommodate variations in internal pressure due to changes in atmospheric temperature, the tank is filled to only about 80% of its capacity, the space remaining being termed the *ullage* space. Since overfilling could be dangerous, any or, more usually, all of three measures are taken as follows. First, a float-actuated valve may be incorporated in the filler connection near the top of the tank. Secondly, the dial gauge indicating the contents of the tank is always sited adjacent to the filler. Thirdly, also installed adjacent to the filler is an ullage valve in the upper end of a tube extending down to the level to which the surface of the fuel rises when the tank is full. The ullage valve should be opened when the tank is being filled: invisible gas will escape from it until the level rises to the maximum permissible, when liquid fuel will squirt out, signifying that the valve should be screwed shut and the filler nozzle uncoupled.

Since liquid fuel has to be introduced under pressure into the tank, the dispenser gun for filling the tank differs from that for gasoline in that it has to be either screwed on to the filler, or coupled in some other way that renders it pressure tight. For instance, in the Landi-Hartog system, Fig. 10.6, the filler cap is an assembly containing two non-return valves in series, both of which are opened by the pressure of the fuel being delivered, but delivery can begin only after a lever on the dispenser gun has been locked on to the filler assembly on the tank. While the upper of these two valves is spring-loaded in the closed position, the lower one is held on its seat by only the vapour pressure in the tank.

Fig. 10.6   The Solex/Landi-Hartog LPG filler valve

Grouped around the filler cap are: the outlet connection from which the fuel is taken to combined evaporator and pressure regulator unit; a safety valve set to blow off if the pressure in the tank exceeds 17.2 bar; the ullage valve and the liquid contents gauge. The tank illustrated in Fig. 10.4 is for installation where filling can be done from above, so the plate carrying this group is set at an angle of 45°. For installation in a commercial vehicle in which access can be gained only from the side, it could be set vertically on the side of the tank, in which case the ullage tube would be a stack pipe extending up to the maximum permissible level of the fuel. Similarly the safety valve would be in the lower end of a stack pipe, which would be taken right up to the top of the tank, in the area filled with vapour: if it were to terminate any lower, there would be a risk of liquid fuel's blowing off and immediately evaporating to form a large volume of highly inflammable mixture. Even worse, the latent heat of vaporisation might cause the valve to freeze in the open position.

In some installations, direct access to the tank is difficult or even impossible to arrange. In these circumstances, an extension pipe connected to the filler can be taken to second filler assembly, also containing a spring-loaded non-return valve. Thus filling could be done remotely at, for example a point on the side or rear of a vehicle or other equipment. Remote fillers should be in what is termed a *valve box*, containing also the ullage valve, so that, in the event of spillage, the vapour would not enter the body or equipment. In such installations, it is generally preferable to install also in the box the fuel contents gauge. This gauge, incidentally, has to be magnetically actuated, since electrical connections inside the tank might generate a spark and ignite the gas in the ullage space, especially if the tank were nearly empty.

10.4   The mixing unit

Liquid fuel is forced, by the pressure in the tank, to a pressure regulator and evaporator unit and thence to a mixing unit which, as its name implies, mixes the gas with the air before it passes the throttle valve and on into the engine. Since the rate of delivery of gas is determined by the demand from the engine, and this is signalled by the mixing unit to the vaporiser and pressure regulator, it is appropriate to describe the mixing unit first.

This unit centres on a venturi for measuring the volume of air flowing into the engine, just as does a conventional carburettor. Around the throat of the venturi is an annular gallery connected by a pipe to the combined vaporiser and pressure regulator unit which, as previously mentioned, supplies the gas to the engine. Holes drilled radially from the gallery into the venturi distribute the gas into the air flow, Fig. 10.7.

The mixing unit has to be matched not only to the needs of the engine but also to the characteristics of the vaporiser and pressure regulator unit. Landi-Hartog make four different types of mixing unit: one is for sandwiching into the carburettor system between the gasoline carburettor

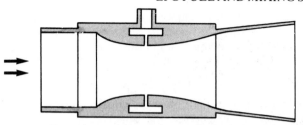

Fig. 10.7   A mixing unit of the trunk type

and throttle barrel; the second is simply flange-mounted on the carburettor assembly; the third is for insertion in a trunk between a remotely mounted air filter and the carburettor; while the fourth, termed the top mounted type, is for clamping between the carburettor horn and the air filter. If an engine breather pipe is connected into the induction system, it should be done upstream of the mixer unit. On engines equipped with gasoline injection equipment, the preferred sites for the mixing unit are either on the throttle body or between it and the air filter. Only installations for engines with carburettors will be covered in what follows, up to Section 10.10.

10.5   Delivering the fuel from the tank

Leaving the tank, the liquid fuel is delivered through a pipe taken from what is termed a *service valve* assembly containing two valves. One can be shut off manually, to isolate the tank, but the other is an automatic safety valve sensitive to the pressure in the delivery line: should the pressure be suddenly released, perhaps by fracture of a pipe, the latter closes instantly.

Landi-Hartog also supply three cocks for switching over from LPG to gasoline and for priming with gas to assist in cold starting. All three are solenoid actuated, but the gasoline cock can be overridden by a manually operated lever so that fuel will always be available for getting home even if the electric system fails. The gasoline and LPG supplies are controlled by a three-position switch, the central position of which is off so that the float chamber can be run dry before changing over to gas. In one of the other two positions it of course activates the solenoid for the gasoline cock and in the other that for the LPG. Since there is no filter in the LPG tank, one is incorporated in the gas priming solenoid valve mounted on the backplate of the vaporiser, Fig. 10.8. This valve is controlled by an on-off switch.

10.6   The vaporiser

Vaporisation and pressure regulation are performed successively in a single sub-assembly Fig. 10.8. In the first stage, the liquid is converted into vapour, by reducing its pressure from its 6.9 bar to 0.49 bar, that is 7 lbf/in^2 above atmospheric, and adding heat to make good the loss due to the latent heat of

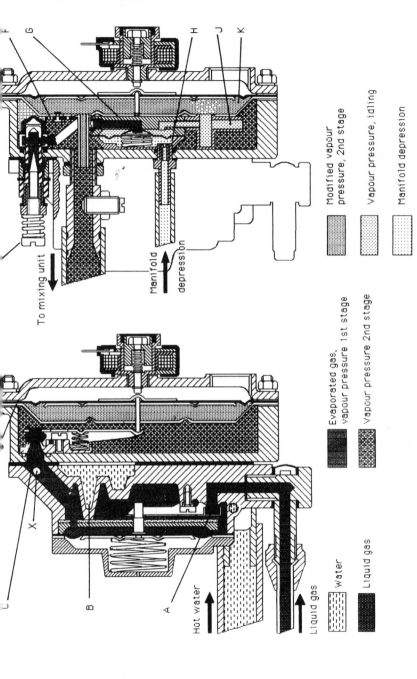

Fig. 10.8 Solex/Landi-Hartog vaporiser and pressure regulator assembly

A: Fuel inlet valve to vaporiser, B: Heat exchanger, C: Inlet valve to pressure regulator, D: Dished aluminium plate, E: Starting mixture adjustment screw, F: Idling mixture adjustment disc, G: Diaphragm-actuated starting valve, H: Small diaphragm chamber subject to manifold depression, for starting, J: Large diaphragm chamber subject to mixing unit depression, K: Port from vaporiser unit to small diaphragm chamber in pressure regulator unit vaporisation. Then, in the second stage, the pressure is reduced to atmospheric or below, to convert the vapour into a dry gas (as was pointed out in Chapter 2, LPG is a gas at atmospheric pressure).

In Fig. 10.8, the vaporiser is shown on the left-hand side of the left-hand diagram: in the right-hand diagram, it is shown only in outline. For an air-cooled engine, the gas has to be exhaust heated before being passed into the vaporiser. Otherwise, the heat required is obtained from the engine coolant, which enters through the larger diameter of the two pipes on the left. After passing through ducts in the casting, it comes out into a heat-exchange chamber of horse shoe shape, the arms pointing downwards on each side. All we see of it in the illustration, therefore, is a section through only B the upper, or bridge portion, higher up and adjacent to the pressure regulator. After the heat exchange has occurred, the water returns, again through passages in the casting, to an outlet pipe alongside the inlet, and therefore invisible in this illustration. Both, however, are very obvious in the foreground in Fig. 10.9.

The liquid gas enters through the smaller pipe on the left, in Fig. 10.8, below that for the water. From here, it passes first upwards and then is turned back parallel to the direction of its entry, until it encounters a valve head. This head is mounted on the lower end of a channel section rocker A, the upper end of which carries a push-rod extending horizontally back through a clearance hole in an aluminium plate and connected to the centre of a diaphragm. The right-hand face of the aluminium plate screens the diaphragm from heat from the engine coolant, while its other face is coated with an absorbent pad, to mop up any heavy liquid contaminants in the LPG. Additionally, when the engine is cold, it absorbs unevaporated liquid, ready to release it again as vapour when the engine is restarted. The pivot pin for the rocker can be seen clamped beneath the head of the screw immediately above that of the valve.

A large diameter coil spring pushes the diaphraghm to the right, holding the valve open until the incoming LPG fills the chamber between diaphragm

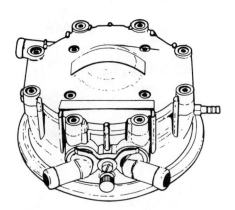

Fig. 10.9   Vaporiser unit, showing the engine coolant inlet and outlet

and aluminium plate. As the pressure rises, it pushes the diaphragm back, against the force exerted by the coil spring, until the inlet valve closes. This happens when the pressure in the chamber rises to that at which the liquid vaporises freely (0.48 bar). The latent heat of vaporisation being replaced by that from the heat exchanger. From this chamber, the vapour leaves through the rocker-actuated valve C, at the top, to enter the pressure regulator, thus allowing the pressure inside the vaporiser to fall until the inlet valve, at the bottom, opens again and more LPG enters, and so on continuously as long as the engine is running.

10.7   The pressure regulator

In the pressure regulator, there are two systems: one serves the engine under normal operating conditions, while the other takes over when it is idling. The control valve for the idling system is shown in the right-hand of the two diagrams in Fig. 10.8, while that for the normal operation system is in the left-hand diagram. Both valves are diaphragm actuated. In this connection, to understand principles on which regulation is based, particularly in the case of idling, it is important always to bear in mind that because the gas flow to the engine can be induced only by differential pressures, the depression causing the diaphragm to deflect is inevitably less than that in the gas as it leaves the outlet port to the engine.

Consider first the system for normal operation. Gas leaving the vaporiser enters the pressure regulator past a rocker valve, C, similar to that already described for regulation of the flow of liquid into it. However, whereas the former valve is normally open and is closed by the diaphragm return spring, that controlling entry into the pressure regulator is normally held open by a spring beneath the rocker and is closed by another diaphragm which, because smaller pressures are involved, is significantly larger than that in the vaporiser.

As before, the valve head is mounted on one end of the channel section rocker, while the other end carries a pushrod connected to the centre of the diaphragm. A solenoid, on the cover, acts on the centre of the other side of the diaphragm, but it is for cold starting so we can for the time being ignore it. As before, the pivot pin for the rocker is clamped beneath the head of the screw that secures the assembly to a pedestal mounted on the main casting.

The dished aluminium plate that is interposed between the diaphragm and the chamber containing this rocker assembly does not affect operation of the unit under normal running conditions. Its function is to form a cradle, or seat, for the diaphragm, keeping it clear of potential damage by the rocker and adjacent pipes and other components to be described later.

In the engine induction tract, the volume flow of air into the engine, is indicated by the depression in the venturi of the mixing unit, which is signalled to the chamber to the left of the larger diaphragm in the pressure regulator. This signal is transmitted through the large diameter pipe (shown only in the right-hand diaphragm), and through which the gas is delivered, back in the opposite direction, to the engine. The right-hand side of the diaphragm is subject to atmospheric pressure. As the depression increases, the diaphragm progressively opens the valve wider and therefore allows increasing quantities of gas to flow from the vaporiser, through the pressure regulator into the engine, thus continuously maintaining the correct air:fuel ratio.

From a smaller venturi, in the outlet from the pressure regulator to the engine, a pipe is taken coaxially to a hole through the dished aluminium plate. As the engine throttle approaches the wide open condition, and the rate of delivery of gas through that venturi section therefore becomes high, the depression induced in it is transferred by the pipe directly to the diaphragm to enrich the mixture, for obtaining maximum power output.

10.8   Pressure regulation for idling and cold starting

Prior to starting and under idling conditions, because the volume of air flowing through the venturi in the mixing unit is zero or so small, there is zero or little depression acting on the diaphragm. It is for this reason that a separate starting and idling system has to be incorporated. The depression is taken from a point downstream of the throttle valve where, with the throttle closed or nearly so, it is very powerful. This depression is made to act upon a much smaller diaphragm in a separate chamber to the left of the centre of the main chamber, as shown in the right-hand diagram. It is signalled to the pressure regulator unit through the pipe on the left, well below the centre of the chamber containing the small diameter diaphragm.

The supply of fuel vapour for starting and idling is entirely separate from that for normal running. It leaves the vaporiser through the small hole that can be seen, in the left-hand diagram of Fig. 10.8, just upstream of the head of the now closed valve C. From here it passes through an idling mixture adjustment needle-valve E, and on through a pipe to a valve port G, leading into the small diaphragm chamber H. The idling mixture is adjusted by screwing the needle valve in to reduce the flow of gas, or out to increase it.

For starting, a control similar to that for a strangler valve, or choke for a carburettor, switches on the solenoid on the outer face of the cover-plate for the large diameter diaphragm. The solenoid pushes the main diaphragm to the left, causing a push rod extending to the left from the centre of the diaphragm to depress the lever to open the valve in the port G to allow the gas to flow from the vaporiser into the diaphragm chamber K. Alternatively, an electrically actuated automatic primer control can be installed. This is designed to remain only for only a limited period, and thus of avoiding over-enrichment when the engine is warm.

When the engine is cranked, the depression downstream of the throttle valve acts on the diaphragm to hold the valve G open against the force exerted by its central coil type return-spring, the degree of opening being dependent on the value of that depression. As the throttle is opened, and the depression in the induction manifold therefore falls, this valve progressively closes again, cutting the idling system out of operation and allowing the normal running system to take over.

For idling, the vapour flows out of the small diaphragm chamber, through the port J below its centre, and on down through a passage that discharges it into the main diaphragm chamber K and thence out to the engine by the same route as that for normal running. On its way down the passage from the small diaphragm chamber, it passes a hole in a passage at right angles to it, from the remote side of the dished aluminium plate that divides the main chamber in two. The venturi effect of the flow past this hole increases the depression in the main diaphragm chamber, and thus contributes towards a smooth take-over from the idling to the normal running systems.

This depression induced beneath the large diaphragm is regulated, during assembly of the unit in the factory, by rotating a small disc F having a series of holes of different sizes near its periphery until that which is found to give the most appropriate performance lines up with a larger bleed hole in the dished aluminium plate. The absolute pressure to the left of the dished aluminium plate is always higher than that adjacent to the diaphragm because of the outflow of gas from the left to the engine.

In service, the regulator disc can be adjusted to obviate a flat spot during the take-over from idling to normal running. However, such adjustment should not be undertaken unless equipment is available for checking its effects on exhaust emissions. Incidentally, if the flat spot is found to occur also when the engine is running on gasoline, it is obviously a function of the engine and not of the gas supply system.

ELECTRONIC CONTROL

10.9   Landi-Hartog LH II Autogas system

To meet the demands arising out of the increasingly stringent emission control regulations, and the consequent development of closed loop electronic control systems, Landi-Hartog introduced a system, Fig. 10.10, based on an electrically controlled evaporator and pressure regulator unit, Figs. 10.11 and 10.12 respectively. It has been developed from the unit illustrated in Fig. 10.8, and operates on the same basic principles. However the two versions differ considerably in detail.

As can be seen from the layout of the whole system Fig. 10.12, there are three connections in right-hand side of the evaporator-regulator unit, two vertical and the central one horizontal. Gas at a pressure of 0.3-1.2 MPa is delivered from the tank, through a solenoid-actuated LPG valve to the central, horizontal connection which, in Figs. 10.11 and 10.12, is shown as item 1. It delivers the liquid gas through the *1st stage valve* 2, into the *1st stage chamber*, to the left of diaphragm 3 in Fig. 10.11.

So long as there is no pressure in the 1st stage chamber, the first stage valve is held open by the spring 4. The liquid gas entering the chamber then evaporates, compensation for the thermal loss due to the latent heat of

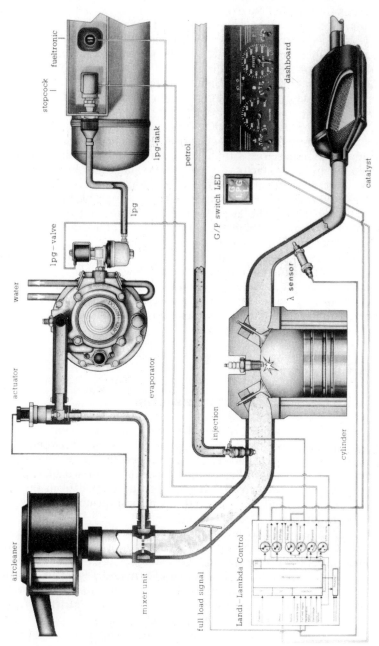

Fig. 10.10   Diagram showing the overall arrangement of the Landi-Lambda Autogas System

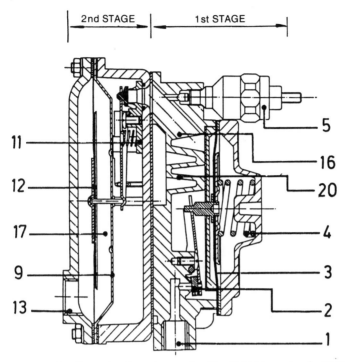

Fig.10.11   From this illustration, it can be seen that Fig. 10.12 (drawn to a larger scale to show its final detail) is not a true section, the second or pressure regulator stage having been rotated in the latter through 90° about its axis

vaporisation being effected by the heat exchanger, item 20 in Fig. 10.11. The hot coolant enters through the connection below that for the gas, passes through the horseshoe shape jacket around the gas passages, and leaves from the connection above it. For air cooled engines, a slightly different arrangement is used, what are termed *evaporator probes* being placed in or on the exhaust system.

As the liquid vaporises, the pressure in the 1st stage chamber increases until it approaches the value of 44 kPa. At this point, acting on the diaphragm 3, it overcomes the force exerted by the spring 4, and thus allows the valve to close under the influence of its return spring (not shown in the illustration). The gas passes through port 16, to the *2nd stage* valve, which is opened and closed appropriately to regulate the pressure in the *2nd stage chamber*, whence it is delivered to the engine. As the pressure in the 1st stage chamber falls following the opening of the 2nd stage valve, the 1st stage valve opens to allow more liquid to enter, the sequence of evaporation and delivery to the 2nd stage chamber being repeated continuously.

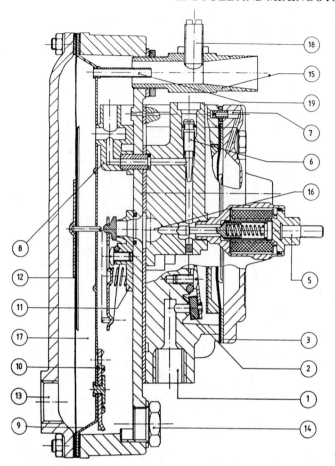

Fig. 10.12   In the Landi-Lambda Autogas System, liquid gas enters the evaporator (shown in detail in Fig. 10.11) at connection 1, and passes as a gas through port 16 in Figs. 10.11 and 10.12, into the pressure regulator, which is the larger diameter left hand port

The left-hand side of the 1st stage diaphragm, as viewed in the illustration, is subjected to the pressure of the gas in that chamber. Note however that the right-hand side is not connected directly to atmosphere. Instead, a connection is made through the restrictor 7 (Fig. 10.12) to a point adjacent to where connection 15 is screwed into the 2nd stage chamber. It is therefore subjected to the depression transmitted back from the venturi in the mixer, through connection 15 into that chamber.

Consequently, a rapid increase in flow of air into the engine, such as might occur if the rev/min were suddenly to increase owing to a shedding of the load, causes the differential pressure across the 1st stage diaphragm to increase and the rate of delivery of fuel into the 1st stage therefore to be reduced, until the bleed through restrictor 7 has progressively restored equilibrium across it. As in the earlier version, an absorbent pad is mounted on the inner face of the diaphragm protection plate, to absorb liquid gas when the engine is cold and release it again as the heat exchange matrix opposite it becomes warm.

During and immediately after cold starting, the gas flow into the 2nd stage chamber is controlled by the solenoid valve 5 but, during normal running, by the diaphragm that directly actuates 2nd stage valve carried on the pedestal 11. Finally, the gas passes out through connection 15 to what Landi-Hartog term the *actuator*, Fig. 10.10, and on to the mixing unit. While the previously mentioned solenoid-actuated LPG valve is simply an on-off valve, the actuator is a valve moved by a stepper motor connected into the closed loop electronic control system, to regulate the flow of gas to the engine.

10.10 Operation

When the ignition key is turned on, the electronic control unit signals to two solenoids, one to open the safety stopcock on the tank and the other the LPG valve, Fig. 10.10. If subsequently the engine stalls, both these valves are automatically closed until the ignition key is again turned.

For cold starting injected engines, the fuel is automatically switched over to gasoline, to ensure that the injection system is primed before running on the gaseous fuel. Otherwise, with this new Landi-Hartog system, a solenoid-actuated idling valve 5, which has replaced the former depression-actuated cold starting device in the evaporator, controls starting from cold. Immediately the ignition is switched on, the valve 5 opens and remains so for only 1.5-2 s, to allow the gas to flow from the evaporator passage 16, through the ejector tube 8 into the gas delivery chamber and out through connection 15 to the mixing unit, ready for starting. Subsequently, as the engine is cranked and its rotational speed rises above 50 rev/min, the valve again opens and remains so. The rate of flow of gas, and therefore the mixture, for idling can be adjusted by means of the screw 6.

The flow of gas through the ejector tube creates a slight depression in the hole drilled into it from the left, as viewed in Fig. 10.12. For starting and idling, the value of the depression communicated to the chamber 17 is just enough to cause the diaphragm to deflect until the pushrod attached to its centre comes into contact with end of the lever carrying the main valve. Note that Fig. 10.12 does not show a true section, and that the push rod attached to the centre of the diaphragm, does not act directly on the main valve, but instead acts on the opposite end of the valve actuation lever.

The actual value of the depression in the chamber during starting and idling is in general equivalent to a few mm of water, and is influenced by not only the rate of flow though the ejector tube but also the leakages, including past the pushrod, and the total of the pressures induced in tube 19, by the gas delivered into the connection 15 and the depression communicated back from the diffuser to that connection.

As in the previous unit, adjustment of the basic value of the depression in chamber 17 is effected by rotating a disc, item 10 in the illustration, to a position in which either none or one of a series of bleed holes around its periphery lines up with a hole in the dished aluminium plate 9, which separates it from the gas delivery chamber. The diameters of the bleed holes are 2, 3, 4, 5, 6 and 7 mm. Access for adjustment is gained by removing plug 14. During assembly in the factory, the 4 mm diameter hole is aligned with that in the dished plate.

As the throttle is opened to take up the load, the depression generated in the mixing unit is transmitted back, through tube 19, to chamber 17. Since the outer face of the diaphragm 12 is subjected to atmospheric pressure, this depression moves it inwards to open the 2nd stage valve. The degree of opening of this valve is proportional to the differential pressure across the diaphragm, which basically depends on the rate of flow of air through the diffuser venturi. However, the outflow of gas from the unit to the actuator and on to the diffuser, in other words the basic mixture strength, can be adjusted by means of screw 18 projecting radially into the connection 15. As full load is approached, the depression communicated to chamber 17 peaks, opening the 2nd stage valve to its maximum delivery position.

When the throttle is closed for deceleration, little or no depression is communicated back to the diaphragm, so the 2nd stage valve closes and gas

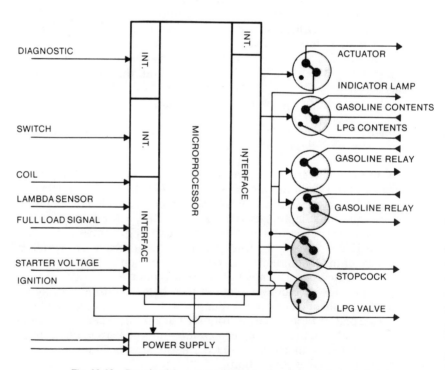

Fig. 10.13   Details of the connections to the Landi-Lambda control

is supplied through only the solenoid valve into the idle system. Switching off the ignition closes both the idle and LPG solenoid valves.

10.11 The Landi Lambda control

The principle of operation of the lambda control system can be seen from Figs. 10.10 and 10.13. When the lambda sensor in the exhaust detects a rich mixture, the controller signals the stepper motor in the actuator to reduce the gas flow and, when a weak mixture is detected, *vice versa*. The control logic differs for engines designed to run solely on LPG and those which can be run on either. With carburetted engines not designed for unleaded fuel, it may be desirable to run initially on gasoline and then to switch over to LPG.

With an injected engine, there is an overlap between running on gasoline and LPG. When, after starting a carburetted engine on gasoline, a change to LPG is required, there has first to be a brief pause for emptying the carburettor float chamber before switching on the gas. In both circumstances, the stepper motor is regulated by the control unit to supply an appropriate progressively increasing flow of gas. A special situation arises if the engine is started on LPG from cold: the lambda sensor will not begin to operate at all until its temperature has risen to about 250-280°C and, should it subsequently rise above about 850°C, it would again cease to function. Consequently, the control system is automatically switched to open loop control for a period of about 1.5 minutes following such a start and, in the event of overheating of the catalyst, the stepper motor again moves into its open loop control position.

Chapter 11

Gasoline injection

Gasoline injection is not the modern invention that it is widely thought to be. The first example was in the 1899 Gorbron Brillè car, which had a spline-driven rotary fuel injection pump. In 1910, Antoinette-Wright produced some aero-engines with injection equipment. Bosch and Bendix introduced systems in 1936 and Fiat and Caproni in 1939, all mainly for aero-engines. In 1940, Caproni Fascaldo experimented with injection on an Alfa Romeo car.

For cars, injection was not seriously considered until after World War II when, as early as 1946, Mercedes was developing it for production cars. The Hilborn Travers continuous injection system was used on an Indianapolis racing car engine in 1948 and, by 1951, the Goliath 2-stroke engine had direct injection into the cylinders. This was followed in 1953 by the introduction of indirect injection for the Connaught racing engine.

By 1954, Mercedes had advanced far enough to introduce their 300SL and some of their racing cars with a Bosch direct injection system based on the use of a cam-and-plunger, or jerk type, pump. Two years later, in 1956, with the aim of overcoming the disadvantage of high costs of injection, a pumpless system was invented by Bond, but the major milestone in the history of gasoline injection, also in 1956, was the introduction of the Bendix Electrojector, on which virtually all the modern systems are based. It, in turn, was based on the application of the then state-of-the-art electronic technology to electrically controlled systems that had been first experimented with in 1932 by the Atlas Diesel Co. and later, in 1940, by Caproni-Fascaldo.

In 1960, a Lucas system involving the use of shuttle valves was introduced, but no mechanical system could compete against other fast evolving hydraulically and electronically controlled ones. Indeed, the subsequent advances relative to the original Bendix concept, initially by Bosch from 1967 onwards, and later by Weber, GM, and Lucas, could not have been made without the developments in electronics and computer control systems that have since occurred.

By 1957 Rochester had developed the Electrojector for continuous injection on the Chevrolet production cars. The Lucas shuttle valve system went into production for the Maserati V8 engine in 1958, and the Bosch system on a Ferrari Formula 1 racing car in 1961. In 1962, an interesting jerk pump system made by Kugelfisher went into some Peugeot production cars, and Lucas injection was used on several racing cars. Then, in 1964, the Tecalemit-Jackson injection system was introduced. Some years later, in

1968, this was taken up by Brico, but soon dropped as it became obvious that the Bosch electronically controlled system was the ultimate answer. In that same year, however, the Spica system was applied to the Alfa Romeo Montreal.

The introduction of the Bosch D-Jetronic injection system on VW and other cars in 1968, was the commercial breakthrough and led ultimately to the establishment of the subsequently developed systems. Then, following the introduction of electronically controlled injection systems, the next major advance was the development by Bosch of the Lambda sensor, Section 11.4. This is a device for detecting the presence of oxygen in the exhaust, and thus enabling control to be exercised on the closed loop principle. Without closed loop control, satisfying the requirements of the latest emissions regulations would be impossible.

TYPES OF INJECTION SYSTEM

11.1 Which injection system?

Among the first things that had to be decided when considering gasoline injection was what type of system to use. In view of the success of both direct and indirect injection with diesel engines, thoughts of course were in the first instance directed towards jerk pump systems. However, diesel experience had shown that such pumps were heavy, costly and noisy and, furthermore, with gasoline instead of diesel oil, they were difficult to lubricate. Moreover, the potential for further development of such systems was poor, they were difficult and costly to interface with electronic sensors, so the exercise of control in relation to both the ambient and engine parameters was very difficult.

Consequently, some alternative systems had to be considered. With the introduction of strict emissions regulations, it soon became obvious that the required degree of accuracy could be obtained only with closed loop electronic control, which is the basis of most of the modern systems. Basically, fuel is delivered by an electric pump at the pressure needed for delivery through injector nozzles, the timing of the opening and closing of which is regulated to obtain the required air:fuel ratio.

Such an arrangement has the advantage that it is independent of any mechanical drive from the engine. Its main critical components are: the pump, which must deliver reliably, without pulsations in flow, at a closely controlled pressure; the injectors, which must contribute to accurate metering, without pre- or post-injection dribble, and deliver the fuel in a very fine spray; and the electronic control unit. Sensitivity of the control unit to engine parameters and ambient conditions is of course essential, and the sensors that serve it must therefore function both reliably and accurately.

11.2 Where to inject?

Injecting the fuel into a pre-chamber increases the complexity of the cylinder head, reduces the space available for valves, and introduces losses due to both thermal conduction and throttling of the gases in the passage interconnecting the pre-chamber and the cylinder. Moreover, with both indirect injection into pre-chambers and direct injection into the cylinders, the hydraulic pressure needed to overcome the compression pressure in the gas is high, introducing problems of noise, wasteful consumption of power by the pump and, potentially, fuel leaks. Another disadvantage is that the time available for completion of injection, and evaporation and mixing after injection is very short.

Injecting into the manifold or some other part of the induction system overcomes all these objections and, by virtue of low pressures, dribbling of fuel from injectors is much easier to avoid. Furthermore, because injection can start before the inlet valve is opened, it allows the fuel more time to evaporate into and mix with the air than if it were to be injected into the cylinder.

If the fuel is injected actually into the inlet ports in the cylinder head, it can be directed at the hot inlet valves, which greatly assist evaporation. Additionally, there is little possibility of condensation on the walls of the manifold, especially when the engine is warm, so acceleration, distribution and fuel consumption are improved. Manifold design is of course simplified

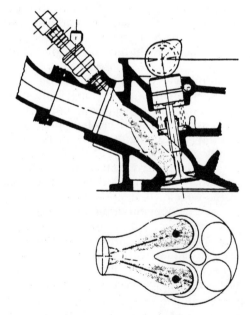

Fig. 11.1   On the Vauxhall/Opel 3 litre, 6 cylinder 24-valve engine for 1990, twin-jet injectors direct the fuel on to the inlet valves

too. On the other hand, the cylinder head casting may be complicated by the need to accommodate injectors in it.

An interesting arrangement for injecting into a four-valve head with siamesed ports for its two inlet valves is that of the Vauxhall/Opel 6-cylinder, 24 valve, 2969 cm^3 engine introduced late in 1989 for the 1990 models. It has a single injector per cylinder delivering twin jets, Fig. 11.1. The jets are directed into the ports and at the inlet valves. However, to keep both the manifold and the cylinder head castings simple, the injectors are screwed into short sleeves, flanged at their ends, and interposed between the ports and the branch pipes of the manifold.

11.3   The alternatives

Continuous injection has the advantage of simplicity and low cost relative to *timed* or *phased injection*. With low pressure continuous injection, the fuel is injected unceasingly into the manifold or ports, premixing it with air to form a cloud of rich mixture just upstream of the inlet valves, ready for induction into each cylinder in turn. When each valve opens, this rich mixture is swept by the incoming air into the cylinder, where swirl and turbulence convert it into an ignitable mixture.

For continuous flow systems, control over air:fuel ratio can be exercised by varying the pressure of the fuel delivered to the injectors but, with many such systems, there is a short time lag between its receiving signals from the control unit and effecting the required changes in air:fuel ratio. A better alternative is to keep the injection pressure constant but vary the volume of fuel delivered, by incorporating a flow control valve, or fuel distributor, Section 11.11. With the application of electronic control to such a system, the mixture can be appropriately and accurately enriched for cold starting, acceleration and development of maximum power.

Timed injection, in which control over air:fuel ratio is exercised by regulating the duration of flow through the injector, or timing it, is another practicable possibility. In most such systems, all the injectors open and close simultaneously and, partly because their response is virtually instantaneous, extremely close control can be exercised over air:fuel ratio, though at added cost. The fuel can be injected into either the manifold or, much more commonly, its branch pipes or directly into the ports. This type of system is attractive for the middle market range of saloon cars.

With *phased, or sequential, injection*, not only is the duration limited, but also the start of injection through each injector is phased relative to the opening of the inlet valve of the cylinder that it serves, thus further reducing the possibility of transfer of fuel intended for one cylinder into another. Again, control can be extremely accurate.

An advantage of both timed and phased injection into the ports of manifold branch pipes is ease of integration of the electronic controls that regulate injection and ignition, to avoid detonation. Either a single detonation sensor operating in conjunction with a crankshaft angle-of-rotation sensor, or a sensor for each cylinder or pair of cylinders can provide a signal indicating to the electronic control unit (ECU) which cylinder or cylinders are detonating. Corrections can then be applied by such a system either to enrich the mixture supply or modify the ignition timing for the individual cylinder or cylinders that are detonating. Obviously, optimum emission quality is obtained by applying the corrective measures to only the cylinder or cylinders that are detonating.

The benefits of close control over fuel supply include avoidance of overheating of a catalytic converter in the event of ignition failure in one or more cylinders, as described in Section 13.6, and the exercise of even closer control over emissions. With both timed and phased injection, it is relatively easy to enrich the mixture appropriately for starting, acceleration, and the development of maximum power. Phased injection is particularly attractive for high performance and luxury cars. Some detailed comments on injector firing strategies are given in Section 11.24.

Yet another option is *single point injection* into either the induction manifold or the throttle body. The latter is sometimes referred to as *throttle body injection* (or TBI) and the former as *central fuel injection* or *single point injection* (CFI or SPI). With TBI, not only the injector but also the injection control unit is usually integrated with the throttle body. If it is not, the fuel may have to be transferred through an external pipe, instead of a short duct, from it to the injector.

Single point injection systems suffer the problems associated with carburation. These include unequal mixture distribution, and the deposition of fuel on, followed by its uncontrollable evaporation from, the walls of the manifold with variations in manifold pressure. Additionally, throttle body heating becomes necessary both to avoid icing and to assist evaporation and mixing. However, with the whole injection system and throttle valve grouped together as a single compact sub-assembly, throttle body injection is significantly less costly than a multi-point system and, therefore, is perhaps most suitable for the highly competitively priced small family saloon or fleet cars.

Weber, prior to developing their PT multi-point injection system, drew up a table comparing the relative merits of the different methods of metering the fuel to the engine (Table 11.1). In it, the designation C represents

Table 11.1:   FUEL METERING SYSTEMS COMPARED

Feature	Simple carb.	Electronic carb.	Single point injection	Timed injection	Phased injection
Fuel cons.	C	B	B	B	A
Economy	B/C	B	B	A	A
Power/torque	A/B	A/B	A/B	A	A
Emissions	C	B	B	A/B	A
Cost	A	B	B	C	C
Reliability	A/B	A	A	A	A
Limp home capability	A	A	C	C	C

acceptable; B represents good, and A extremely good. Weber elected to go for a multi-point phased injection system, Fig. 11.52 because it had the highest score of all and, in their opinion, offered the best prospects for meeting future requirements. However, unlike most other multi-point injection systems, it relied on measurements of absolute pressure and temperature of the air in the manifold, together with throttle valve opening angle, for assessment of the volume of air entering the engine.

CLOSED LOOP CONTROL

11.4   The lambda sensor

The lambda sensor, first introduced by Bosch in 1976, is essential for operation on a *closed loop control* basis. Consequently, we need to understand how it functions before describing in detail the injection systems that are based on its use. While it is applicable to, and desirable for, all engines, it is virtually indispensable for those equipped with catalytic converters in their exhaust systems. This is because, without closed loop control, unburned hydrocarbons can be discharged into the exhaust and be burned in the converter, which can thus not only overheat to the point of being destroyed but also become a fire hazard. Even so, control is temporarily switched from closed to open loop when enrichment is required for cold starting, acceleration or maximum power operation.

By closed loop control, we mean in this case, that deviations from complete combustion of all the air-fuel mixture supplied to a computer-controlled engine are detected by an instrument (the lambda sensor) that signals back to the computer the onset of those changes, so that it can instantly correct them. In contrast, an open loop control system is one in which various parameters such as coolant temperature, load and rotational speed are communicated to a control system that is designed to keep the engine operating within the defined parameters. The main difference, however, is that if it drifts outside these parameters, the control system is unaware and therefore cannot correct directly, but has to wait for signals from other, less precise indicators, that will trigger appropriate control action. Such signals might arise from, for example, changes in engine temperature, speed, load or throttle opening.

The lambda sensor detects deviations from a zero oxygen content of the exhaust which, if positive, are indicative of inefficient combustion leading to either high specific fuel consumption and loss of power or, if negative, carbon monoxide and unburned hydrocarbons in the exhaust gas, with similar adverse effects on performance and exhaust emissions. Incidentally, the control has to be calibrated to take into account the fact that, even with excess fuel at lambda 0.95, there is still about 0.2 to 0.3% oxygen by volume in the exhaust gas. As indicated in Section 12.7, lambda is the ratio of the actual mixture strength to that theoretically required for complete combustion of all the air and fuel.

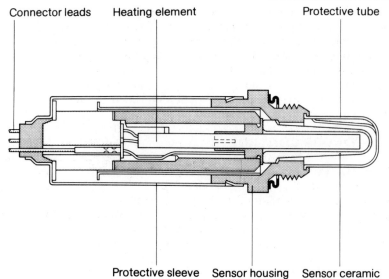

Fig. 11.2   *Bosch Lambda sensor. The heating element is of course for bringing it more rapidly up to its operating temperature after starting the engine from cold*

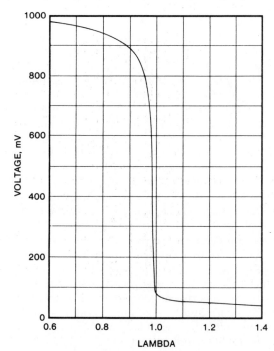

Fig. 11.3   *Plot of voltage characteristic against air:fuel ratio of a lambda sensor at its normal operating temperature (about 600°C)*

As can be seen from Fig. 11.2, the lambda sensor is contained in a steel housing screwed into the exhaust manifold, placing its sensitive element in the gas stream. The sensitive element is a zirconium oxide ceramic thimble, the inner and outer surfaces of which are coated with micro-porous platinum to form electrodes. A louvred metal sleeve is fitted over the thimble to screen it from erosion by solid particles in the exhaust gas stream.

The outer surface is exposed to the exhaust gas stream, and the inner one to atmosphere. At about 300°C, the ceramic begins to conduct oxygen ions, and any difference between the oxygen content of the gases exposed to the two platinum electrodes induces between them a voltage proportional to that difference. The actual characteristics of the voltage difference can be tailored to suit the application, a typical example being illustrated in Fig. 11.3. An important feature of this type of sensor is its extreme sensitivity to deviations from lambda = 0.1. Normally, the exhaust gas brings the electrodes up to the temperature at which they become effective but, should the open loop control be required to come into operation soon after starting at low temperatures, an electric heating element can be added.

THE BOSCH SYSTEMS

11.5   The Bosch hydraulic, electro-hydraulic and electronic systems

Bosch offer six distinctly different types of fuel injection equipment. They are the K-, KE- L- and its variants, including the LE-, LU-, L3-, LH-Jetronic, and the Mono-Jetronic and Motronic systems.

All the components and sub-systems and how they function will be described in subsequent sections, so only a brief outline of the principal differences between the systems will be given now. The K-Jetronic, Fig. 11.4, the K standing for continuous flow, has been in production since 1973. It is multi-point injection system, with a hydro-mechanical control, termed the *fuel distributor*, for opening the injectors and regulating the rate of flow of fuel through them. The output from the pump is delivered at what is termed *the primary pressure* to the fuel distributor, but passing first through a hydraulic accumulator, Fig. 11.5, and then a filter unit. Within the fuel distributor, it passes into the upper end of the cylinder in which the control plunger operates and also into a group of chambers, one per cylinder, below diaphragm-actuated distributor valves. All the sub-systems such as those for fuel flow regulation and valves for warm-up are controlled by signals from sensors of, for example, ignition switch, throttle position, intake air flow, engine speed and temperature. A distinguishing feature of the K-Jetronic is that its sensors are either automatic switches or they trigger switches. They therefore control the components of the system directly, instead of indirectly by sending signals to a computer performing the control function.

In the KE-Jetronic, introduced in 1976, an electronic control unit replaces the hydro-mechanical unit. Fuel is delivered through a diaphragm type

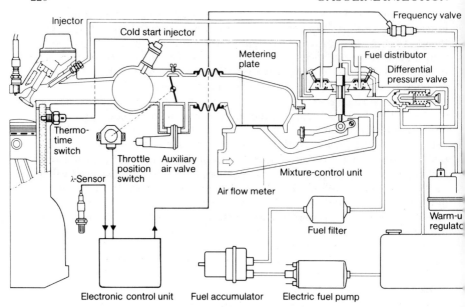

*Fig. 11.4   The electronic control unit, throttle position switch, frequency valve and its connec-
tion to the lower chambers of the fuel distributor, as shown here, are included in the Bosch
K-Jetronic hydro-mechanical system only if closed loop control is required. For open loop
control, they are unnecessary*

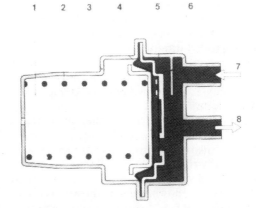

*Fig. 11.5   The plate valve, which is riveted to the baffle between the diaphraghm and the fuel
inlet, lifts off its port, to enable the fuel accumulator to charge rapidly. Since the fuel discharge
rate required is inevitably relatively small, the valve subsequently seats on its port, leaving open
only the smaller hole in its plate*
*1. Spring chamber, 2. Spring, 3. Stop, 4. Diaphragm, 5. Fuel chamber, 6. Baffle, 7. Fuel in,
8. Fuel out*

primary pressure regulator, simultaneously to the electro-hydraulic pressure actuator and the space above the control plunger. Whereas in the K-system, the pressure below the diaphragms in the fuel distributor is the same as the constant primary pressure, and the rate of injection is regulated by varying the pressure above them, in the KE-system the pressure above is kept constant and the rate of injection regulated by varying the pressure below the diaphragms in the fuel distributor. This is done by an *electro-hydraulic pressure actuator*, regulated by an *electronic control unit*, so there is no warm-up regulator.

Other features include fuel supply cut-off which comes into operation in the over-run condition, thus further helping to reduce fuel consumption, and a safety circuit that breaks the electric circuit to the fuel pump if the engine remains switched on after it has stopped or stalled, for example immediately following an accident.

Sensors additional to those in the K-system are required, for signalling to the electronic control unit the deflection of the air metering plate (volume inflow of air), the throttle position (idling, overrun or full throttle), and the engine speed, from the ignition system. An engine coolant temperature sensor is included, in addition to the thermo-time switch, and a lambda sensor is placed in the gas stream in the exhaust manifold. An engine start signal is obtained from the ignition circuit. The output from the electronic control unit controls the electro-hydraulic pressure actuator.

The L-type systems, also introduced in 1973, are all electronically controlled, the fuel being delivered in each instance directly to a rail on the engine, instead of through a hydro-mechanical distributor, to the individual injectors. They differ from the K-type systems in that a swinging gate, instead of balanced plate, type of air flow sensor is employed.

An exception is the LH-Jetronic, in which a hot wire anemometer, measures the mass flow, instead of volume flow of the air into the engine. The LE- has open loop control for Europe and LU-Jetronic system has closed loop control for the USA, while the L3-Jetronic has a digital control unit bolted on to the air flow sensor, to simplify interconnection between the two, and is available with both closed and open loop control. In all the L-series, the fuel is delivered to what is termed the *fuel rail*. Because the fuel rail together with the pressure regulator mounted on one end serves as a plenum chamber, helping to damp out pulsations, a fuel accumulator is unnecessary.

In contrast to the L-Jetronic control system, the LH-Jetronic has no major mechanical control components. Instead, it has a microcomputer with data as well as program memories, by means of which the air:fuel ratio is regulated at all times to conform with values plotted against speed and load in the data memory. Its microcomputer, operates in conjunction with a power supply pack and a stable clock. The clock is based on a quartz oscillator, which provides the pulses for sequencing the operations.

Mono-Jetronic is a low cost, single point, throttle body injection system. Its throttle serves, together with signals from air intake temperature and engine speed signals, to indicate rate of air flow into the engine.

The Motronic is a digitally controlled combined fuel injection and ignition, or engine management, system. It converts the analogue signals from the sensors into digital signals, for processing and comparison with data stored in the memory of an on-board computer. Calculations, based on the analogue data, are made by the computer to enable it to issue the appropriate control signals to the injection and ignition systems. It has a swinging gate type air flow sensor.

In what follows, first the individual elements, or sub-systems, of the Bosch K-, KE-, and L-Jetronic variants will be used to exemplify the basic principles of fuel injection. Then, the Mono-Jetronic and Motronic systems will be separately described, because their sub-systems are either closely integrated with, or their functions performed by, their electronic control systems.

11.6 Elements of modern injection systems

With virtually all modern injection systems, the quantity of air supplied to the engine is regulated by means of a conventional butterfly type throttle valve. The actual mass of the air in-flow, however, has to be measured by a separate sub-system. Other essential elements of an injection system may include an idle air control, a fuel pump, fuel filter, a cold start enrichment system, fuel pressure regulator and a control unit, which may be either hydraulic or electronic or a combination of both and, possibly, fuel rail or some form of fuel flow pulsation damper.

The control unit needs sensors to supply it with information about the engine operating conditions and requirements. These may include an air flow sensor, a throttle switch, and sensors for indicating engine temperature, engine speed, crankshaft angle, throttle opening, manifold pressure, and air temperature in either the manifold or the air intake.

AIR FLOW METERING

11.7 Air flow sensors

The traditional way of measuring air flow is to interpose in the flow path a plate in which is a calibrated orifice. However, this is impracticable for engines: if the orifice were large enough to cater for full throttle operation without significantly restricting the flow and therefore reducing volumetric efficiency, it would be much too large for accurate measurement of the low rates of flow typical during idling and slow running.

Volume air flow meters, such as the vane or cup types, are either too inaccurate or, if accurate enough, too bulky, complex or fragile for automotive applications. An alternative that has been considered however is the Kármán vortex type, Fig. 11.6. The incoming air flows past vortex generators, the frequency of generation of the vortices being a measure of

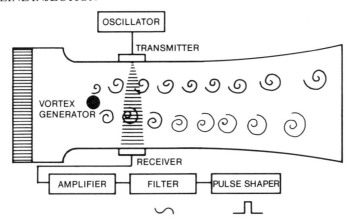

Fig. 11.6   Kármán vortex flowmeter

the velocity of flow. This frequency is measured by transmitting ultrasonic waves through the air stream, in a plane normal to its axis, to a receiver, signals from which are then processed electronically. The presence of the vortices affects the propagation velocity of the ultrasonic waves, and therefore the output signals from the receiver.

In some instances, for example in the Bosch Mono-Jetronic, Weber and GM systems, the measurement of the quantity of air inducted is effected on a *volume-density*, or *speed-density*, basis simply by using either throttle valve position or engine speed indicators, and sensors for air pressure and temperature in the induction manifolds. The two last mentioned sensors are necessary because it is not the volume but the mass of the air that has to be measured for establishing what mass of fuel must be metered into it to obtain a chemically correct mixture. Measurements of volume alone are impracticable owing to inaccuracies introduced, because of variations of density with temperature and manifold pressure.

With the addition of an electronic control system, it is possible to increase the accuracy of measurement by storing in the memory a map of engine volumetric efficiency plotted against speed. Also, by storing records of changes in flow experienced with increasing age of that type of engine in terms of hours run or mileage covered, it is possible to take into account the effects of wear on mixture requirements.

Throttle position indicators may be used also for signalling, to electronic controls, rates of opening of the throttle for acceleration. In simpler forms, they can be simply switches indicating that the throttle is closed for idling or overrun, or approaching the wide open condition for maximum power operation. This simplification, however, is practicable only if an air flow sensor other than the throttle is used.

Systems based on measurement of throttle angle have the advantage of simplicity as regards mechanical components but, in view of the wide range of air flows between idling and full throttle under all conditions of speed and load, sufficient accuracy for attaining acceptable reductions of emissions is virtually impossible without electronic control. However, compensation for wear is not automatically effected, as it is with air flow meters that measure more accurately the quantity of air flowing into the engine.

Therefore, Bosch install upstream of the throttle valve in most of their systems one of three different types of air flow sensor. These are: a balanced plate, a gate type metering device and a hot wire anemometer. The signals from them are supplemented by a throttle position indicator, for signalling a need for enrichment for starting etc.

11.8   Suspended plate type air flow meter

In the Bosch K- and KE-Jetronic injection systems, a suspended plate type air meter is used in conjunction with the hydraulic fuel delivery control. Basically, a circular plate is carried on one end of a lever arm pivoted at its opposite end. This plate is suspended in a throat in the air intake, Fig. 11.4. As the air flow into the engine increases, it lifts the plate against a control force exerted by a plunger, termed the *control plunger*, which presses down on the lever arm at a point nearer to the pivot. How the balancing force is exerted by the control plunger is regulated is described in Section 11.11.

The mass of the plate is counterbalanced by a small weight on the end of the lever opposite to it so that, when the engine is switched off, it settles gently down to its zero position.

As the throttle is opened downstream of the plate, the increasing flow of air forces the plate upwards in the progressively varying section of the throat. The pressure exerted on the plate is always balanced by that of fuel acting on the upper end of the control plunger. At very low rates of flow, the deflection of the arm is large enough to be measured accurately yet, by virtue of the conical section of the throat, it is still within practical limits at maximum flow.

If the throat of the air flow meter were of straight conical section, the air:fuel ratio would be constant over the whole of the range of deflection of the plate. The more obtuse the angle, the leaner would be the mixture and *vice versa*. In practice, therefore, the angle is changed in three stages, for idling, part load and full load, the first and last mentioned conditions requiring enrichment of the mixture.

The suspended plate air flow meter also automatically provides for enrichment for acceleration. If the throttle is opened rapidly, there is sudden inrush of air to relieve the depression in the manifold. This causes the suspended plate to overswing, and then return to its new equilibrium position as the manifold pressure stabilises. Consequently, the rate of flow of fuel is momentarily increased to the value that would be required if the throttle were to remain in the overswing position.

To release the considerable pressure that can be generated in the intake in the event of a backfire, the plate is free to swing back beyond the narrowest portion of the throat until it hits a rubber stop. A leaf spring, bearing on the underside of the plate returns it to its zero position and, when the engine has been switched off, helps to support it there. The upward travel of the end of the leaf spring is limited by a rubber stop.

As can be seen from Fig. 11.4, the control plunger does not in fact bear directly on the lever on which the sensor plate is mounted, but on a roller carried by a second lever parallel to it. The two levers pivot about a common spindle and, in the end of the secondary lever remote from the pivot, is an adjustment screw the end of which rests on the upper face of main lever. This is for setting the zero position of the plate in the throat.

11.9 Swinging gate type air flow meter

This type of air flow meter, Fig. 11.7, is used in the Bosch Motronic and the L-Jetronic variants, Fig. 11.8. It has several advantages. First, because the angular inertia of the gate is inherently lower than that of the linear inertia of

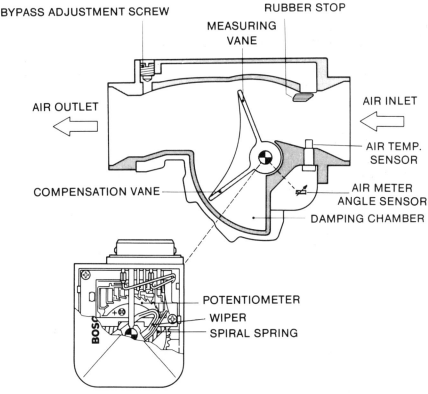

Fig. 11.7   L-Jetronic air flow sensor, showing the screw in the bypass duct for manual adjustment of the idling air:fuel ratio. In the potentiometer sub-assembly, there is a contact wired into the circuit that drives the pump; so, if the engine has stalled but the ignition is still switched on and the throttle pedal released, the pump will not continue delivering fuel

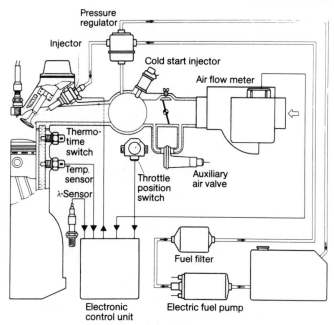

Fig. 11.8   *The Bosch L-Jetronic injection system. The idle speed adjustment screw in the throttle bypass should not be confused with the idle mixture adjustment screw in the air metering gate bypass shown in Fig. 11.7. From the filter, the fuel is delivered into one end of a fuel rail, Fig. 11.17, on the opposite end of which is mounted the pressure regulator. The pipes to the injectors are appropriately spaced along the length of the fuel rail and not, as they appear to be in this illustration, taken from the pressure regulator*

the balanced plate, its response to changes in throttle opening is potentially more rapid. Secondly, with the electronic controls of these three injection systems, full advantage can be taken of the fact that, on depression of the accelerator pedal, the sensor valve opens fractionally in advance of the actual inflow of air into the engine, so the increase in the rate of injection, needed to make up for the condensation in the manifold and to enrich the mixture for increased power demanded for acceleration, can be made to occur correspondingly earlier.

As can be seen from the illustration, the gate is spring loaded and is of the twin leaf, or twin flap, type. It is swung open by the air flow, against the torque applied by its spiral return spring. The second leaf is fixed at rather more than 90° to the main one. Its function is to damp out oscillation due to the effect on the twin leaf assembly of the pulsation of the air flow, which increases with throttle opening. It does this because adjacent opposing faces of the leaves are equally subjected to the pressure oscillations, so that the resulting moments on the assembly cancel out. By virtue of the profile of the passage in which the main leaf swings, there is a logarithmic relationship between its angle and volume of air passing through. Consequently, at low throughput, when small errors of measurement would otherwise represent a

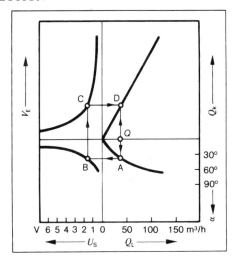

Fig. 11.9   Relationship between air quantity, sensor flap angle, voltage at potentiometer and quantity of fuel injected. If Q is the quantity of air flowing through the meter at a flap angle A, then D is the quantity of fuel required. The potentiometer transmits a voltage signal B to the control unit, which then causes a pulse such as will deliver to the injectors a quantity of fuel equal to D

high percentage of the total flow, a high degree of accuracy is in fact obtained.

The angular position of the flap is sensed by a potentiometer, which converts it into a voltage inversely proportional to the air throughput. This potentiometer has two arcuate tracks comprising very narrow conducting segments, or data points, connected to thick film, ceramic-metal resistors on a ceramic baseplate, which are unaffected by either high or rapidly changing temperatures. One track picks up the voltage, varying as the air sensor plate deflects, while the other transmits it to the electronic control unit. The arm that carries the brushes is attached to the sensor plate spindle but insulated from it.

Fine wire brushes have the advantage that the individual wires apply only a very light pressure to their tracks, so the rate of wear is extremely low. Moreover, by virtue of the multiplicity of wires, good electrical contact is obtained even though the surfaces of the tracks may not be absolutely even and regardless of the speed at which they are wiped. To prevent damage in the event of a short circuit, a thick film fixed resistor is placed in series with the wipers, which are free to travel beyond the ends of the tracks, to avoid damage in the event of a backfire.

Both ageing and the temperature characteristic of the potentiometer could be sources of error in the translation of flap angle into a voltage. So, to avoid them, resistance ratios instead of absolute values are evaluated by the control unit. The relationships between quantity of air flowing, angle of sensor flap, potentiometer voltage and fuel injected are shown in Fig. 11.9.

A small quantity of air is taken through a bypass around the sensor plate.

This is adjustable by the screw shown in Fig. 11.7, for setting the idling air:fuel ratio.

11.10   Hot wire anemometer

The hot wire type *mass flow* meter, Fig. 11.10, measuring the air mass directly instead of on the volume-density principle, has many advantages. It regulates the air:fuel ratio more precisely, and offers minimal obstruction to the air flow. Correction of fuelling with altitude is automatic. Errors do not arise from either pulsation or variations in ambient air temperature and therefore density. Response is extremely rapid. The instrument is of simple design and has no moving parts.

The air flow sensor used in the LH-Jetronic system, Fig. 11.11, is of the hot wire type, in which an electrically heated platinum wire, 70 μm thick and forming one arm of a Wheatstone bridge, is placed in the airstream. A current passing through this wire is regulated, between 500 and 1200 mA according to the rate of air flow, to keep its temperature constant relative to that of the incoming air. The voltage drop across a precision resistor in the circuit, Fig. 11.12, is a measure of the current variations due to the air flow.

In the other arms of the bridge circuit, the resistors are of high impedance, so the currents flowing through them are only a fraction of that through the hot wire and precision resistor. The current through the temperature compensation resistor, which has a constant resistance of about 500 ohm, is similarly low. This resistor, because it must be corrosion resistant and have a rapid response, is of platinum film. Its compensation effect can be adjusted by means of the series resistor R_1, and a temperature sensor compensates for the intake air temperature. By virtue of the low mass of the sensor and its

Fig. 11.10   A Bosch photogaph showing, left, a hot wire carrier sub-assembly, another of which can be seen secured by two screws in the main housing of the complete hot wire air metering unit on the right

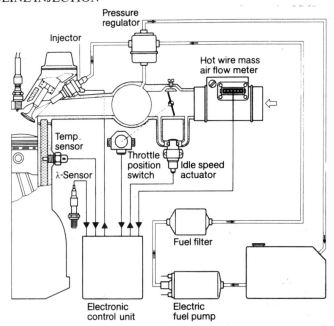

Fig. 11.11   The principal difference between the L- and LH-Jetronic systems is the use in the latter of a hot wire instead of the gate type air metering unit

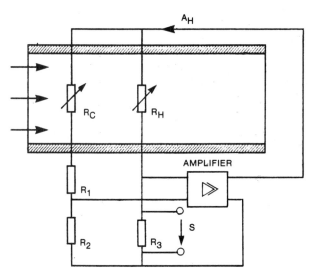

Fig. 11.12   Bridge circuit for the hot wire mass-flow meter
R_H: Hot wire, R_C: Temperature compensation sensor, R_1, R_2: High impedance resistors, R_3: Precision resistor, S: Signal voltage for air flow rate, A_H: Heating current

connections, a time constant of only 3 s or less is obtained. This allows accurate matching of the sensor to output signal. Also in the housing for the hot wire air mass meter is a potentiometer that can be adjusted for setting the idling mixture.

Contamination of the surface of the hot wire can cause inaccuracies, so a cleanse command is given by the electronic control unit each time the ignition is switched off. On the issuing of this command, the wire is raised to a high temperature for 1 s, to burn off any contamination that might be there.

From Fig. 11.10, it can be seen that the hot wire is carried in a plastics measuring tube. The tube contains the hot wire carrier ring, the precision resistor and the air temperature sensor. A printed circuit board, hybrid circuit, and power transistor are mounted in a housing on top of the unit. The hybrid circuit embodies some of the bridge resistors, and the control and self cleaning circuits.

By virtue of the very low mass of the hot wire and time constants of only a few milliseconds, the response of the heating circuit is extremely rapid. Consequently, despite the increase in pulsation of the flow as full load is approached, measurement remains accurate. Errors can occur only if the throttle is wide open at low speeds, when some large amplitude return flow pulsations might be experienced, but even then correction can be effected electronically.

FUEL FLOW METERING

11.11   Continuous flow systems

With continuous flow systems, fuel metering is effected by varying the rate of flow at either constant or varying pressure. As mentioned previously, rapid response is difficult to obtain with variable pressure systems. In the K-Jetronic system, the rate of flow is varied while the pressure is kept constant in the delivery lines to the injectors. This is done as follows.

In Section 11.8, it is stated that the balancing force acting on the end of the lever opposite to that carrying the suspended plate of the air flow meter is imposed by a control plunger. The upper end of this plunger, Fig. 11.4, is subjected to what is termed the *control pressure* in the fuel system. Over most of the operating range, this pressure is constant though, for warm-up and full load operation, it is increased appropriately for enriching the mixture.

Basically, the injectors are opened automatically by the fuel delivery pressure, as it rises above its nominal value of 3.3-3.6 bar. The rate of flow through them is then regulated by a variable restrictor forming part of the *fuel distributor* assembly. This restrictor is in fact the upper edge of the waisted section of the control plunger which, to a degree that is varied with the rate of flow of air past the suspended plate type meter, partially covers slots, termed *control slots*, through which the fuel passes on its way to the injectors. The greater the upward deflection of the plate and, therefore, the longer the uncovered length of the slot, the greater becomes the volume of fuel passing through it at a constant delivery pressure.

The fuel is delivered first into the lower chambers of the distributor, which are all interconnected by a ring main. From here, it goes radially into the bottom of the waisted section of the control plunger, and then up and finally radially out again through slots into the upper chambers. Each of these chambers is isolated from its neighbours. The function of the fuel distributor is to distribute the fuel at rates of flow that are varied to meet the operational requirements of the engine, at a constant pressure equally through each injector into the individual induction ports.

As can be seen from Fig. 11.4, the fuel is delivered into the distributor at a point adjacent to the primary pressure regulator. The latter component is simply a relief valve which maintains a constant pressure in the primary system, and releases fuel in excess of engine requirements back to the tank. Although, as previously indicated, the main flow is directed to the chamber beneath the diaphragm valves of the fuel distributor, a branch from the duct between the pressure regulator and the lower chambers takes off some of the fuel into the *control circuit*. Entering this circuit, it passes first through a restricting orifice and then up into the space above the control plunger, which it leaves through another restricting orifice to the warm-up regulator.

The function of the first restriction is to de-couple the pressure in the control and primary fuel circuits, while that of the second is to damp out oscillation of the air flow sensor plate owing to the pulsation of the air flow, which increases as the throttle is opened. In some installations, there is a spring above the control plunger, to help to prevent it from being drawn up by thermal contraction of the fuel when the engine cools after being switched off. Under this condition, compensation is effected with fuel from the accumulator replacing that which is contracting.

The warm-up regulator, Fig. 11.13, is a bimetal controlled, diaphragm type valve mounted so that it senses engine coolant temperature. It also is electrically heated to prevent enrichment for too long a period in very cold conditions. When the engine is cold, it reduces the constant control pressure, by releasing back to the tank a proportion of the fuel delivered to the control chamber. Indeed, the control pressure can thus be reduced initially, to as little as 0.5 bar but, as the engine temperature rises, it is progressively increased until, under normal running conditions, it levels out to become constant at about 0.1 bar higher than the delivery pressure to the injectors. When the control pressure is reduced relative to its normal constant value, the air flow metering plate deflects further. This lifts the control plunger, increasing the open areas of the control slots, thus enriching the mixture.

There is one diaphragm and control slot for each cylinder in the engine, the uncovered length of the slot being determined, as previously indicated, by the establishment of equilibrium between the forces exerted on the lever by the rate of flow of the air past the suspended plate and the control pressure exerted by the fuel on the upper end of the plunger. Incidentally, the presence of the fuel above the plunger also ensures that the latter follows precisely and instantly the movements of the arm carrying the sensor plate.

The pressure differential across each diaphragm actuates a *differential pressure valve* to maintain, regardless of the uncovered length of its associated slot, a constant pressure of delivery of fuel to the injector that it serves. This valve is simply a vertical tube against the lower end of which abuts a circular plate centrally fixed to the top face of the diaphragm. Consequently, it is opened if the diaphragm falls, and closed if it is lifted.

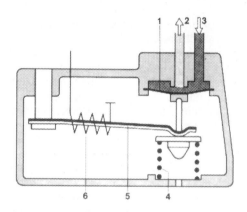

Fig. 11.13   Warm-up regulator shown with its setting appropriate for a cold engine condition 1. Diaphragm, 2. Fuel return, through primary pressure regulator to tank, 3. Control pressure, 4. Valve spring, 5. Bimetal strip, 6. Electric heating element

Compression in a spring, supplemented by the delivery pressure, above the diaphragm, tends to open it but the primary pressure acting upon the lower face of the diaphragm tends to close it. A differential of 0.1 bar will open or close the valve. Since both the primary pressure below and that exerted by the spring above are constant, the force required to hold the diaphragm in its equilibrium or mean position, and thus to keep the distributor valves just open, must also be constant. Therefore, so also must be the delivery pressure to the injectors.

The rate of flow to the injectors is of course proportional to the cylindrical area opened up between the circular plate and the bottom edge of the tube but, as has already been explained, overall control over the total rate of flow (to all the cylinders) is exerted by the control plunger. Viscosity and resistance to flow of the fuel will cause a slight pressure drop between the distributor valves and injectors.

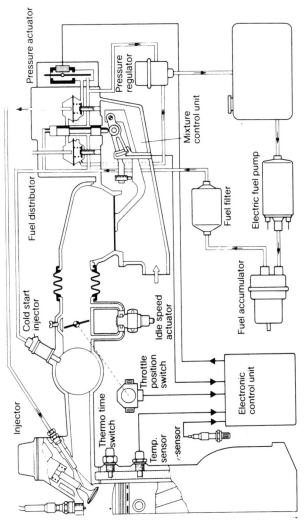

Fig. 11.14   In contrast to the K-Jetronic system, in which a warm-up regulator and frequency valve modify respectively the pressures above the control plunger and below the diaphragms, the KE-Jetronic has an electronically controlled pressure actuator regulating the pressure below the diaphragms of the distribution valves while that above them remains constant

Pressure actuator

Pressure regulator

Mixture control unit

Fuel distributor

Electric fuel pump

Fuel filter

Cold start injector

Fuel accumulator

Idle speed actuator

Injector

Throttle position switch

Thermo time switch

Temp. sensor

sensor

Electronic control unit

As so far described, the K-Jetronic fuel metering system is suitable for use only with open loop control. If a closed loop control using a lambda sensor for maintaining the air:fuel ratio at lambda = 1.0 is required, an extra circuit has to be introduced, to vary the pressure beneath the diaphragms of the differential pressure valves. Lowering this pressure correspondingly increases the differential pressure across the slots uncovered by the control plunger, thus increasing the rate of flow of fuel into the upper chambers and on to the injectors.

As has already been mentioned, the control and primary pressure circuits are decoupled by the restrictor in the entrance to the duct supplying the control circuit. For lambda control, an extra connection is taken from the lower chambers to allow a proportion of the fuel to pass out of them through a variable restrictor, termed the *frequency valve,* back to the tank. For operation on the closed loop principle, the electromagnetic frequency valve is opened and closed cyclically by electric pulses from the electronic control system on the basis of signals from the lambda sensor. This reduces the pressure in the lower chambers in proportion to the ratio of open to closed time. For operation on the open loop principle (for example for cold starting and warm-up) the variable restrictor is fully closed in response to appropriate signals from a throttle position switch and engine temperature sensor.

This arrangement, however, represents only minimal application of electronic control, based on a relatively simple computer for doing little more than modifying the characteristics of the system through the medium of the lambda sensor. A more comprehensive conversion to electronic control came in 1976, with the introduction of the KE-Jetronic system.

11.12   Fuel metering in the KE-Jetronic continuous flow system

For the KE−Jetronic, Fig. 11.14, a more elaborate electronic control system is employed, to perform the fuel metering function accurately in response to variations in operating conditions of the engine. Extra components are introduced, mainly sensors, including one to signal to the computer the angular deflection of the air flow metering plate (volume air flow), so that an electro-hydraulic pressure actuator can be substituted for the mechanical regulation of the control pressure, as a means of metering the flow to the injectors.

The sensors include the following: the potentiometer measuring the deflection of the air metering plate, to indicate volume inflow of air flowing into the engine; a throttle position switch to indicate an idling, overrun or full throttle requirement; and a sensor in the ignition system to indicate engine speed. An engine coolant temperature sensor is included too, as also is a thermo-time switch, the function of which is described in Section 11.18, and a lambda sensor is placed in the gas stream in the exhaust manifold. An engine start signal is obtained from the ignition circuit. The output from the electronic control unit regulates the electro-hydraulic pressure actuator.

Among the incidental advantages of the use of comprehensive electronic control are the ease with which fuel economy can be further improved by speed limitation and overrun cut-off of the fuel supply. Speed limitation by cutting the ignition would be unacceptable for modern engines used in conjunction with catalytic converters, because the oxidising stage would overheat, Section 13.6. Instead, therefore, the electronic control unit of this, and incidentally also the various L-Jetronic systems, optionally compares the engine speed signal with a limit recorded in its memory and, if it is too high, suppresses the injection signals. Similarly the overrun fuel supply can be cut off at a predetermined speed, on the basis of signals received from the throttle valve switch and the engine speed and temperature sensors.

11.13   The KE–Jetronic pressure regulator

The diaphragm type pressure regulator, Fig. 11.15, used in the KE- is more accurate than the spring-loaded plunger type of the K-Jetronic and, moreover, performs the additional function of retaining throughout the system, after the engine has been switched off, a pressure below that which lifts the injector valves. This is to enable the engine to be re-started instantly while it is still hot, which could otherwise be difficult since, at atmospheric pressure, heat from the engine could cause bubbles of vapour to form in the injectors, their pipelines or the distributor.

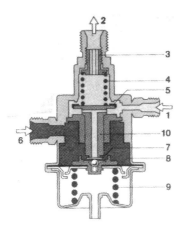

Fig. 11.15   KE-Jetronic primary pressure regulator
1. Return from the fuel distributor, 2. To tank, 3. Adjustment screw, 4. Counter-spring, 5. Seal, 6. Inlet, 7. Valve plate, 8. Diaphragm, 9. Control spring, 10. Valve body

As compared with the K-Jetronic system, the advantages obtained include rapid response to changing driving conditions, improved driveability and good low speed torque. Fuel economy is better and there is no jerking when the supply of fuel is resumed after it has been cut off for overrun operation, during which there is zero emission of toxic gases. Exhaust gas pollution over the whole range is lower and can be even better if closed loop control is incorporated.

When the engine is started, the pump progressively increases the primary pressure in the system until the return spring in the accumulator, Fig. 11.5, is fully compressed and the diaphragm seated on its stops. Meanwhile, the fuel has been entering the pressure regulator valve through the connection on the left in the illustration. As the pressure rises, the diaphragm in the pressure regulator is forced downwards against the lower spring, but the upper spring, acting on the valve body, keeps the port closed until the diaphragm assembly comes down upon the lower stop. The pressure ultimately attains its constant working value of 5.4 to 6.4 bar, according to engine application. At this point, the valve body is lifted upwards against the influence of the upper spring, to open the port and release the fuel surplus to requirements (together with that just beginning to be released through the connection on the right from the fuel distributor) out through the connection at the top into the pipeline back to the tank.

The pressure regulator valve is connected in parallel with the main flow circuit, and maintains at the previously mentioned constant primary pressure, the simultaneous deliveries of fuel to the space above the control plunger and to the electro-hydraulic pressure actuator. This pressure must be accurately maintained because, acting on the upper end of the control plunger, it is utilised primarily to keep the mixture strength consistently at lambda = 1.0.

When the engine is switched off, and the flow from the pump therefore ceases, the accumulator discharges and the primary pressure falls. As it does so, the diaphragm rises but the valve, under the influence of the upper spring, remains closed and, ultimately, the seal around the upper edge of the lower seating for that spring comes up against its stop. This prevents further flow of fuel back through the restrictor in the duct from the lower chamber of the fuel distributor to the tank.

At this stage, the primary pressure has fallen sufficiently for the flow to the injectors to have been cut off by closure of the gap between the edges of the control plunger and the slot through which the fuel enters the upper chambers of the fuel distributor. Consequently, the pressure in both the primary system and injector delivery pipes remains constant at a level below that which would lift the injector valves. The chamber beneath the diaphragm of the primary pressure regulator is connected by a pipe taken to a point downstream of the air sensor plate. Therefore, the pressure at which the valve is held closed is influenced by that in the air intake downstream of the air sensor and thus also to the differential pressure across the valves in the individual injectors.

Other features of the KE-system include fuel supply cut-off, effected in the overrun condition by the electronic control unit, further to reduce fuel consumption. Also the electric circuit to the fuel pump is automatically broken if the engine remains switched on after it has stopped or stalled. This is valuable as a safety measure immediately following an accident.

An electronic control unit regulates the actual rate of injection, through the medium of the electro-hydraulic pressure actuator, which is flange-mounted on the distributor unit. It does so by varying, according to engine operating conditions (idling, cruising, maximum power etc), the pressure below the diaphragms in the fuel distributor. This pressure, unlike that in the K-Jetronic, is not the primary pressure.

As has been mentioned previously, the fuel supply from the pump to the accumulator and filter is the same as in the K-Jetronic. Before the fuel enters the fuel distributor, ferromagnetic contamination is removed by a fine filter with a magnetic separator. In the KE-system but only for starting when the engine temperature is low, it passes straight through the distributor to the cold start valve as described in Section 11.18.

Under all other conditions, it passes into two lateral ducts in the distributor. The upper one goes through a damping restrictor, as in the K-Jetronic system, into the space above the control plunger, while the lower one delivers across the unit, through the electro-hydraulic pressure actuator, and back to the chambers below the diaphragms of the differential pressure valves. Immediately before the lower branch enters the electro-hydraulic actuator, a connection is taken off to the primary pressure regulator which, as previously mentioned, releases fuel in excess of engine requirements back to the tank.

Fuel flows continuously through the lower chambers into a duct in which there is a restrictor, and out to join the return flow from the primary pressure regulator to the tank. The part played by this flow in the functioning of the electro-hydraulic pressure actuator is explained in Section 11.14, while the function of the restrictor is to create a back-pressure for operation of the diaphragm type differential pressure valves.

Some fuel of course leaks down the control plunger. In the KE-Jetronic, an O-ring seal at the bottom of the plunger prevents it from passing into the air intake, and it is taken away by a duct, not shown in the illustration, to join that which returns from the primary pressure regulator to the tank.

11.14   The electro-hydraulic pressure actuator

As previously mentioned, fuel delivered from the electro-hydraulic pressure actuator passes to the chamber below the diaphragms in the fuel distributor. The function of the pressure actuator is to vary the pressure in the chamber below the diaphragms, in response to signals from the electronic control unit.

As shown in Fig. 11.14, a plate tends to block the flow issuing as a jet from a nozzle to which is connected the pipeline delivering fuel from the accumulator. This plate, pivoted at its opposite end, is pushed away from the

nozzle by the jet, against the reaction from control torques applied to it. In
so doing, it regulates rate of flow through the nozzle.

The plate deflects to the rear until equilibrium is established between the
force exerted on it (due basically to the constant delivery pressure multiplied
by the area of the orifice of the nozzle) and those due to the torques applied
to it by magnetic fields from both a permanent magnet and electro-magnet
regulated by the electronic control. The fuel deflected from the plate fills the
electro-hydraulic actuator housing and flows continuously out through the
lower chambers and restricted duct back to the tank, as described in Section
11.13.

The manner in which the control torque is applied by the plate is
illustrated in Fig. 11.16. An armature having two poles at each end, and
subjected to two magnetic fields, is secured to the centre of the plate. One of
the fields, represented by the dotted lines, is that of a permanent magnet.
The other is an electromagnetic flux, regulated by the electronic control
unit. These fields are additive across gaps 2 and 3, and subtractive across 1
and 4. While the strength of the field of the permanent magnet remains
constant, any increase in the control flux tends to increase the reaction of the
plate to the flow through the nozzle. Such an increase causes a drop in the
pressure downstream of the nozzle, but without any change in that before it,
since this is held constant by the primary pressure regulator.

The strength of the permanent magnet flux is such that when no current is
flowing through the electro-magnetic coil, the relative pressures in the
various parts of the distributor, and therefore flows, are appropriate for
supplying fuel to the injectors at a rate that gives an air:fuel ratio of

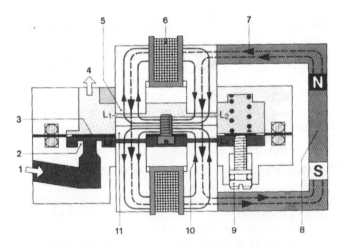

Fig. 11.16   Section through electro-hydraulic actuator
1. Fuel inlet, 2. Nozzle, 3. Baffle plate, 4. Fuel outlet, 5. Magnetic pole, 6. Electro-magnet coil, 7.
Permanent magnet flux, 8. Permanent magnet drawn in at 90° to its actual position, 9. Screw for
adjustment of basic moment of force, 10. Electromagnetic flux, (full line), 11. Air gaps of the four
segments of the armature, L_1 to L_4

lambda = 1.0. This enables the car to be driven to a service station for attention should the control system fail.

Application of the control current to the electro-magnet to enrich the mixture, for instance for warm-up or maximum power, increases the resistance of the plate to the flow from the orifice. This, because there is an outlet from the chambers below the diaphragms in the fuel distributor to the tank, reduces the pressure below these diaphragms. Since the pressure differential across the diaphragms is held constant, in this system about 0.2 bar, the pressure above them is also reduced. Consequently, the differential pressure across the slots in the control plunger is increased and so, therefore, is the rate of flow through the upper chambers to the injectors.

By virtue of both the very small electromagnetic time constants and inertia of its moving parts, the pressure actuator reacts extremely rapidly to commands from the electronic control unit. In any case, the maximum reduction in pressure required between the primary circuit and the actuator is only a few hundredths of a bar.

Two other functions, fuel cut-off in the overrun condition and speed limiting, can be performed by the pressure actuator. For either, the current in the electromagnet can be reversed by the electronic control unit, to reduce to zero the pressure drop across the differential pressure valves. This causes these valves to close under the influence of their return springs and so to shut off the fuel supply to the injectors. Thus, speed limiting is effected without detriment to exhaust gas emission content. To avoid hunting of the overrun cut-off, the switching is effected at speeds that differ according to whether the speed is increasing or decreasing. Additionally, to avoid stalling, the switching points are at higher speeds at low than at high engine temperatures.

Another parameter that can be taken into account by the electronic control unit is atmospheric pressure. At high altitudes, the mass flow for a given deflection of the air flow sensor plate, would be smaller than that at lower levels, so the mixture would be too rich. Compensation can be made provided an extra sensor is incorporated to signal ambient atmospheric pressure to the electronic control unit. In response to low ambient pressure signals, the electronic control unit reduces the current to the electro-hydraulic actuator.

11.15   Fuel distribution in the KE-Jetronic system

Variations in the open areas of the slots in the control plunger, in response to signals from the air flow sensor, determine the rate of flow into the chambers above the diaphragms of the differential pressure valves and on to the injectors. At the same time, the pressures in these chambers, which are sealed off from each other, must remain constant to provide an air:fuel ratio of lambda = 1.0. To this end, the differential pressure valves are held open just wide enough to maintain equilibrium, to within a nominal 0.2 bar, between the pressures above and below the diaphragm.

As mentioned previously, control over the air:fuel ratio is effected, regardless of the volume of fuel passing through, by varying the pressure below the diaphragms instead of, as in the K-system, varying the control pressure. This is done by the electronic control unit through the medium of the electro-hydraulic pressure actuator, as described in Section 11.14.

When the engine is switched off, the control plunger sinks until it is stopped by the O-ring seal around its lower end. This seal is located by a ring-nut screwed up below it, so that its height can be adjusted to ensure the plunger falls down far enough for the slots to be closed completely in this condition. As mentioned previously, closure of the slots is essential so that the accumulator cannot discharge through them and on past the clearance between the plunger and its bore back to the tank. The K-Jetronic does not have this O-ring and adjustable stop nut, so its plunger sinks on to the arm that carries the sensor plate, and any leakage of fuel past it is drawn into the air intake.

11.16   Fuel metering with intermittent or timed injection

Intermittent injection calls for a greater degree of precision in control, which is therefore effected electronically instead of hydro-mechanically, as in the K- and KE-Jetronic systems. So, in the L-Jetronic system, a gate type air flow meter is employed, the fuel accumulator and distributor are eliminated, and the pressure regulator is simplified. For the LH-Jetronic and Motronic systems, a hot wire anemometer is substituted for the gate type air sensor. In all instances, the systems are more compact and therefore installation easier except, possibly, in that instead of individual pipe connections being taken from the metering unit to the injectors, a single connection is taken to a fuel rail, for which space has therefore to be found alongside the cylinder head.

From a roller-cell type pump, the fuel is delivered at about 2.5-3 bar, according to the application, through a 10 μm filter, directly to one end of a fuel rail, Fig. 11.17. At the far end of the rail are the connections to the pressure regulator and start valve: the latter is described in Section 11.18. The principal function of the fuel rail is to ensure that the injection valves are all subject to the same pressure. Additionally, its volume is large enough for it to act as a damper, for the avoidance of interference due to pressure pulses as injector valves open and close. By virtue of a continuous flow through the rail and back to the tank, the fuel in it is cool enough to help to prevent the formation of vapour bubbles in it and thus ensures good hot starting. With an alternative design, the rail can be pulled down directly on to sealing rings on the ends of the injectors. This obviates the need for branch pipes and short hose connections for delivering fuel to the injectors.

The principle of mechanical operation of the pressure regulator, mounted on the end of the fuel rail, is obvious from Fig. 11.18. A feature to be noted is that a connection is taken from the base of the chamber that houses the diaphragm return spring to a point downstream of the throttle valve. Consequently, fuel delivery pressure to the injector nozzles is a function of

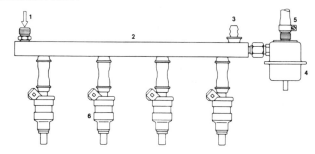

Fig. 11.17   The fuel rail assembly
1. Inlet from tank, 2. Gallery, 3. Connection to start valve, 4. Pressure regulator, 5. Return
connection to tank

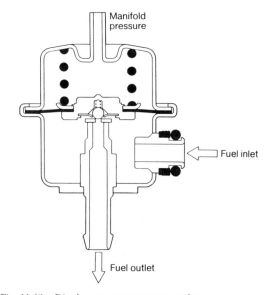

Fig. 11.18   Diaphragm type pressure regulator

the absolute pressure in the manifold and therefore the pressure drop across their valves, and so it remains constant regardless of throttle opening.

11.17   Fuel metering controls of the L- and LH-Jetronic systems

For these systems, the electronic control converts all analog to digital signals. The two that indicate air flow and engine speed are the main variables and provide the basis on which the control system calculates the rate of air consumption per stroke. Engine speed is taken from either the contact breaker circuit or, for breakerless ignition systems, the ignition coil.

The other variables call for either, on the one hand, simple or, on the other, precision compensation. Those requiring only simple compensation are signalled by the engine temperature sensor and throttle switch, Fig. 11.19. For instance, starting, warm-up and load adaptation require the mixture to be modified in response to the engine temperature signals, while compensation for idling, overrun, or part or full throttle is based on signals from the throttle valve switch. Precision compensation is required for coping with transitional conditions during acceleration, speed limitation and overrun, and has to be based on the signals already mentioned plus those from the air flow potentiometer.

The control unit processes the impulses from the ignition system in stages, as indicated in Fig. 11.20. The upper section of this diagram illustrates the inlet valve overlap in a 4-cylinder engine and the passage of the spark. Below this, the damped oscillations of the ignition triggering pulse for each cylinder are shown. These are then passed through a pulse shaping circuit to convert them into rectangular pulses. Next, they are processed by a frequency divider to provide two working pulses for each working cycle regardless of the number of cylinders so that, for each 360° rotation of the crankshaft, each injection valve opens and closes once regardless of the position of the inlet valve. If the inlet valve is closed, the mixture is held in the manifold until it opens.

Since the duration of injection depends on both the quantity of air entering and the engine speed, there are three more stages. In the first, a division control multi-vibrator generates the basic injection time signal. Secondly, a multiplying stage lengthens the time signal to apply the corrections for engine and operating conditions and to adapt for variations

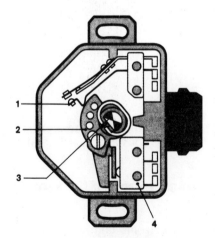

Fig. 11.19   Throttle valve switch
1. Full load contact, 2. Air flow sensor, 3. Throttle spindle, 4. Idle contact

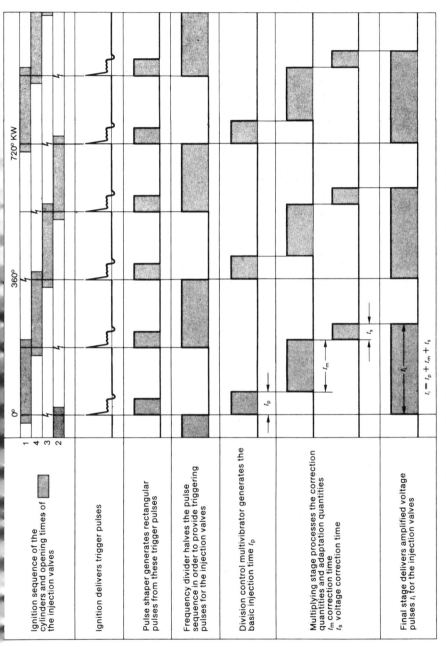

Fig. 11.20 Generation of the injection pulses in a control unit for a 4-cylinder engine

in battery voltage. The final stage delivers amplified voltage pulses to the injection valves. As mentioned in Section 11.5, the LH-Jetronic system regulates the air:fuel ratio electronically at all times to conform with plots of load against engine speed recorded in the memory.

11.18   Cold starting and idling

For starting from cold, extra fuel must be supplied to compensate for condensation on the walls of the induction manifold and valve ports. In most systems, a solenoid-actuated *start valve*, such as the Bosch unit in Fig. 11.37, is screwed into the main tract of the induction manifold into which it injects extra fuel for a period dependent on engine temperature. It comes into operation as the starter motor is switched on and, in the case of the K-, KE-Jetronic systems, its duration of operation is controlled by a thermo-time switch in a tubular housing screwed into the cylinder block coolant jacket, Fig. 11.21.

The switch is actuated by a bimetal strip subjected to not only the heat from the coolant but also that coming from an electrical heating element. Its duration of opening is basically engine coolant temperature dependent. If the engine is started hot, the solenoid circuit will already be broken owing to the heat transmitted to the strip from the coolant in the cylinder block jacket. However, the electrical heating element is added in case starting is prolonged, in which case the mixture could become too rich and the engine

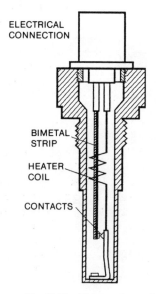

ELECTRICAL
CONNECTION

BIMETAL
STRIP

HEATER
COIL

CONTACTS

Fig. 11.21   Thermo-time switch

would not start at all. As a result, at moderately cold temperatures, the start valve injects extra fuel for a period of 4.5 s but, at for example −20°C, the flow of current through the heating element will cause the bimetal strip to break the circuit in about 7.5 s.

The engine temperature switch, also screwed into the coolant jacket of the engine, is of the negative temperature coefficient, semi-conductor resistance type. As the temperature rises, its resistance falls.

An alternative method of cold start enrichment can be employed in the L- and is standard on the LH-Jetronic system. It is simply the utilisation of the electronic control system to prolong the opening period of the injection valves. This function is performed on the basis of signals from only the ignition switch and engine temperature sensor, so the thermo-time switch is eliminated. However, a constant load signal is substituted for that from the air flow sensor which, with the throttle closed, is misleading because of the large amplitude of the pulsations of flow at cranking speeds.

When the solenoid is energised, the cold start valve is lifted off its seat, and the fuel flows through and then tangentially into a tiny swirl chamber. It finally passes out, through a hole in the outer end of this chamber, as a fine spray into the main tract of the manifold. As soon as the contact to the solenoid is broken by the bimetal strip, a coil spring returns the valve on to its flat seat.

11.19 The auxiliary air device

To develop the power required for overcoming the viscous drag of the lubricant during warm-up, extra mixture must be supplied. This provision of the extra air and fuel helps to reduce the time taken for warm-up, but too great an increase in supply of course adversely affects both fuel consumption and emissions. In the Bosch K-, KE- and the L-Jetronic variants, extra air is supplied through a throttle bypass, which is opened and closed by an auxiliary air valve. This valve is actuated by a bimetal strip, again subject to engine temperature and surrounded by an electric heating coil. The electric element limits, for economy, the time during which the extra mixture of air and fuel is supplied. Heat from the coolant ensures that the device does not come into operation when the engine is warm.

As can be seen from Fig. 11.22, as the engine cools, the bimetallic strip pushes down a lever extension of a rotary valve plate, against the influence of a coil type return spring. This brings the hole in the rotating plate progressively into alignment with that in the stationary one, thus opening the bypass. The extra flow through the air sensor upstream of the throttle and its bypass lifts the plate, causing the fuel distributor to increase the flow of fuel and thus to maintain the required air:fuel ratio.

An alternative, for use where closed loop control is required, is an idle speed control in the form of a rotary idle actuator. This is widely applied to the KE- and is standard on the LH-Jetronic system. It maintains the appropriate idling speed regardless of engine temperature and changes in

ELECTRICALLY HEATED
AUXILIARY-AIR DEVICE
(SECTION)

1 PLATE OPENING
2 AIR PASSAGE
3 PERFORATED PLATE
4 PIVOT
5 ELECTRICAL HEATING

ELECTRICALLY HEATED
AUXILIARY-AIR DEVICE

1 ELECTRICAL CONNECTION
2 ELECTRICAL HEATING
3 BIMETAL STRIP
4 PERFORATED PLATE

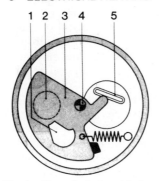
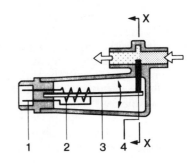

Fig. 11.22   Auxiliary air device with electrically heated bimetal strip control: left, cross section
on XX (not to scale); right, longitudinal section

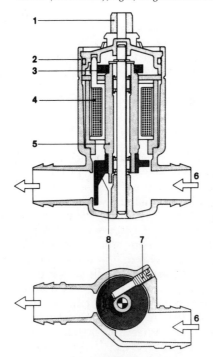

Fig. 11.23   Rotary idle actuator
1. Electrical connections, 2. Housing, 3. Spiral return spring, 4. Winding, 5. Rotating armature,
6. Bypass, 7. Adjustable stop, 8. Rotary slide-valve

load on the engine by, for example, the switching on of screen heaters. Moreover, it does so throughout the life of the engine, regardless of wear.

The drive for the rotary idle actuator is an electro-magnet the rotation of which is limited to 60°. At the lower end of its armature is a rotary slide valve, Fig. 11.23, and at its upper end a spiral return spring. Idle speeds relative to engine temperatures and degrees of throttle opening are programmed into the memory of the ECU, and the closed loop control circuit is supplied with signals from the corresponding sensors on the engine and injection equipment. The idle speed signal is converted into a voltage which is compared with the optimum value, as programmed into the memory. On the basis of the difference between the actual and recorded voltages, the ECU, by varying the on/off ratio of DC current applied to the armature coil, adjusts the actual speed to make it coincide with the optimum. At the maximum on/off ratio, the bypass is fully open. In the event of a malfunction leading to a total absence of current, the spring closes the slide valve on to its adjustable stop.

11.20 Idling speed regulation and warm-up

After starting, idling speed is of course dependent upon the quantity of mixture supplied which, at normal temperatures, is related to the quantity of air supplied. All the Bosch systems have a throttle bypass, projecting into which is a screw for regulating the air supply when the throttle is closed on to its stop. Those with swinging gate type air flow meters have, in addition, a channel bypassing the gate. This again has an adjustment screw projecting into it. However, this screw is for manual adjustment of the mixture strength under idling conditions.

Generally, to enable the engine to fire at very low starting temperatures, the mixture might have to be enriched by a factor of as much as two or three. After start-up, it must be rapidly reduced over a period of about thirty seconds to between 60% and 30% enrichment. During warm-up, condensation of the mixture in the induction system, and initially the cylinders, progressively reduces and so also, therefore, must the enrichment of the mixture, over a period of perhaps two minutes, to lambda = 1.0 or less, according to the type of engine and emission control system used.

Where there is no electronic control, as in the Bosch K-Jetronic system for example, a thermo-time switch is needed. This is generally actuated by a bimetal strip subjected to both engine coolant temperature and an electric heating element either surrounding or adjacent to it. If the engine is already warm when started, the circuit through the switch will already be broken, but in cold conditions it will be closed until opened by either the combined effects, on the bimetal strip, of the heating element and the rising engine temperature or, in extreme cold, possibly the former alone. In most other systems, control is effected by the electronic control unit, on the basis of signals transmitted to it from its clock (for elapsed time), the engine temperature sensor and thermo-time switch. In this way, the degree of enrichment can be more precisely matched to the requirements for different starting temperatures.

The effects on the enrichment commands passed from the electronic control unit to the injectors, of both the increase in temperature due to the electric heating element, curve AB, and that due to the rising temperature of the coolant, curve CD, are shown in Fig. 11.24. On starting the engine from very cold temperatures, the influence of the heating element is at first predominant; subsequently the engine temperature takes over, and the electronic control unit blends AO and OD in a smooth transitional curve so they do not in fact cross over at O.

After the engine has fired, the enrichment is therefore reduced progressively to zero over a period related to the start-up temperature. For example, in mild conditions, for example starting from a temperature of +20°C, the Bosch system would continue at the start-up level for a period of perhaps about 3.5 s, determined partly by the rate of increase of engine temperature. Then the electronic control unit would progressively decrease the enrichment to zero over a further 20 s.

In the K-Jetronic system, which is not electronically controlled, a warm-up regulator valve is incorporated, as described in Section 11.11 and illustrated in Fig. 11.13. Under all conditions of steady state operation except when the engine is not fully warmed up and possibly, as explained later, at full power at constant speed, the valve is closed. Consequently, the pressure above the control plunger is constant, and the exposed height of the slots in the control spindle therefore varied by only the air sensor.

In three circumstances, however, the control pressure is modified by the warm-up regulator valve. These are: first, for starting from cold and during

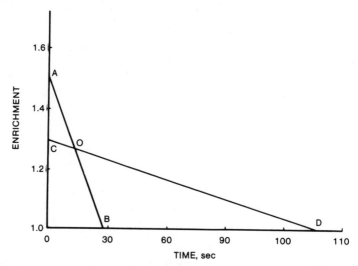

Fig. 11.24   Warm-up enrichment as influenced by: AB the electrical heating element; CD engine temperature

the subsequent warm-up period, when it enriches the mixture to a degree over and above that provided by the profiling of the air sensor funnel; secondly, for some applications only (Section 11.22) when it similarly enriches the mixture for obtaining maximum power output. Thirdly, closure of its return line to the tank retains some pressure after the engine has been switched off, so that bubbles of vapour will not form in the fuel in the system and cause difficulties in restarting when the engine is still hot.

Essentially, the warm-up regulator comprises an electrically heated bimetal strip, which lowers or lifts a diaphragm-actuated valve to reduce or increase respectively the counter pressure on the upper end of the control plunger. The lower the pressure is above the control plunger, the higher will be the deflection of the air flow metering plate for any given air flow, and the greater the uncovered length of the slots in the fuel distributor. Typical curves of control pressure and enrichment factors are illustrated in Fig. 11.25.

The third function of the warm-up valve is effected indirectly. A non-return valve installed coaxially within the primary pressure regulator

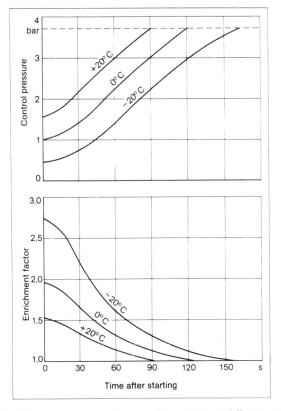

Fig. 11.25   K-Jetronic warm-up regulator characteristics at different temperatures

valve, Fig. 11.4, is held open by the pressure regulator plunger so long as the engine is running. However, when the engine is switched off and the control valve plunger therefore returns to its zero position, it is closed by its return spring. This closes the return line from the warm-up valve to the tank, so that some pressure is retained in both control and fuel delivery circuits.

11.21 Enrichment for acceleration

As was explained in Section 11.8, the K-Jetronic system, enrichment for acceleration is obtained by virtue of overswing of the air flow metering plate when the throttle is opened suddenly. In the KE-Jetronic system, to take into account the fact that extra enrichment is necessary for acceleration when the engine is cold, additional control is exercised by the electronic control unit, in response to signals from the engine temperature sensor and a potentiometer. The latter, described in Section 11.9, is installed on the air flow sensor spindle. The output from the potentiometer is a maximum when the accelerator pedal movement starts from idling and it decreases as engine power is increased. Not only, therefore, does the signal pulse transmitted from the electronic control unit to the electro-hydraulic pressure actuator increase in length with magnitude, as well as speed of deflection of the air flow meter, but also it is longer at low than at high temperatures. At 80°C or less its duration is 1 s.

11.22 Full load enrichment

As previously mentioned, the profile of the orifice containing the floating plate air flow meter of the K-Jetronic system is such as to provide the extra enrichment for full load operation. However, some engines designed to cruise on exceptionally weak mixtures require for operation at full load, a greater degree of enrichment than is provided by the profiling of the air sensor funnel. This extra enrichment can be effected by using a modified warm-up regulator having, beneath its diaphragm valve, an extra return spring inserted coaxially within the original one, Fig. 11.26.

Whereas the lower end of the main spring is always seated on the housing, that of the extra one seats on top of a diaphragm the upper face of which is subjected to manifold depression. During slow running and cruising, this diaphragm is lifted until it seats on its upper stop, so the valve is then under the influence of both return springs. However, as the throttle is opened further, and the manifold pressure therefore increases, the diaphragm sinks, ultimately seating on its bottom stop, at which point, the valve and, when cold, the bimetal strip are subjected to only the force exerted by the main spring. A typical curve showing the control pressure characteristic obtained with such a device is shown in Fig. 11.27.

In the KE-system, a wide open throttle signal from a throttle-actuated switch, together with an engine speed signal from the ignition system,

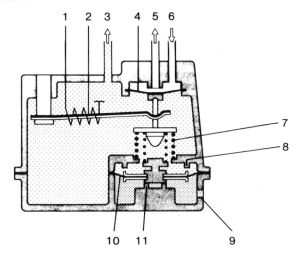

Fig. 11.26   A warm-up regulator incorporating a diaphragm-actuated enrichment valve for
lean-burn engine operation at full load
1. Electric heating element, 2. Bimetal strip, 3. Connection to induction manifold, 4. Warm-up
valve diaphragm, 5. To fuel tank, 6. Control pressure from fuel distributor, 7. Diaphragm return
springs: outer, warm-up and, inner, enrichment, 8. Upper stop, 9. Vent to atmosphere, 10.
Enrichment diaphragm, 11. Lower stop

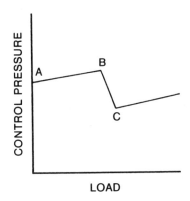

Fig. 11.27   Characteristic curve obtained with regulator of Fig. 11.26. As the throttle is opened
from A the curve comes up to point B, where the manifold depression has risen to the point at
which the lower diaphragm first brings the inner spring into contact with the upper spring seat.
Point C is where the lower diaphragm hits stop 8 in the other illustration

triggers the electronic control unit to impose a correction on the fuelling rate
signalled by the air meter orifice profile. This provides closer control and
better fuel economy. In the L- and LH-Jetronic systems, on the other hand,
full load enrichment is effected by the electronic control unit, entirely in
response to signals from the throttle switch and ignition system.

INJECTORS

11.23 Some aspects of injector design

Naturally, designers of petrol injection systems initially sought to benefit from the experience with diesel injection. This led to the widespread attempts to use pintle type injectors, though in some instances solenoid-instead of cam-actuated, so that they could be controlled electronically. However, with the increasing stringency of emission controls, and demands for lower fuel consumption coupled with better performance, greater accuracy of metering of the fuel became essential. Among the injectors currently in use are those illustrated in Figs. 11.29, 33, 34, 35, 36, 39 and 50.

To enable the electronic control to meter with precision the supply of fuel to the engine, a primary essential is a linear relationship between quantity of fuel delivered and pulse width, over its full range from maximum (the pulse repetition period) to zero. This would imply both instantaneous starting and stopping of flow, and a linear relationship between quantity of fuel delivered and time.

In practice, however, there is inevitably a delay between the beginning and end of the electronic control pulse and the actual starting and stopping of the flow of fuel. Consequently, the point of zero delivery will be offset along the time axis from the origin, Fig. 11.28. Except for pulses of very short width, it is not difficult to arrange for the flow to be virtually linear from start to finish, up to but not including the pulse repetition point. At the latter point, the flow is continuous so, in effect, the start is no longer offset from the origin.

The difference between the shortest linear pulse width and the offset is termed the *minimum linear duration of injection*. This of course must be as

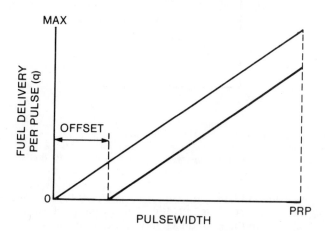

Fig. 11.28   Fuel delivery plotted against pulse width: top, theoretical perfect; bottom, perfect injector delivery with offset

small as practicable, to maximise the *dynamic range* of delivery of the injector, the dynamic range being defined as the ratio of maximum to minimum duration of injection. Ideally the point of origin and that of zero delivery would be coincident, in which case the dynamic range would of course be infinity.

Within limits that might be imposed by the characteristics of the injector, the maximum duration of injection is primarily a function of the rotational speed of the engine and whether the injector is fired once or twice per revolution. On the other hand, the minimum duration of injection is determined to a major degree by injector design and the consequent offset of the delivery characteristic.

Linearity of injection improves with both the ratio of the actuation force to the mass of the delivery valve and the appropriate matching to them of the electrical and time constants of the solenoid circuit. Since the time required to close the injector is a function of the current in the solenoid at the point at which its circuit is broken, delivery errors are difficult to avoid when the pulse width is shorter than that required to allow the current to build up to a stable value.

11.24 Injector firing strategies

There are two injector firing strategies: *sequential*, or one injection for every two revolutions, and *simultaneous double-fire*, which is one injection per revolution of the engine. For simultaneous double fire, the electronic control system is simpler than that for sequential injection, and therefore significantly less costly. Therefore, the sequential firing strategy is generally employed only for turbocharged and other high performance types of engine. These generally call for high ratios of maximum to minimum linear deliveries of fuel, or a large dynamic range since, otherwise, injection at narrow pulse widths with a simultaneous double fire strategy may entail operation in the non-linear range, which can lead to poor driveability.

11.25 The Lucas injector

To meet all these requirements, Lucas Engine Management Systems designed the D Series injector, Fig. 11.29. Instead of a pintle, it has a disc type armature held down on the valve seat by a coil spring plus the fuel pressure. It is designed for fuel pressures ranging from about 2 to 4 bar, and flows from 80 to 400 g/min. An electrical pulse triggered by the electronic control energises the solenoid and, when the magnetic force has built up to a value exceeding that exerted by its return spring plus the hydraulic pressure, the armature is lifted from the seating ring around the valve port, Fig. 11.30, until is stopped by the shim above. When the solenoid circuit is broken, the current decays until the spring force dominates and closes the armature on to

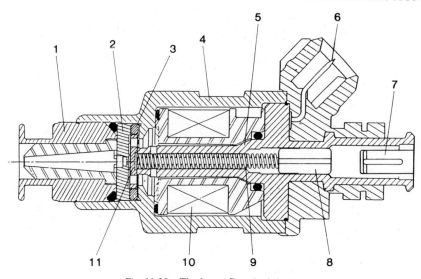

Fig. 11.29   The Lucas D-series injector
1. Nozzle, 2. Valve seat, 3. Shim and spacer, 4. Body, 5. Core, 6. Electrical connection, 7. Filter,
8. Calibration slide, 9. Spring, 10. Winding, 11. Armature

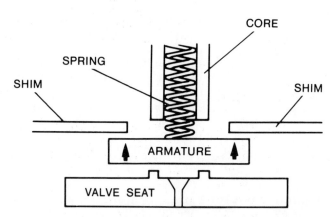

Fig. 11.30   Diagram showing how the armature deflection is limited to the distance between the
valve seat below and a shim above

the sealing ring, at which point, the additional force exerted on it by the fuel
pressure ensures that it does not bounce.

As can be seen from Fig. 11.31, the mass of the armature disc may be as
much as an eighth of that of a pintle and between a third and a quarter of that
of a spherical seating valve. This correspondingly increases the force:mass
ratio, and therefore also the rate of acceleration of the armature. The
outcome is a shift of the zero point of the delivery line, Fig. 11.28, towards

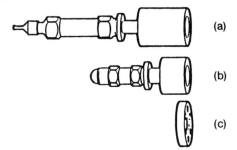

*Fig. 11.31   Comparison between effective masses of three injector valve types: (a) Pintle type,
4.0g; (b) Ball type, 1.8g; Lucas CAV armature, 0.5g*

the origin. Indeed, the D Series injector can be operated in the linear range
with a simultaneous double fire strategy as defined in Section 11.24. This is
because, at static flow rates of less than 250 g/min, and a pulse repetition
period of 10.0 ms, it has a dynamic range greater than 20:1.

To take advantage of the rapid response of this very light armature, the
impedance of both the drive circuit and the solenoid were reduced and the
static flow rate increased. However, it was found that improvements beyond
an offset of 0.77 ms did not significantly increase the dynamic range, but did
lead to high sensitivity to variations in supply voltage and tended towards
unstable injection. For the D Series injector, typical resistance values for the
solenoid coil winding are 2.35 ohms for current mode systems and
16.2 ohms for voltage mode operation.

11.26   Deposits in nozzles

Deposits have tended to accumulate in the delivery orifices of injectors of
some earlier designs. They generally comprise carbon, and hydrocarbon
gums and varnishes. As they build up, there is a gradual shift towards lean
mixture and partial blockage. The outcome is progressive loss of power,
misfiring, surging and poor driveability.

Pintle type injectors can be surprisingly noisy, up to about 57 dB(A)
overall and perhaps 62 dB(A) maximum. However, by virtue of the low
mass of the plate valve of the D Series unit, it is about 9 dB(A) quieter
overall with the engine stopped and the injectors cycled, reducing to about
2 dB(A) with the engine running. Leakage would adversely affect both
engine start times and emissions but, with the flat disc of the plate valve
seating on a flat surface of the valve seat in the Lucas injector, tight sealing is
assured. This is because centring is not critical and lapping to very close
tolerances is relatively easy.

Accuracy of aiming of the spray at the induction valve is important for
obtaining low HC emissions at full load. The normal spray pattern, with a
single hole, is a cone with 10° included angle, and this is adequate for most

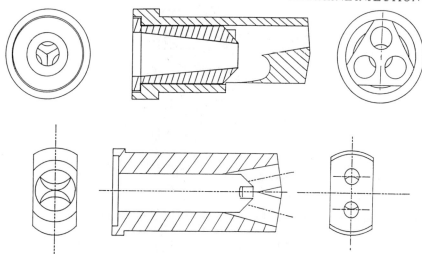

Fig. 11.32   Alternative nozzles: top, three hole, wide angle cone jet; bottom, two hole divided jet
for 4-valve heads

applications. To produce sprays of different forms, Lucas produce spray
director inserts in the injector nozzle, as shown in Fig. 11.32.

11.27   Some other injectors

The lightweight injector valves used in the Bosch K- and KE-Jetronic
systems are opened by the relatively low fuel pressure of about 3.3-3.6 bar,
acting on their heads: the actual value depends on the engine application and
local quality of fuel. They vibrate axially at a frequency of 1500 Hz to
atomise the fuel as it is continuously injected into the manifold. When the
engine is switched off, they are returned to their seats by light springs, Fig.
11.33. The vibration is initiated by the sudden increase in an area exposed to
the opening pressure, as the valve first lifts off its seat. Since this is instantly
followed by an equally sudden local release of pressure it seats again, and the
whole process is repeated cyclically until the ignition is switched off and the
injection pressure therefore drops.

In some instances, the Bosch injectors are air shrouded as follows.
Around the injector body is what might be termed an air jacket. Its upper
end is connected to a pipe from the air intake, and its lower end, around the
nozzle, is open to the induction manifold. The low pressure in the manifold
induces a flow of air through the jacket and out as a funnel shape shroud
around the fuel spray directed at the inlet valve. This helps atomisation and
evaporation, especially with the K- and KE-continuous injection systems.

Injection valves for the L-Jetronic variants and Motronic systems, Figs.
11.34 and 35 respectively are heavier, as also are their return springs. This is

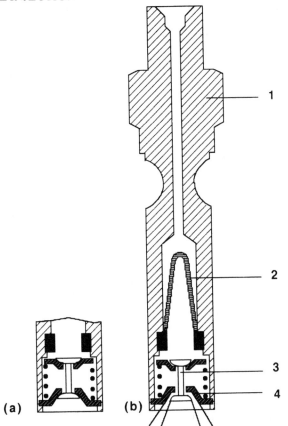

Fig. 11.33   Injector for K-Jetronic system; (a) valve closed, (b) valve open
1. Valve housing, 2. Filter, 3. Valve needle, 4. Valve seat

because they are integral with the armatures of their solenoids which open
them for timed periods. These solenoids are energised by electric pulses
from the electronic control unit. The valve lifts are 0.1 mm and the pick-up
and release times between 1 and 1.5 ms.

In both systems, after passing through a filter at the top of the injector,
fuel flows down through slots in the sides of the armature and needle into a
chamber in the tip of the valve. Consequently, the lifting of the valve is
accelerated by the sudden exposure of the area of the needle seating face to
the delivery pressure. A collar towards the upper end of the needle limits its
axial travel. Atomisation is assisted by a head ground on the tip of the pintle
of the L-Jetronic injector.

The injector for the Motronic system is designed so that the fuel rail can be
clamped down directly on to its upper end. The needle has a polished
straight flanked pintle on its tip, to atomise the fuel as it passes through the
precision hole in the nozzle. A needle lift of 0.1 mm and breakaway and
release times of 1.0-1.5 ms are quoted.

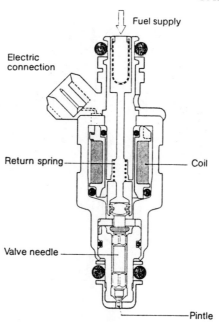

Fuel supply

Electric
connection

Return spring

Coil

Valve needle

Pintle

Fig. 11.34   L-Jetronic injector (Mk1)

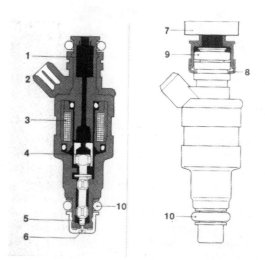

1

2

3

4

5

6

10

7

9

8

10

*Fig. 11.35   The nose of the Motronic injector, with an O-ring seal around it, is a push fit in a boss
in the induction manifold. After all the injectors have been inserted, the fuel rail complete with one
branch pipe (or boss) per injector, is then assembled over their upper ends, which are similarly
fitted with O-ring seals
1. Filter, 2. Electrical connection, 3. Solenoid iwinding, 4. Armature, 5. Needle valve, 6. Pintle,
7. Branch pipe on fuel rail, 8. Safety clip, 9. Upper O-ring, 10. Lower O-ring*

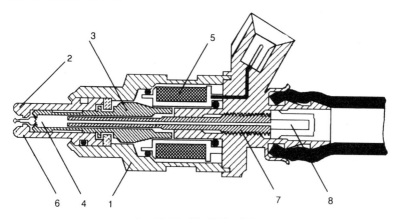

Fig. 11.36   The Weber Injector
1. Injector body, 2. Needle, 3. Armature, 4. Spring, 5. Winding, 6. Nose piece, 7. Adjuster thread
(spring compression), 8. Filter

Normally the Bosch injection valves, including those that are air shrouded, are not screwed into the manifold. Instead, both their noses and the upper ends of their bodies are a push fit in rubber rings. The lower ring seals the boss in which the injector is carried in the manifold and the upper one is held in a hole in a bracket. For holding the injectors in a spanner if a screw type connection is made to them, there are hexagon shape collars near their upper ends.

The rubber rings insulate the units from excessive vibration and heat, mainly to avoid formation of vapour bubbles locally in the fuel, which could lead to difficulties in starting the engine when hot. For the avoidance of fuel spray deposition in the manifolds, especially when the engines are cold, the jets are preferably aimed at the valves in the inlet ports.

The Weber injector illustrated in Fig. 11.36 is, in principle, similar to those produced by Bosch, but has a tubular instead of solid armature. This would appear to offer some advantages as regards magnetic properties and accuracy and stability of guidance and support for the valve but, possibly, makes it heavier and introduces more friction.

11.28   Start valves

A start valve is a form of injector valve but, because it is not in continuous use and sprays fuel into the induction manifold trunk instead of into the inlet valve ports, it does not have to be of such a sophisticated design. Bosch incorporate start valves in all their multi-point systems, but most other manufacturers rely on the electronic control unit to signal the injectors to supply the extra fuel needed for cold starting. The Bosch unit for the KE-system is illustrated in Fig. 11.37. That for the L-Jetronic is similar but

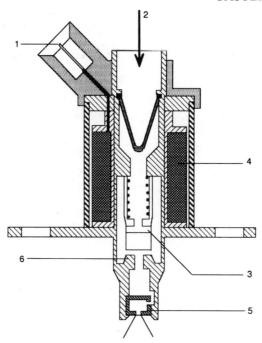

Fig. 11.37   Cold start valve shown open
*1. Electrical connection, 2. Fuel supply, through strainer, 3. Armature with valve seating face on
its lower end, 4. Solenoid winding, 5. Swirl nozzle, 6. Valve seat*

more compact: its fuel inlet, also containing a filter, is on the side of the unit, the solenoid coil and armature are shorter, and the electrical connection is made at the upper end of the unit.

THROTTLE BODY INJECTION

11.29   Bosch Mono-Jetronic system

The Mono-Jetronic and Motronic injection systems, as well as those of some other manufacturers, although having many features similar to those of the Bosch L-variants, are so different from them that they will now be described separately. Incidentally, Bosch offer a Motronic M3 and two Mono-Motronic versions. The M3 is for use with three-way catalyst systems, while the latter two are digitally controlled variants of the Mono-Jetronic for use respectively with and without automatic ignition control. Among those of other manufacturers are the Weber IAW, and GM Multec single- and multi-point injection systems.

Bosch produce their Mono-Jetronic system, Fig. 11.38, for applications where low cost is a prime requirement. A single injector intermittently

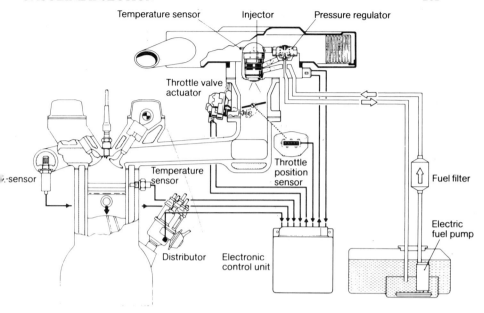

Fig. 11.38   Mono-Jetronic injection system

injects fuel into the throttle body. With this system, the angular position of the throttle valve is utilised as an indication of the volume air flow, thus eliminating the need for an additional air sensor.

A low pressure vane type pump, as described in the last paragraph of Chapter 5, is installed in the fuel tank. It delivers, at a pressure of 1 bar, through a filter directly to the throttle body injection unit. The latter unit also houses the diaphragm type pressure regulator valve, which maintains a constant differential between the pressure of the fuel and that of the air into which it is injected, regardless of the quantity of fuel passing.

The ignition system provides the engine speed signal for the controller. Other sensors include the throttle valve potentiometer which, in association with the engine speed and air temperature signals, indicates the mass air flow. The air temperature sensor is incorporated in the air passage through the throttle body. Signals for enrichment for the idle, acceleration and full load conditions are also provided by the throttle valve potentiometer as also, in association with the engine speed indication, are those for cutting off the fuel supply in the overrun condition or, if required, to limit the engine speed. A sensor in the cylinder block coolant jacket signals engine temperature to the controller, for regulation of cold starting, immediate post-start operation and progressive warm-up. Battery voltage affects the response time of the injector valve, so the controller has to compensate for this as it signals to the solenoid valve for opening and closing the injector valve.

Open loop idle speed control is effected through the medium of the

thermo-actuator, which regulates the position of the throttle stop. The
throttle valve potentiometer signals to the controller the need for extra fuel
to maintain the appropriate air:fuel ratio. If a closed loop idle speed control
system is incorporated, the thermo-actuator is replaced by a servo-motor
which, by adjusting the throttle opening in response to engine speed and
temperature signals, regulates the air supply to the engine to correct any
deviation of the actual from the required idling speed. Both systems are
maintenance-free, since no adjustment has to be made manually to either
the engine speed or mixture for idling and, in the case of the closed loop
system, compensation is made automatically for drift due to wear of the
engine or injection system.

11.30   Mono-Jetronic control and operation

Basically, the digital control unit processes the input signals and uses them to
compute the duration of injection at constant pressure, and thus the quantity
of fuel to be injected per engine cycle. It comprises an analog-digital
converter, a microcomputer, and program and data memories. For
determining the basic injection period, it refers to an engine characteristic
map comprising 15 throttle angle and 15 engine speed points, making a total
of 225 data points for maintaining the air:fuel ratio at lambda = 1.0, for part

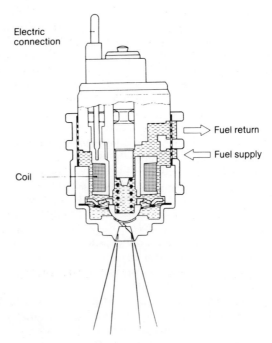

Fig. 11.39   Low pressure fuel injection valve assembly

load operation. Superimposed on this 15 × 15 map is an adaptive map comprising 8 × 8 data points and, if the air:fuel ratio deviates beyond prescribed limits, an adaptation alogarithm writes correction values into the former. This compensates for drifts in the performance of either the engine or injection equipment, owing to wear in service

The injection pulses are timed relative to signals from the ignition system. Enrichment for cold starting, post start and warm-up, full load and acceleration are effected in response to the signals as described in the last paragraph in Section 11.29. Because all cylinders are supplied through the one injector, the volume injected per cycle is large, so a single hole unit would be inadequate. Therefore, in the tip of the injector, Fig. 11.39, are six angled radial holes producing a conical spray. This is divided into two segments directed one into each of the crescent shape apertures opened up between the edges of the butterfly valve and the bore of its housing. The spray characteristics are optimised by a combination of baffle and swirl effects.

FUEL INJECTION AND ENGINE MANAGEMENT

11.31   Bosch Motronic combined fuel injection and ignition system

Given the presence in the engine installation of a microcomputer for regulating fuel injection, there is good reason for optimising its utilisation by designing it for performing other control functions. The Motronic system does just that. Primarily it integrates injection and ignition controls, but it can also encompass other parameters such as exhaust gas recirculation and evaporative emission canister purging, which are explained in Sections 13.18 and 13.23 to 26. Comprehensive information on the electronic components of the Motronic and other injection systems is given in the Bosch publication *Automotive Electric/Electronic Systems*.

The intermittent injection system is basically identical to that of the L-Jetronic, but all its signal processing functions are done digitally. For the ignition system, the conventional centrifugal and manifold depression actuated spark advance mechanism has been abandoned. Instead, it has a spark advance characteristic map stored in the memory of its control unit, which modifies the spark advance to take into account not only throttle position but also engine coolant and air intake temperatures.

11.32   Electronic ignition control in the Motronic system

The Motronic electronic ignition system is fairly conventional. When a spark is required, the electronic controller momentarily opens the circuit to earth, whereupon the collapse of the field around the primary coil generates the spark voltage in the secondary coil. The resultant high voltage current is passed through the distributor to the sparking plug. An important feature is the absence of a mechanical contact breaker and its centrifugal and pneumatic advance and retard system. However, some high speed 6-cylinder engines do have a centrifugal mechanism.

The difference between the ignition advance characteristic as supplied by the conventional mechanically actuated system and the actual requirements stored in the memory of the Motronic electronic control system can be seen from Fig. 11.40. To obtain the data points for the complex map used in the Motronic system, the engine is run on a dynamometer, where they are optimised as regards fuel consumption, emissions, and driveability. The optimum ignition points are then recorded and stored electronically for reproduction in the memory of the controller micro-computer. In operation,

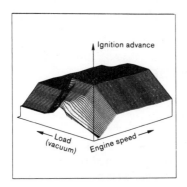

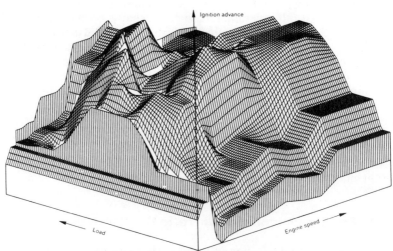

Fig. 11.40   From this illustration, the complexity and accuracy of the Motronic ignition timing map can be seen compared with that, to a smaller scale above left, of a conventional system with a mechanical advance mechanism

the microcomputer, following the occurrence of each spark, determines the point at which the next spark should be triggered, and it does so on the basis of the points registered on the engine speed and load map stored in its memory, together with any corrections necessary in relation to coolant and air temperatures, and throttle position.

An inductive engine speed sensor signals directly from the crankshaft, which is more precise than using a Hall effect sender in the distributor. Consequently, the spark advance can be set closer to the ideal, without risk of detonation. Therefore, fuel utilisation is better and higher torque can be obtained. With digital records, the ignition points for each condition of operation can be set independently of all the others, which again increases engine efficiency and reduces fuel consumption.

There are in fact two inductive pulse senders on the flywheel. That for engine speed senses the passage of teeth past its permanent magnet core, while the other, for indicating crank angle, senses the passage of either a pin or hole in the flywheel. Signals thus obtained are processed in the control unit to render them suitable for processing by the computer.

The parameters involved in setting the ignition points include fuel consumption, torque, exhaust emissions, tendency to knock, and driveability. However, the weighting given to each differs according to the type of operation. For example, for idling, the priorities are low emissions, smoothness and fuel economy; on the other hand for part load operation, they are driveability and economy while, for full load, the main criteria are the maximum torque requirement and absence of detonation

For starting and all types of operation other than part throttle light load, correction factors are applied to the map values. There is also, for example, a switch in the control unit to cater for different fuels and grades of fuels. Its effect, however, is felt only during operation in the high load range. Additionally, starting is improved by virtue of the incorporation of a correction routine for adjusting spark timing in relation to cranking speed.

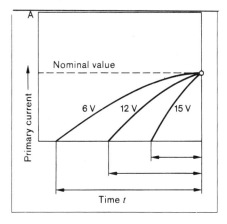

Fig. 11.41   Primary current at different voltages

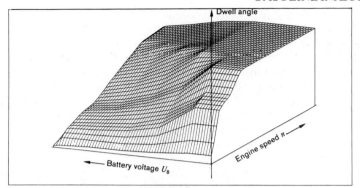

Fig. 11.42   Relationship between the dwell angle of the current in the primary circuit of the
ignition coil, battery voltage and engine speed

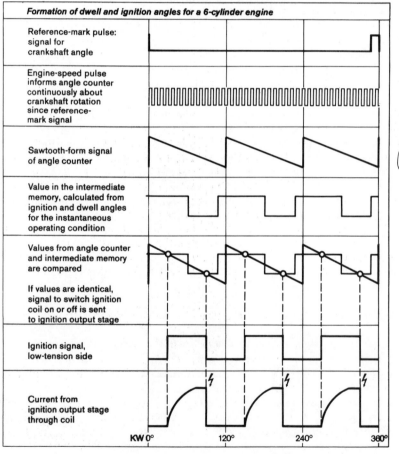

Fig. 11.43   Dwell and ignition angle processing for a 6-cylinder engine

After the generation of each spark, a finite time, Fig. 11.41, is required for the re-establishment of the current in the coil to its nominal value, ready for the next firing. The higher the engine speed, and therefore frequency of sparking, the longer is the dwell time needed to allow the current to build up in the coil. Consequently, the relationship between current flow time in the coil and supply voltage has to be regulated, by reference to a dwell angle characteristic map like that in Fig. 11.42. As soon as the current has risen to the appropriate level before the next ignition point, it is held there by the output stage. This holding function ensures that, even as the dwell time shortens during acceleration from low engine speeds, the appropriate current is maintained throughout.

An indication of how the electronic control unit regulates injection and ignition simultaneously can be gleaned from Fig. 11.43. To keep the breakaway and release times of the valves as short as possible, without using current limiting resistors, a special integrated circuit in the electronic control unit regulates the current to the injectors. For a six cylinder engine, for instance, the valve opening current is 7.5 amp and, at the end of the injection period, reduced to a holding current of 3.5 amp.

11.33 Motronic fuel supply system

As can be seen from Fig. 11.44, the fuel system differs slightly from some of those previously described. From the tank, the roller-cell type pump delivers at a pressure of 2.5-3 bar through a 10 µm pore filter directly to one end of a fuel rail. At the other end is the pressure regulator, Fig. 11.18, from which the return flow to the tank passes through a pulsation damper, Fig. 11.45, to the tank. This, by reducing fluctuations in the pressure in the return line, suppresses noises arising from both the operation of the pressure regulator or the opening and closing of the injector valves.

By virtue of its large volume relative to the quantities of fuel injected per cycle, the fuel rail acts as a hydraulic damper and ensures that all the injectors connected to it are equally supplied with fuel. Injection occurs once per revolution, or twice per cycle, and is directed into the ports.

11.34 Overall principle of operation of Motronic system

For air flow measurement, a sensor of the swinging gate type described in Section 11.9, for the L-Jetronic is employed in the Motronic system, Fig. 11.44. The duration of injection required for maintaining lambda = 0.85-0.95, for engines equipped with three-way catalytic converters, is assessed in relation to engine speed and on a basis of per piston stroke, instead of per unit of time. Corrections are applied, as required, in response to signals received from detonation, temperature, time and other sensors, and in accordance with plotted values on engine performance maps. The sensors are as previously described for the L- and LH-Jetronic systems.

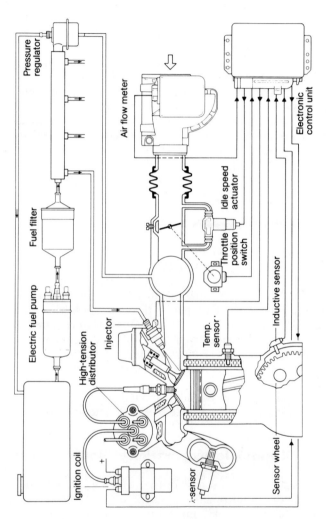

Pressure regulator

Air flow meter

Fuel filter

Idle speed actuator

Throttle position switch

Electric fuel pump

Injector

High-tension distributor

Temp. sensor

Inductive sensor

Ignition coil

λ-sensor

Sensor wheel

Electronic control unit

Fig. 11.44   The Bosch Motronic system exercises control over both injection and ignition

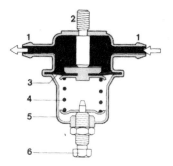

Fig. 11.45   *Pulsation damper of the Motronic system*
1. Fuel connections, 2. Threaded mounting, 3. Diaphragm, 4. Damper spring, 5. Housing, 6.
Adjustment screw

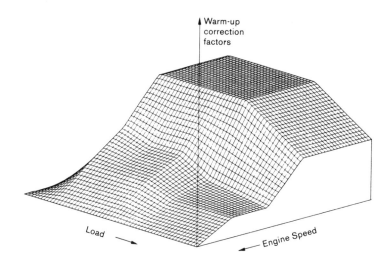

Fig. 11.46   *Map showing how warm-up correction varies with speed and load (high load and*
speed, small correction)

as also are the principles of operation of the ancillary devices such as those
for regulating air flow through the throttle bypass. Consequently, it is
unnecessary now to do other than to present the features in the form of a
Table and footnotes, as follows.

Table 11.2: ADJUSTMENTS FOR VARIOUS OPERATING CONDITIONS

IN this table, the following symbols are used to indicate the various sensors: TTS thermal time switch, TVS throttle valve switch, and ET, AT and K respectively engine and air temperature and knock sensors, but since all control functions call for signals from the air flow, intake temperature and engine speed sensors (reflecting load), these are omitted to avoid repetition.

Operational variables	Fuel supply	Additional sensors	Ignition timing	Additional sensors	Relevant notes
Cold start	Enriched	TTS, TVS	Retarded	TTS, ET	1, 2, 3
Post start	Enriched	TTS, ET	Advanced	TTS	4
Warm-up	Enriched	ET	Advanced	ET	5, 6
Hot idling	Normal	ET	Normal	ET	7, 8
Full load	Enriched	TVS, ET	Controlled	ET, AT, K	9
Acceleration	Enriched	TVS, ET	Controlled	TVS, ET, K	10
Overrun	Cut-off	TVS	Retarded	TVS	11

(1) **Cold start** Extra fuel is delivered either by using the electronic control to increase the duration of opening of the injection valves or through the cold start valve, not included in Fig. 11.44, into the manifold upstream of the injectors, or both. For most engines, there is no need for a cold start valve: instead, the number of injections per revolution may be increased and, since at very low speeds the quantity of air inducted is constant, the duration of the injections is regulated on the basis of cranking speed, starting temperature and number of revolutions since starting began. At higher cranking speeds throttling occurs, so the duration of injection is reduced.
(2) Sharp variations in speed during starting would lead to inaccurate air flow signals, so a fixed load signal, weighted by engine temperature, is utilised by the control unit.
(3) The lower the cranking speeds and the higher the engine temperature the more retarded must be the timing. In a cold engine, timing earlier than $10°$ btdc can induce reverse torques damaging the starter. On the other hand, with high compression engines, if the spark is retarded too much, knocking can occur at high intake temperatures. At high cranking speeds, starting is improved if the ignition is advanced.
(4) **Post start** At low temperatures and fast idle speeds, the ignition is advanced to improve both performance and fuel economy. After a short time, it is progressively reduced to normal as the engine temperature rises.
(5) **Warm-up** Both enrichment and spark advance are progressively reduced as engine temperature rises but, if a cold start valve is incorporated, its cut-off point must be compensated for, by increasing the flow through the injectors. To improve driveability, spark point is further advanced during part load operation. In general, after start-up, the ignition timing is adjusted on the basis of engine temperature for idling, overrun, part and full load.
(6) To overcome oil drag, either an auxiliary air device or a rotary actuator, Section 11.19, bypasses the throttle, the Motronic electronic control supplying the extra fuel needed to maintain the appropriate air:fuel ratio. This control operates on the basis of not only engine temperature but also speed, load and an additional map, Fig. 11.46. For lean-burn engines, this is especially important, since it enables extra enrichment to be applied in operational ranges in which driveability and good throttle response are critical and, in others, where fuelling to be reduced.
(7) **Hot idling** By virtue of the application of the Motronic ignition control, enrichment is unnecessary except during overrun when, if no overrun fuel cut-off is incorporated, a slight degree of speed-related enrichment can improve driveability and reduce emissions.
(8) Ideally, the ignition timings for starting and idling should be different. With electronic control, the spark can be advanced as speed is reduced, to increase torque for normal idling: consequently, the idling speed does not have to be set so high to cater for loads from ancillaries, so both fuel consumption and emissions are reduced.
(9) **Full load** With Motronic, the degree of enrichment is engine speed dependent and modified by the map in the memory to cater for pulsations in flow and avoidance of knock. Maximum torque is obtained with lambda = 0.9-0.95. The ignition point is set on the basis of the map but, to obtain maximum torque without knock, modified in response to signals from the knock sensor. Thus high power output is obtained with good fuel economy.
(10) **Acceleration** The degree of initial enrichment is based on the signal from the throttle valve switch and lambda sensor. The electronic control calls for a mixture at lambda = 0.9, for maximum torque and avoidance of a flat spot. For acceleration during warm-up, further enrichment is applied in response to engine temperature signals. Ignition timing is adjusted in response to engine load and speed signals and, if a preset rate of change of load is exceeded, the ignition timing is slightly retarded, to avoid knocking and generation of NO_x.
(11) **Overrun** After an initial lag, the ignition is first retarded (for a smooth transition) and then, a few cycles later, the fuel is cut off completely. It cuts in again, over a few cycles, at an engine speed slightly higher than idling and, once more, the ignition is first retarded and then, as the fuel begins to flow again, progressively advanced back to normal. All this happens during stop-start situations in city traffic and normal braking and down-hill operation, thus saving fuel and obviating emissions.

11.35 Other variables

Intake air temperature. A sensor positioned in air the intake, Fig. 11.7, signals to electronic control unit, which reduces fuelling to compensate for lower density, or mass, of charge and reduces ignition advance to avoid detonation at higher temperatures, especially for turbocharged engines, in which the higher temperature may not be offset by a lower density of charge.

High altitude. A sensor signalling the reduction in pressure with altitude can be incorporated in the electronic control unit, for reduction of the rate of fuelling with increasing altitude.

Battery voltage. Battery voltage falls off rapidly with not only increasing load, but also decreasing temperature and deterioration with age. Self induction causes a lag in both the opening and closing of the electro-magnetic injection valves. Breakaway time depends to a significant degree on battery voltage, but release time only little. Therefore, a fall in battery voltage causes a decrease in injection time. Fig. 11.47 shows how the electronic control unit reduces injection time as battery voltage increases.

Fuel quality. Some Motronic electronic control units contain two maps for ignition advance relative to load and speed, and the driver can switch from one to the other. Generally, the program retards the ignition only at high loads.

Speed limiting. As in the L-Jetronic system, if required, injection can be inhibited to limit maximum engine speed, the device cuts in and out respectively at speeds of 80 rev/min above and below the required limiting value.

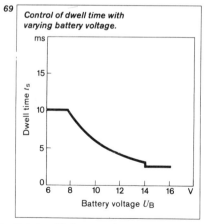

Fig. 11.47   Relationship between dwell time and battery voltage

Engine stopped. To obviate danger of fire after an accident, a power transistor in the control unit controls an external pump relay in a manner such that the pump can operate only if the circuit between the starter and the battery is closed or the engine speed is higher than a preset minimum relative to the throttle position. Furthermore, to prevent the coil from overheating if the engine is left switched on after it has been stopped or stalled, the microcomputer turns off the ignition if the speed is less than, say, 30 rev/min.

Stop-start. To save fuel in heavy traffic, an additional controller can be installed to signal either *stop* or *start* to the electronic control unit. To stop the engine, the driver depresses the clutch pedal, and to start it again, he depresses both the clutch and accelerator pedals simultaneously. However, the engine will stop only if the speed is less than 2 km/h and start only when the throttle is one third open. A function of the additional controller is to assess whether, in the light of the fact that each start uses extra fuel, economy is in fact obtainable: if it is not, the engine will not stop.

Computer-aided transmission control. Fuel economy, gear shift quality, and transmission torque capacity and life expectancy can be improved by adapting the Motronic electronic control unit for use also in automatic transmission control. Additional signals needed by the unit, for controlling the transmission's hydraulic pressure regulator, its solenoid valves and malfunction warning, include transmission output speed, kick-down switch, and program (economy or sporting performance, and manual shift). Gear shift performance curves in an electronic memory are much more effective than their hydraulic counterparts for controlling gear changing. Furthermore, the torque of the engine can be regulated during shifts, by momentarily retarding the ignition during a shift, to obtain a part load feel with a full load shift.

Exhaust gas recirculation. Exhaust gas recirculation can adversely affect driveability, especially at low speeds and light loads. By employing the electronic control unit for regulation of exhaust gas recirculation (EGR) in relation to the engine performance map, these difficulties can be overcome. The electronic control unit, through the medium of a pneumatic valve, regulates the quantity of exhaust gas recirculated so that NO_x is reduced at high loads, and good driveability retained at light loads and low speeds. Further information on EGR is given in Section 13.18.

Evaporative emissions. Canister purge, as described in the Sections 13.22 to 26, can also be controlled by the electronic control unit.

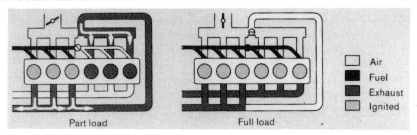

Fig. 11.48   The Motronic cylinder cut-out system

Boost pressure control. With turbocharged engines, the onset of knock can be delayed by either reduction of boost or retardation of the ignition. However, reduction of boost reduces performance, and retardation of the ignition can cause overheating of the turbocharger. On the other hand if, as soon as knock is detected, both are effected simultaneously in an interrelated manner by the electronic control unit these drawbacks can be largely avoided. The ignition retard is effected immediately and then there is a lag before the boost falls; during this lag, the control progressively advances ignition to its optimum value.

Cylinder cut-out. Where, in the interests of economy, it is required to cut one or more cylinders out of operation, the Motronic electronic control unit can do so by cutting the fuel supply to the cylinder or cylinders and, as more power is required, restore it either to one at a time or to groups of cylinders. Moreover, it can control a valve to direct hot exhaust gas through the inactive cylinders, Fig. 11.48, to keep them at normal operating temperature, and therefore with normal friction between their moving parts. Another significant advantage is that the working cylinders operate with the throttle opened wider, so there is less throttling of the idle cylinders. At the time of writing, such schemes are only experimental.

SOME OTHER SYSTEMS

11.36   The GM Multec single-point system

Many features of the GM Multec single- (or throttle body) and multi-point injection systems are similar to those of the Bosch Mono-Motronic and Motronic systems respectively. Consider first the single-point, or TBI, system illustrated in Fig. 11.49, of which twin barrel versions are also available.

From the submerged twin turbine type pump, fuel is delivered at a pressure of 0.83 bar and rates from 19 to 26 g/sec, through a 15 micron filter to the throttle body unit. A water separator/fuel strainer is attached to the fuel pick-up beneath the base of the pump.

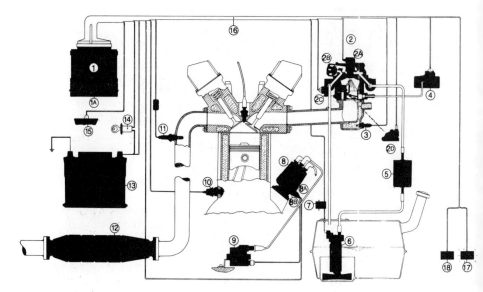

Fig. 11.49   GM Multec single point, or throttle body, fuel injection system with ignition advance
as well as closed loop fuelling control
1. Electronic control module and (a) plug-in and calibration software EPROM, 2. Throttle body
(a) injector (b) fuel pressure regulator (c) idle air control valve and (d) throttle position sensor, 3.
Coolant temperature sensor, 4. Manifold absolute pressure sensor, 5. Filter, 6. In-tank fuel
pump, 7. Fuel pump relay, 8. Ignition distributor (a) magnetic pick-up and (b) electronic ignition
module, 9. Ignition coil, 10. Oil pressure switch, 11. Exhaust oxygen sensor, 12. Catalytic
converter, 13. Battery, 14. Ignition switch, 15. Diagnostic connection socket, 16. Harness, 17.
Check engine warning lamp, 18. Vehicle speed sensor

Rates of injection are regulated by an electronic control module (ECM),
while a separate electronic ignition module (EIM) controls the spark timing.
Air flow is metered by a conventional throttle valve. Sensors signal to the
ECM the throttle position, and temperature and absolute pressure in the
manifold. These and the other sensors used in the system can be seen in Fig.
11.49.

A diagrammatic representation of the throttle body unit is shown in Fig.
11.50. It is mounted on a riser, which is water jacketed to help to vaporise
the fuel and prevent icing in cold and damp ambient conditions. A coolant
temperature sensor is screwed into the base of this jacket.

Within the fuel inlet is a fine mesh screen. The fuel circulation path is from
the bottom of the chamber housing the injector, up to the pressure regulator
at the top, so any bubbles of vapour developing will float up and be returned,
with the fuel in excess of engine requirements, to the tank. Fuel injection is
regulated by a solenoid which, when energised, lifts the ball type metering
valve fully off its seat. It is eventually closed again by a coil spring. When the
valve is open, the constant pressure maintained by the regulator projects a
conical spray into the bore upstream of the throttle valve. Regulation of the

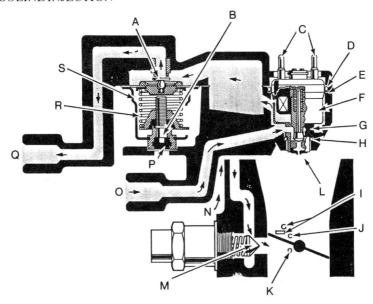

Fig. 11.50   GM Rochester throttle body injection unit
A: Diaphragm and self seating valve assembly, B: Regulator screw (factory adjusted), C: Injector
electrical terminals, D: 'O' ring (large), E: Back-up washer, F: Fuel injector, G: Injector fuel
filter, H: 'O' ring (small), I: Typical vacuum ports (for EGR and spark), J: Timed canister purge
(optional), K: Constant canister purge (optional), L: Nozzle, M: Idle air control valve (shown
open), N: Air in, O: Fuel inlet (from fuel pump), P: Dust seal, Q: Fuel return (to fuel tank), R:
Regulator spring, S: Fuel pressure regulator assembly

total rate of delivery of fuel through the valve can be effected by varying
either the open duration or the frequency of fixed duration pulses.

The pressure regulator is a diaphragm type valve opened against the
resistance of a calibrated spring, by the pump delivery pressure. It reduces
the injection pressure to 0.76 bar. As previously indicated, its primary
function is to maintain a constant pressure across the metering jet. The
maximum recirculation rate is 27 g/s.

Enrichment for cold starting, warm-up, acceleration and maximum power
are effected by the ECM, as also is idling speed. When the throttle is closed
on to its stop, extra air bypasses it through a duct in which is a tapered pintle,
idle air control valve actuated by a stepper motor. This valve is moved by the
ECM in response to signals from the engine speed sensor.

11.37   The Multec multi-point system

In principle, this multi-point system so resembles the Bosch Motronic,
Sections 11.32-35, that a full description would be largely repetitive.
Therefore, only a few brief comments will be necessary here. It is a complete
engine management system, Fig. 11.51, regulating EGR, ignition, fuelling,

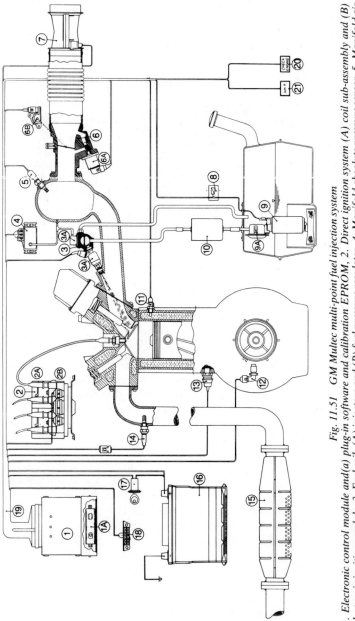

Fig. 11.51   GM Multec multi-point fuel injection system

1. Electronic control module and (a) plug-in software and calibration EPROM, 2. Direct ignition system (A) coil sub-assembly and (B) electronic ignition module, 3. Fuel rail, (A) injectors and (B) fuel pressure regulator, 4. Manifold absolute pressure sensor, 5. Manifold air temperature sensor, 6. Throttle body (A) idle air control valve and (B) throttle position sensor, 7. Mass air flow sensor, 8. Fuel pump relay, 9. In-tank fuel pump and (A) pulsator, 10. Fuel filter, 12. Crankshaft sensor, 13. Oil pressure switch, 14. Exhaust oxygen sensor, 15. Catalytic converter, 16. Battery, 17. Ignition switch, 18. Socket for diagnostic connection, 19. Harness, 20. Check engine warning lamp, 21. Vehicle speed sensor

overrun cut-off, air flow control, including during idling, and open or closed loop control over emissions. In the Multec system, however, the ECM, served by signals from the throttle position indicator and manifold pressure and temperature sensors, meters the air flow on the speed-density principle and controls the rate of fuelling in relation to it. Among the features of the system are on-board diagnostics, back-up fuel and ignition circuits, and an assembly line diagnostic link. Mass flow air metering with a hot wire anemometer is an optional alternative. Another option is either direct or distributor ignition timing.

Extracts from the specification include the following. The direct ignition system, which obviates the need for a distributor and separate coil, is capable of making 35 kV available. It typically produces a 1700 microsec spark at 18 kV. For a 4-cylinder engine, a dual tower, twin-spark, epoxy-filled coil is used, the current of which is closed-loop controlled, and there is back-up control over ignition timing.

The injectors are of GM design, with alternative ratings of 12 or 2 ohm at 3 bar, and flow rates ranging up to 15 g/s. They are a push fit in bosses on an extruded aluminium fuel rail, where they are retained by spring clips and sealed by O-rings. The fuel pump has a vane and a roller type impeller, the former both centrifugally removing any vapour bubbles present and priming the latter. A pulsation damper is mounted on top of it and, in its base, a fuel strainer/water separator sleeve is fitted to the fuel inlet. At 3.5 bar, a delivery rate of 19 g/s is typical.

The oil pressure switch that can be seen in Fig. 11.51 controls a parallel circuit to drive the fuel pump in the event of failure of either the pump relay or the electronic control. Rated at 1000°C exhaust temperature, the oxygen sensor is based on a zirconium element. Signals from the vehicle speed sensor indicate to the ECM when overrun cut-off and idle speed control should be brought into operation.

Incorporated in the ECM are an 8 bit microprocessor, a co-processor, AC/DC converters to enable the digital microprocessor to read the analog signals from the sensors, and drivers for the actuators and back-up hardware. Software and calibration are programmed into a 16 kByte EPROM customised to meet the requirements for specific applications. The co-processor relieves the microprocessor of interruption by the engine timing functions.

Software alogarithms continuously check the status of the ECM outputs and the validity of its inputs. If a fault is detected, a code is stored in the memory and a warning lamp on the instrument panel illuminated. Service technicians can then read the code indicating the nature of the problem and, if necessary, connect to the system a diagnostic facility to obtain further details.

11.38   Weber IAW injection-ignition system

In the Weber IAW system, Fig. 11.52, a roller type pump delivers at up to 5

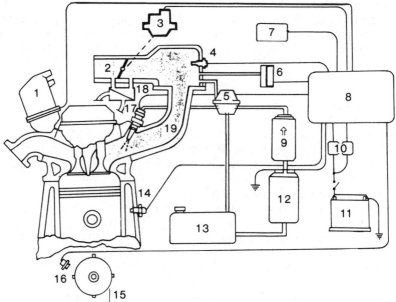

Fig. 11.52   The Weber IAW combined injection and ignition control system
1. Phase sensors, 2. Throttle body, 3. Throttle position sensor, 4. Air temperature sensor, 5.
Pressure regulator, 6. Absolute pressure sensor, 7. Ignition assembly, 8. Electronic control, 9.
Fuel filter, 10. Relays, 11. Battery, 12. Fuel pump, 13. Fuel tank, 14. Coolant temperature sensor,
15. Crankshaft pulley, 16. Engine rev/min sensor, 17. Injectors, 18. Extra air valve, 19. Induction
manifold

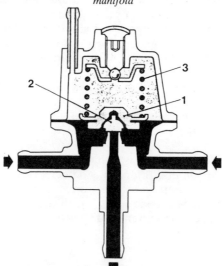

Fig. 11.53   The Weber fuel pressure regulator is adjustable but a cap inserted over the socket
screw discourages tampering in service
1. Diaphragm assemby, 2. Valve head with return spring beneath it, 3. Calibrated spring

bar to a paper element filter having a surface area of 1200 cm^2 and a pore size of 10 micron. From the filter, the fuel passes through a diaphragm type pressure regulator, Fig. 11.53, which maintains a constant pressure of 3 bar in the delivery lines to the injectors. Since the diaphragm is exposed on one side to the fuel pressure and the other manifold depression, the differential pressure across the injector nozzles is unaffected by changes in atmospheric pressure.

The Weber injector has been commented upon in Section 11.27 and illustrated in Fig. 11.36. It is opened by a solenoid energised by a signal from the electronic control unit and closed by a return spring, the compression setting of which can be adjusted by means of a screwdriver slot in the upper end of its tubular seating. The included angle of the conical jet of atomised fuel leaving the injector is about 30°.

Air flow metering is effected on the speed-density principle, with throttle position, manifold air temperature and absolute pressure sensors signalling to the electronic control unit. In a throttle bypass duct, a manually adjusted valve, Fig. 11.54 is used to set the basic idling speed, while a thermostatically controlled rotary sleeve valve, Fig. 11.55, regulates the idling speed for cold starting and warm-up. During warm-up, a water jacket next to the coiled bimetal strip progressively increases its temperature, causing it to rotate towards the closed position until, when the engine attains its normal operating temperature, it has closed the valve completely.

The electronic control unit triggers each injector to deliver in turn one shot phased in relation to the induction stroke of its cylinder. To regulate the quantity of fuel injected in relation to the air flow into the engine, the control unit varies timing of the start of injection. Spark advance is also regulated by the control unit, through the medium of a power module, coil, and dissipator sub-assembly. All this is done on the basis of a data map stored in the memory, and the system is programmed to take account of changes in requirements owing to wear over the life of the engine.

Input signals include the temperature and absolute pressure in the manifold, coolant temperature, rev/min and crankshaft angle, battery

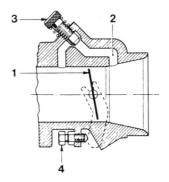

Fig. 11.54   Throttle stop and bypass adjustment screws
1. Butterfly valve, 2. Bypass duct, 3. Idle speed adjustment screw, 4. Throttle stop

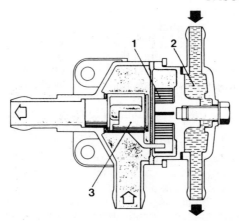

Fig. 11.55   Extra mixture for cold starting and warm-up is supplied through this rotary valve and
hoses of a throttle bypass system in the Weber IAW system
1. Coiled bimetal strip, 2. Coolant, 3. Rotary sleeve valve

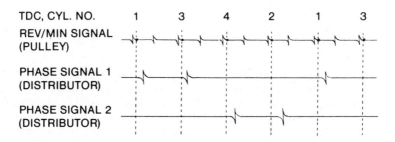

Fig. 11.56   The signals that indicate to the electronic control the crankshaft phase and engine
rev/min

voltage and throttle position (closed, cruising and wide open). Engine speed
is derived from variable reluctance sensors detecting the passage past them
of four lugs projecting radially from the periphery of the crankshaft pulley.
Crankshaft angle is detected by two inductive sensors in the ignition
distributor. The relationships between the various signals are shown in Fig.
11.56.

Chapter 12

Combustion and Combustion Chambers

As will be explained in greater detail in Chapter 13, burning the air-fuel mixture in the internal combustion engine is oxidation, and the aim, at least for satisfying the emissions regulations during steady state cruising operation, is at combining all the hydrogen and carbon atoms in the fuel with all the oxygen from the air with which it is mixed. This process has to be completed in the shortest practicable time, but not explosively. In other words, in a gasoline fuelled engine, the flame should spread progressively throughout the combustion chamber, without spontaneous ignition occurring ahead of it.

Ignition is initiated by the passage of a spark, though catalytic initiation of ignition has been accomplished in the Merritt Catalytic Compression ignition, or MCC, engine. As has been mentioned in previous chapters, to obtain maximum power, a slightly rich mixture is required for ensuring that all the oxygen in the cylinder is burned. This can lead to emissions of CO and unburned hydrocarbons in the exhaust. For maximum economy, on the other hand, the need is to ensure that all the fuel is burned, which entails supplying a slightly weak mixture. In this case, there is a risk that oxides of nitrogen might be formed, though it must be admitted that enriching the mixture does not necessarily solve this problem.

THE MERRITT CONCEPT

12.1   Catalytic ignition

Since most readers will be familiar with spark ignition, but fewer with catalytic ignition, the latter will be explained first. The idea was originated in 1985 by Dr Dan Merritt, of Coventry Polytechnic, and made public in 1987. It is based on the idea that the platinum and other catalysts that can cause the unburned hydrocarbons to ignite in exhaust systems can surely ignite the much more combustible mixture drawn into the cylinder during the induction stroke.

How a catalyst functions is not entirely understood. However, it is believed that it strongly attracts and adsorbs some of the hydrocarbon and oxygen radicals into its surface, thus breaking the chemical bonds of the hydrocarbon molecules so that they can then combine with the oxygen present and releasing them, ultimately to form CO_2 and H_2O. This generates enough heat locally for the combustion to spread throughout the remaining fuel-air mixture. The catalytic action is totally independent of both the mixture strength and the actual type of hydrocarbon fuel used, and it occurs at temperatures much lower than those normally required for initiating combustion.

12.2   The MCC catalytic combustion engine

The layout of the engine as originally designed is illustrated diagrammatically in Fig. 12.1(a). The development work began using a single cylinder of a conventional four cylinder four-stroke engine with push rod rather than overhead camshaft actuation of the valves. It was fitted with a modified head, to contain the combustion chamber, and a separate crankshaft and connecting rod mechanism for actuating the piston in the auxiliary cylinder. Subsequently, 1989, Dr Merritt designed some more versions, four-stroke and two-stroke, Figs. 12.1(b) and 12.1(c), without separate cylinder and crank mechanisms.

As shown in Fig. 12.1(a), the cylindrical combustion chamber is housed in the head, where it is in effect interposed between the two cylinders. Its walls are coated with the platinum catalyst. Air and mixture flow back and forth through two passages in this combustion chamber, one from the auxiliary cylinder and the other from the main cylinder. That from the main cylinder is tangential to the cylindrical chamber to generate the swirl as air enters it during the compression stroke, while that from the auxiliary cylinder is aligned approximately perpendicularly to the axis of swirl, to form a turbulent stratified charge within the combustion chamber as the two pistons move together.

Essentially, the fuel is injected into, and the mixture prepared in, the small auxiliary cylinder, the capacity of which is about one fifth of that of the main cylinder. In the engine illustrated in Fig. 12.1(a) this operation is completed as the pistons in each simultaneously move up to tdc. The clearance above the auxiliary piston at tdc is so small that, ultimately, the charge is squeezed out of its cylinder into the swirl chamber, where it is ignited as, under the influence of centrifugal force, it is swept over the catalyst on the walls. Then the expanding and still burning gases are forced out through a duct into the main chamber, where combustion is completed. Finally, the exhaust stroke begins. The cycle of operations, is illustrated in Fig. 12.2.

In addition to the obvious advantages of low pressure injection (about 8 bar) and absence of an electric ignition system, the MCC engine has many more. By virtue of surface, instead of point ignition, burning is very rapid and therefore high rotational speeds, in theory up to as high as 6000 rev/min, are practicable. Its power output is controlled by regulation of the duration of injection per cycle. Consequently, there are no throttling losses, so part

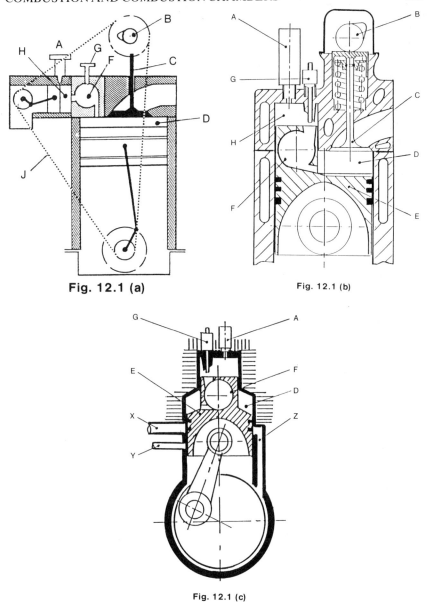

Fig. 12.1 (a)

Fig. 12.1 (b)

Fig. 12.1 (c)

Fig. 12.1   Three versions of the MCC catalytic combustion engine: (a) has a separate crank, piston and cylinder; (b) has not and its combustion chamber is in the piston crown instead of the head; (c) is a 2-stroke version, again with the combustion chamber in the piston crown
A: Injector, B: Overhead chamshaft, C: Inlet valve, D: Main cylinder, E: Shouldered piston, F: Combustion chamber, G: Cold start assistance, H: Mixture preparation cylinder, J: Drive belt for auxiliary crankshaft, X: Exhaust, Y: Inlet, Z: Transfer port

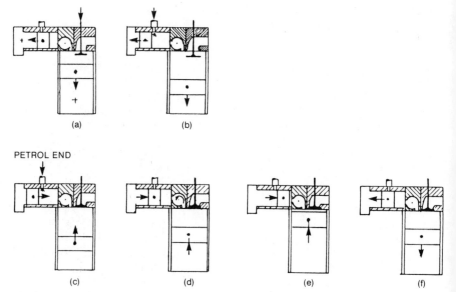

Fig. 12.2   The sequence of operations of the MCC engine: (a) beginning of induction, (b) injection during induction, (c) beginning of compression, (d) mid-compression, (e) end of compression and onset of catalytic ignition in combustion chamber, (f) expansion

throttle economy is outstandingly good. Theory suggests that, because combustion of its premixed charge occurs extremely rapidly at virtually constant volume, it should be more fuel-efficient, and especially at full load, than a conventional diesel unit.

Clearly, this engine cannot function unless the air-fuel mixing process is segregated, and the mixture kept away from the catalytic combustion chamber until the moment that ignition is required which, by virtue of the rapidity of subsequent combustion, is virtually at tdc. Five design features contribute to keeping the mixure from being injected into the combustion chamber too early. First, the passage of air from the main cylinder through the combustion chamber to the minor cylinder guarantees complete purging of the combustion chamber during the induction and compression strokes. Secondly, because the piston-swept volume of the main cylinder is about five times that of the minor one, this purging action continues throughout the compression stroke. Thirdly, evaporation of the fuel in the minor chamber cools, and therefore reduces the pressure of, the gas in it. Fourthly, the centrifugal effect of the rapidly rotating vortex in the combustion chamber builds up a pressure gradient opposing entry of mixture from the minor cylinder. Finally, where two crankshafts are employed, they may be connected slightly out of phase, to retard the transfer from the auxiliary cylinder to the combustion chamber. A more detailed description of this engine is to be found in *The Motor Vehicle*, by Newton, Steeds and Garrett, Butterworths 1989.

FLAME DEVELOPMENT WITH ELECTRIC IGNITION

12.3 Spark ignition

The mechanics and functioning of the electrical equipment for generating and timing the spark are very widely understood and, in any case, do not concern us here. On the other hand, both the ignition process and the progress of the subsequent combustion do. So far as the overall combustion process is concerned, we can regard the ignition as originating at a point, but if calculations or studies in detail have to be made regarding the macro process of igniting the fuel, the fact that the spark has a length equal to the gap between the plug points should not be ignored.

The passage of a high energy spark through an ignitable mixture increases both its temperatures and molecular energy locally. This breaks its constituents down, forming radicals which, being inherently unstable and chemically active, combine to form simpler compounds such as CO_2, H_2O and perhaps some transients. The chemical reaction is exothermic, so more radicals are released and combine, forming a tiny kernel of burning fuel. The process continues at first at a virtually constant and then an increasing rate as a flame front, dependent upon the conditions, moves away preferably at a relatively constant or slowly accelerating velocity, from the source of ignition. Finally, enveloping the whole of the space above the piston, it is checked on reaching the walls of the combustion chamber.

12.4 The flame kernel

When the kernel is first formed, it is in a relatively fragile state, and can be chilled and blown out, or quenched, by velocity of motion of the gas around it, as is the flame of a candle by a draught. During the initial period of ignition, what is termed *flame development* (the formation of intermediate products of combustion) occurs and is evident as *ignition lag*. The duration of this lag in terms of time varies solely with air:fuel ratio but, in terms of crankshaft angle, it increases with speed of rotation, which is one of the reasons why spark timing has to be advanced with increasing engine speed. To overcome the problems associated with the fragility of the flame kernel, the spark plug has in some instances been placed in a small pocket or even in an auxiliary chamber in the main combustion chamber.

The amount of spark energy required to initiate ignition obviously varies with the degree and velocity of motion of the mixture in the area in which the plug points are situated, but it also depends on the air:fuel ratio. In general, for mixtures in the stoichiometric range, an energy of 0.2 mJ is needed and, for rich or lean mixtures, an energy of 0.3 mJ per spark. Too low a spark energy will result in either failure to ignite or a slow rate of flame development, increased ignition lag and delayed completion of combustion.

Both economy and maximum power attained are dependent upon the velocity of propagation of the flame from the kernel. The more rapidly and smoothly combustion is completed, without detonation, the better. This is because, up to a point, the sooner after tdc that the peak combustion pressure can be attained in the cylinder, the higher will be the mean torque and the greater the amount of work that can be extracted from the gas as it forces the piston down the cylinder. Detonation has been explained in detail in Section 2.2

12.5   Spark timing and compression ratio

Economy and power are also dependent upon spark timing in relation to engine speed, ignition lag and velocity of spread of the flame front. The aim is at generating as much of the heat as possible when the piston is appropriately positioned for extracting the highest proportion of its energy into work on the crankshaft. This is generally between approximately 5° and 10° after tdc. Earlier release of the heat results in thermal losses to the walls of the combustion chamber and, possibly, mechanical losses in doing negative work on the crankshaft (tending to rotate it backwards) as the piston is coming up to tdc on compression. Releasing the heat too late means that it can be converted into work over only part of the power stroke. This leaves the exhaust gas hotter at the end of the stroke, and therefore may increase the temperature of the exhaust valves to a level above that which they can withstand.

Generally, the compression ratio of a spark ignition engine is somewhere between about 7:1 and 10:1 (usually closer to the latter figure and sometimes even slightly higher) giving respectively maximum compression pressures from approximately 15 to about 25 bar. The final compression temperature is rarely much above about 600°C, which is well below the autoignition temperature of the mixture.

12.6   Compression ratio and detonation

Part load efficiency can be improved by increasing compression ratio. However, there is a limit above which detonation will arise at full load. Detonation can occur under two conditions. First, when the flame has to travel a long distance before it reaches the combustion chamber wall furthest from the spark, the unburned gas ahead of the flame front, termed the *end gas*, may be compressed and heated to such a degree as to ignite spontaneously, or explode. Incidentally, the heating of the unburned gases due to compression will far exceed that that due to either radiated or conducted heat from the advancing flame.

Secondly, towards the end of the combustion process, the flame front may be advancing at a speed approaching that of sound and, locally, parts may actually attain that speed. Consequently, a series of shock waves may be sent out ahead of the front and trigger spontaneous ignition in the already very hot and highly compressed gas. These shock waves will be reflected from the

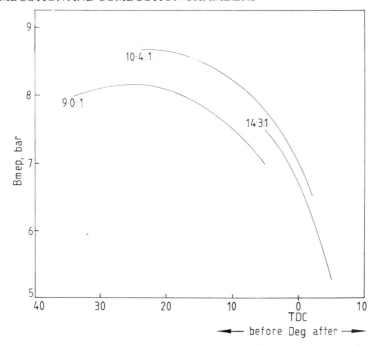

Fig. 12.3   Curves of detonation limited bmep plotted against spark advance for compression ratios of 9.0:1, 10.4:1 and 14.3:1

walls and resonance may occur. The outcome is that serious mechanical or thermal damage may be done to components such as pistons, rings and exhaust valves. Common results are overheating of valves and softening or even melting of light alloys, leading to the punching of holes through piston crowns, collapsed upper lands, and piston ring and valve breakages.

The higher the compression ratio, the more closely must the ignition timing be controlled, by the use of a reliable knock detector and computer controlled ignition, as in the Bosch Motronic system. Knock limits at various compression ratios are illustrated in Fig. 12.3. Here it can be seen that the curve of knock limit at a compression ratio of 9:1 is much less steep than that for a compression ratio of for example 12:1.

As an alternative remedy for detonation, pistons providing continuously variable compression ratios have been made, but these are so heavy that they have tended to be used on slow speed engines. They can hardly be considered seriously for high speed spark ignition engines. Another possibility is to close the inlet valves early: by cutting off the inflow of mixture before the cylinder is full, the effective compression ratio is reduced. Furthermore, the depression induced in the cylinder by the inertia of the outgoing exhaust gases can do on the piston useful work that it would otherwise have expended on inducting additional fresh mixture. Various devices have been invented for increasing efficiency by automatically varying the valve timing while the engine is running, but they have mostly tended to be fairly complex and, consequently, their potential durability and reliability suspect. Undoubtedly, the oldest, simplest, and most reliable method of controlling the compression ratio is to throttle the incoming mixture, though it has the severe disadvantage of causing negative work to be done on the piston.

12.7   Air:fuel ratio

For complete combustion of gasoline in air, the theoretically correct mixture is 14.7 parts of air with 1 part of fuel by weight, which is taken lambda = 1. In other words,if lambda = 0.9 the mixture is 10% rich and, at 1.1, it is 10% weak. In general, mixtures outside the range lambda = 0.8 to 1.2 (11.76:1 to 17.6:1) will not burn cleanly, though they can be burned. At low air:fuel ratios, carbon monoxide and unburned carbon, in the form of soot, will be discharged. On the other hand, at air:fuel ratios above about lambda 1.2, ignition will be irregular so unburned hydrocarbons will be discharged through the exhaust. Incidentally, at lambda = 1.0 a volume of 10,000 litres of air are needed to burn 1 litre of fuel.

Above lambda = 1.25 and below about 0.4, respectively 18:1 and 5:1, ignition cannot be initiated at all, let alone reliably, by a spark. It should be appreciated that these figures are not precise, because factors such as the velocity of motion of the charge and how close the compression temperature is to the autoignition temperature influence ignitability. Indeed stratified charge engines, Sections 12.14-16, have been run on mixtures as lean as 64:1 though the optimum for obtaining low fuel consumption and levels of emission is widely recognised as being of the order of 20-25:1. From the fact that ignition cannot be obtained reliably with mixtures that are outside the range 60% rich to 25% weak, it can be seen that the tolerance below is much higher than that above lambda = 1.0. Therefore, the aim is usually at supplying the region around the sparking plug points with a rich, rather than weak, mixture. Another factor is that the evolving heat tends to evaporate and expand away any droplets of fuel present, thus generating micro turbulence, so the kernel develops faster in a rich than a weak mixture.

MIXING THE FUEL AND AIR

12.8   Mixture formation

The aim when designing a fuel metering system (carburettor or injection) is at forming a homogeneous mixture. This is possible only if all the fuel is vaporised, though it must be borne in mind that vaporisation can continue in the cylinder, right up to and even beyond the point at which the spark is passed. Vaporisation is of course slow during a cold start, which is why extra fuel has to be supplied to ensure that an ignitable mixture reaches the spark plug points.

When the engine is running properly, the main concern, as explained in Chapter 9, is that all cylinders shall receive equal charges at a common air:fuel ratio. If they do not, the strengths of their firing strokes will differ, giving rise to rough running, and if the air:fuel ratios differ, detonation may occur in those that receive weak mixtures. In the past, the cure has been to increase the overall air:fuel ratio at optimum ignition advance (for obtaining maximum bmep) so that even the cylinder that is running weakest is not detonating. Not only does this increase overall fuel consumption but nowadays it is in any case undesirable because it results in exhaust contamination with CO and unburnt hydrocarbons. Some enrichment during cold start up and warm-up cannot however be avoided.

Although of course the degree of uniformity of cylinder charging attained over the whole load and speed range is dependent primarily upon the shape of the manifold and overall rapidity of vaporisation and mixing, the degree of throttle opening also has an effect. Partial closure of the throttle tends to deflect the flow to one side of the riser or manifold and therefore can cause unequal filling of the cylinders. This effect also varies with speed of flow past the throttle valve.

In Fig 12.4, three factors affected by the degree of throttle opening are demonstrated. First, in engines equipped with carburettors and running at

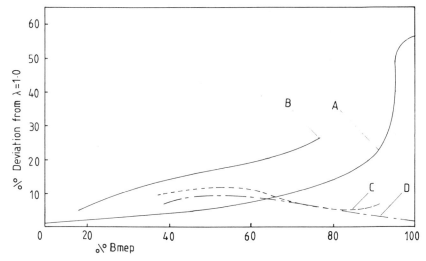

Fig. 12.4   Curves showing deviation from λ=1.0 plotted over the whole range of throttle opening (bmep) at constant speeds, with the spark advanced continuously to the point at which detonation is just avoided
Carburetted or throttle body injected engine: A at 3000 rev/min, three-quarters load; B at 1500 rev/min, light load
Multi-point manifold injected engine: C at 1500 rev/min, light load; D at 4000 rev/min, three-quarters load

constant speed, the distribution of the mixture is better at the lower speed, curve A, than at the higher speed, curve B.

Secondly, as the load is increased at constant speed, so also is the velocity of flow past the throttle valve, and this causes greater deflection of the flow and so the distribution deteriorates correspondingly. This effect is most pronounced at the lower speed, owing to the increasing velocity of flow past the only slightly open throttle valve. At the higher speed, when the throttle is fairly wide open even at lower end of the bmep range, the variation in deflection of the flow with increasing throttle opening is not so severe.

The third effect is attributable to the fact that the rate of evaporation, as influenced by manifold depression, is the overriding influence. With the throttle closed, evaporation occurs more rapidly than with a wide open throttle. This effect is therefore greater when the engine is idling or the throttle is partly closed at high bmep, curve A.

With port or manifold injection, the situation is different in that instead of the distribution of mixture, it is that of the air to the cylinders that is relevant. In these circumstances, distribution is worst at light load, when the deflection of the air flow past the throttle valve is greatest. Since each cylinder receives an equal charge of fuel, those that receive the lightest charge of air will tend to have a rich mixture and *vice versa*. Furthermore, the higher the velocity of air flowing through and the greater the depression in the induction system, the more uniform will be the distribution, as is demonstrated by curve C. At the wider throttle openings and at the higher speed, curve D, the distribution is even better.

12.9   Swirl and turbulence

There are three main types of air motion. They are: *swirl*, and *macro* and *micro turbulence*. Swirl can be generated in several ways. Most commonly, the inlet port is aligned partially tangentially relative to the bore of the cylinder so that the incoming charge swirls about its axis. Further inducement to swirl can be given by additionally incorporating spiral induction ports in the cylinder head.

A point that has to be borne in mind, however, is that swirl and turbulence can be generated only by the application of energy. That for generating swirl can be taken only from the kinetic energy of the incoming gases and therefore inevitably will reduce volumetric efficiency. Turbulence on the other hand which probably consumes more energy, at least in most engines, can come from the flywheel, through the crankshaft and piston.

Curved baffles, more commonly called shrouds, have been welded just inboard of the seats on valve heads to prevent the incoming gases from flowing other than tangentially into the cylinder. However, this is undesirable in spark ignition engines, because of the extra inertia of the rapidly reciprocating valves and the distortion and other problems associated with lack of uniformity of heat distribution in the valve heads. Moreover, it also reduces volumetric efficiency. Even in the slower speed

Fig. 12.5   In this Ford crossflow engine, not only does the inflowing gas stream roll round above the piston crown to form, with its axis parallel to the crankshaft, a vortex which swirls increasingly rapidly as the piston rises but, additionally, as the piston comes up to tdc, a more complex turbulence is induced by the shapes of the flanks of the piston crown, which generate smaller vortices whose axes are also in a horizontal plane but at right angles to that of the primary vortex

diesel engines, shrouded inlet valves are relatively uncommon, though here they are cooler by virtue of the higher expansion ratios: significantly more heat is extracted from the working fluid than in the spark ignition engine and, because the operating speeds are lower, slightly less emphasis needs to be placed on keeping valve mass low.

In crossflow engines (inlet and exhaust ports on opposite sides of the head), Fig. 12.5, a different form of swirl can be generated. With this arrangement, the inlet port can be aligned with its axis parallel to that of the cylinder but directing the flow down its flank so that, as it is deflected up again by the piston crown, swirl occurs about a horizontal axis parallel to the crankshaft. As the piston rises, the vortex thus formed is progressively confined within a smaller space, and its diameter therefore reduced. If we apply the principle of conservation of energy, we see the energy contained in a vortex swirling at a given angular velocity will be the greater the larger is its radius. Consequently, reduction of the radius while its mass remains constant, must increase its velocity if its energy content is to remain constant.

12.10   Macro turbulence, squish and micro turbulence

Macro turbulence is the term for the small eddies that occur naturally owing to the drag between the air stream and the surfaces along which it is flowing. This slows the layers nearest to the surface, leaving those further from it moving at a higher velocity. With two diametrically opposite layers of gas flowing at different velocities, there is a natural tendency for roll-over to occur, in other words, for the laminar flow to break up adjacent to the surface and tiny vortices to form.

Macro turbulence can be generated also by devices such as a squish shelf. This is a surface in the combustion chamber which is both flat and parallel to the piston crown. As the piston comes up to tdc, its crown rapidly approaches the squish shelf until there is so little clearance between the two that the air is forcibly ejected from between them along a plane perpendicular to the axis of the cylinder. This of course superimposes macro turbulence on the vortex of gas which, at this stage is swirling at high velocity.

Squish can be generated also around a bowl-in-piston combustion chamber, which will be described in Section 12.11. Such a combustion chamber is, however, more common in diesel than spark ignition engines. With both types of engine the need is for a combined swirl and macro turbulence that is consistent, or better still varied in a controlled manner, over the whole of the engine load and speed range. Consequently, in this respect, engine design is perhaps as much an art as a science.

Squish, however, is by many regarded as wishful thinking. Realistically, there seems to be no reason why large enough quantities of the mixture should remain between the shelf and the approaching crown of the piston long enough to be forced out in the manner just described. Even so, there probably is a squish effect, but of a magnitude much less than that envisaged by the early enthusiasts for the device. On the other hand, what might be called *reverse squish* probably does occur as the two surfaces are drawn apart. This would undoubtedly be more forceful and cause some additional turbulence, perhaps in a region where, at the instant of its generation, the flame front has not penetrated.

The flame front, itself generates macro turbulence owing to the rapid changes in temperature and therefore high temperature gradients at the interface between unburnt and burning gases. Micro turbulence is created around the progressively increasing number of points of autoignition of tiny groups of molecules as the flame front expands. Both these effects increase the speed of burning and rate of progress of the front across the combustion chamber. In general, the speed of travel of the flame front may range from about 20 to 40 m/s, the rate of combustion being greatest when lambda is approxiately 0.9. Short combustion times are conducive to high thermal efficiency and therefore low fuel consumption.

12.11   Influence of combustion chamber shape

Among the main essentials governing choice of combustion chamber shape is that it must be as compact as practicable. In this respect, a spherical chamber is clearly the optimum for two reasons: it offers the highest ratio of volume to surface area, and therefore least loss of heat; secondly, the distance the flame has to travel from the a central ignition source is as short as possible, so combustion is potentially completed both rapidly and uniformly. However, most so called spherical chambers are not so. To obtain an adequate compression ratio, the piston crown must be at least flat, if not actually domed. In practice, therefore, the combustion chambers are either part spherical, hemispherical or, if I might be forgiven for inventing a word to describe a shape formed by rotation of a crescent about its normal axis, crescentoidal.

Another extremely important requirement is that the spark should occur at the centroid of the combustion chamber, the aim being that the flame should have equal distances to travel in all directions as it spreads away from it. Again, this is an ideal that cannot be achieved in practice. In a truly spherical chamber for example, the points would have to extend a long distance out from the spark plug housing. So, not only would they be fragile and vulnerable to erosion, but also they would become extremely hot and therefore liable to incandesce and cause preignition as defined in Section 2.2. Some compromise may be possible, but extension of the nose of the spark plug into the combustion chamber is severely limited by the difficulty of providing adequate cooling, and various other considerations such as local air flow, swirl and turbulence patterns and velocities.

In practice, considerations such as the need to accommodate valves and, when they are open, to leave clearance between their heads and the crown of the piston rule out a truly hemispherical pocket for the combustion chamber especially in the cylinder head. For obtaining a high compression ratio with a crossflow engine, what is termed the *double penthouse* type of chamber, as illustrated in Fig. 12.6(a), is preferred. The piston is in effect domed, but with flats on each side of the centre of its crown, to clear the valves. Where the induction and exhaust manifolds are on the same side of the engine, however, a *single penthouse* or *wedge* shape chamber, Fig. 12.6(b), is often used. Again, the piston is domed but with a flat on only one side, to clear two valves.

Before high compression ratios became the vogue, for obtaining high thermal efficiency, the *bath tub* type of chamber, Fig. 12.6(c), was widely favoured. This offered the advantage of a squish shelf on one or both sides of the valve pocket. A compromise between the bath tub and single penthouse type is often used so that not only can the valves be inclined and the ports do not have to be turned through 90°, but also a higher compression ratio obtained.

Many variants of these arrangements have been used, only a few having been illustrated here. They range from flat roofs virtually flush with the joint face of the cylinder head and bowl-in-piston combustion chambers to the double penthouse type just described but with a dished instead of domed piston crown. In many instances, recesses have been machined or cast in piston crowns, to clear the valves. In designing such recesses, sharp exposed corners or peaks that could overheat and encourage either detonation or preignition should be avoided. Bowl-in-piston combustion chambers, as in Fig. 12.10 but generally not so deep and concentric with the piston crown, are frequently used with a cylinder head that forms a flat roof in virtually the same plane as the top face of the gasket. Unless very shallow, however, they can be troublesome, because confining the combustion process within the piston crown can cause it to overheat unless oil cooling is applied to its underside. However, to clear the valves, shallow bowls with part spherical chambers in the head, are fairly common.

In general, the shape of the combustion chamber roof is to a major extent determined by the type of layout of the valve actuating gear used. Vertical

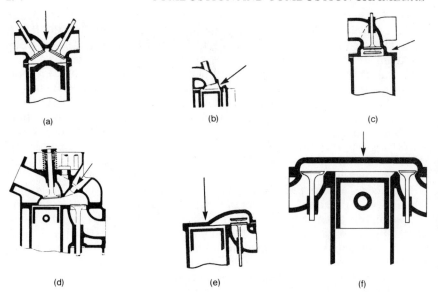

Fig. 12.6   A selection of combustion chamber types with arrows indicating spark plug positions: (a) penthouse, (b) wedge, (c) bath tub, (d) F-head, (e) side valve, (f) T-head (long ago obsolete)

valves in line are convenient for direct actuation by a single camshaft. On the other hand, inclined valves are more suitable for both rocker and twin camshaft actuation. Other advantages of the inclined valve arrangement include reduced overall height and the fact that it enables the ports to be designed so that the air flows more smoothly from the manifold than if they had to be turned through a right angle as they approach the valve seat.

FILLING THE CYLINDERS

12.12   Valve layout

Although the side-valve layout, or L-head, is the worst as regards tendency to detonate, similar conditions can arise with other layouts, so we shall use it here to explain how detonation can occur in the end-gas. Owing to inherent simplicity and low manufacturing cost, engines of this layout remained in production until well after World War II. Probably the last in the UK was one of the Hillman Minx models of the 1950s.

As can be seen from Fig. 12.7, the spark occurs not far from the valves, so the expanding gas forces the flame front into the restricted space between the head and piston crown. As it does so, it compresses the end-gas until, ultimately, if the engine is operating under load with the throttle open fairly wide and the cylinder therefore receiving a full or almost full charge, it ignites spontaneously, or explodes.

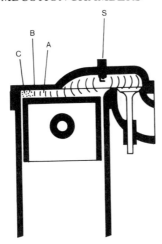

*Fig. 12.7   Showing how compression of, and radiation of heat to, the end-gas causes detonation
A: Spreading flame, B: Flame front, C: End gas, S: Spark plug*

If, on the other hand, the spark plug is for example coaxial with the cylinder, as in T-head engine, Fig. 12.6(f), the end-gas may be compressed into the spaces above the valves where, beneath the red-hot exhaust valve, the heat both radiated and conducted to it will aggravate the conditions locally. However, by moving the spark plug away from the centre an appropriate distance towards the exhaust valve, the end-gas in that region is ignited and burned before it becomes end-gas. Additionally, by lowering part of the top of the T-head towards the piston, turbulence can be generated, as described in the next paragraphs. A major disadvantage is that, with the T-head, high compression ratios are impossible.

The form of L-head in Fig. 12.6(e) was invented by the great engineer Sir Harry Ricardo, founder of what is now Ricardo Consulting Engineers Ltd at Shoreham-on-Sea. From this illustration, it can be seen that, as the piston comes up to tdc, it forces or squishes the gas out, from between its crown and the cylinder head, into the combustion chamber above the valves. This generates turbulence which, encouraging rapid yet progressive combustion of the charge, reduces the quantity remaining to form end-gas. Optimum effect is obtained when the area of the passage between the cylinder head and the combustion chamber is approximately equal to that of the inlet valve port. If it is much larger, the turbulence is inadequate and, if smaller, too violent. However, with the side valve layout, it is impracticable to obtain compression ratios higher than about 5.5:1 without either restricting the breathing capacity or unacceptably increasing the turbulence which is why, by about 1934, the overhead valve layout began to be adopted for applications in which high performance was important.

To obtain large valve ports with a compact combustion chamber, what was termed the F-head, Fig. 12.6(d), was adopted by a few manufacturers. The Rover 80 and 100 models of the 1960s were probably the last to have engines with the F-head layout. This was at least a decade after high compression ratios and the overhead valve layout, having the virtue of better fuel economy, had become virtually universal for automotive engines.

12.13 Influence of number and sizes of valves

As is well known, inlet are bigger than exhaust valves, since the pressure of the gas escaping past the latter is so very much higher than that performing the all-important function of pushing the charge into the cylinder. Since we want to scavenge and then fill the cylinder completely with great rapidity, the overall aim is at incorporating valve ports, both inlet and exhaust, that are as large as practicable.

Until recently, two valves per cylinder have been the norm. Now however, with the constant search for ever higher efficiency, four valves are not uncommon, while the compromise of two inlet and one exhaust valve has been adopted by some manufacturers. Since both multiple valves and complex actuation mechanisms are costly, they are currently used only in engines for the upmarket ranges of cars.

Here we are concerned with only the effects on combustion, not the practical aspects such as actuation mechanisms. Two important considerations in the design of valves are ease of flow into the cylinder and the flow pattern created in the cylinder. Since swirl and turbulence have already been discussed in Sections 12.9 and 12.10, we are now concerned mainly with filling.

We shall now compare the two- and four-valve layouts, as shown diagrammatically in Fig. 12.8. To simplify the calculations and to concentrate on the basis of the comparison, let us assume that we do not have to accommodate valve seats. Let $4R$ be the diameter of the cylinder bore, then the maximum possible radius of the ports in the two-valve layout

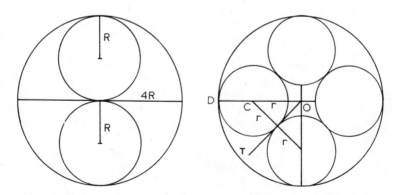

Fig. 12.8   Diagram illustrating relative areas of 2- and 4-valve porting

is R, and their total area is:

$$2 \times \pi R^2 = 6.283\,R^2$$

Now consider the four-valve layout. From the same illustration we can see that r is the radius of the valve ports which, since there are four of them, are smaller. We can express the smaller radius r in terms of the larger one R as follows:

$$OD = 2r + OX, \text{ or } 2r = OD - OX$$

Since OCT is a right angle triangle, $OC = \sqrt{2}r$

So
$$OD = 2R = \sqrt{2}r + r = r(1 + \sqrt{2})$$

Hence
$$r = 2R/(1 + \sqrt{2})$$

and the area of the four valve ports, $4 \times \pi r^2$, is:

$$4 \times \pi\{2R/(1+\sqrt{2})\}^2 \qquad = 4 \times \pi \times \{2R/2.1414\}^2$$

$$= 4 \times \pi \times 4R^2/5.83$$

$$= 8.622R^2$$

It follows that, by having four valves instead of two, the rate of volume flow into the cylinder is increased by a factor of approximately $8.622/6.283 = 1.4$. Another important benefit obtained, however, is that the sparking plug can be situated in the centre of the roof of the combustion chamber, so the distance the flame front has to travel laterally is equal in all directions. Some designers assert that the latter is the more significant benefit, because it enables a higher compression ratio to be used. At first sight, this looks to be unlikely but, if one takes into consideration the fact that four valve stems instead of two obstruct the flow into and out of the cylinder, they might possibly be right.

In some engines, the valve seats or, where inserts have been used, their housings have been machined to a size such that the outermost edges of the port apertures are exactly in line with the bores of the cylinders. This potentially attractive for crossflow cylinder heads where swirl about an axis parallel to the crankshaft is desired. On the other hand, the pockets formed by extending the combustion chambers outboard of the upper ends of bores might contribute to detonation. Furthermore, in the small pockets thus formed, local quenching of the burning gases could lead to contamination of the exhaust with hydrocarbon emissions. With the combustion chamber extended in this way, it might also be difficult to obtain an adequately high compression ratio.

12.14   Influence of valve timing

Valve timing has a profound influence on the volumetric efficiency and both the filling and the scavenging of the cylinder. Volumetric efficiency has been defined previously in this book as the actual volume of air drawn into the cylinder divided by the piston-swept volume. It varies with speed, rising to a peak, rarely much above 80%, at or near the point at which maximum torque is developed. For calculations of volumetric efficiency, the volume left between the piston crown and cylinder head, is not normally taken into account.

Because of gas inertia effects, volumetric efficiency cannot be optimised over the whole speed range, so emphasis is always placed on optimising it for what, for the vehicle into which it is to be installed, is considered to be the most useful part of that range. For a racing car, for example, this would be the higher speeds while, for a family saloon, it would be perhaps about 65 to 75% of maximum speed.

Optimisation is done by appropriate choice of valve timing. Generally, the inlet valve opens somewhere between about 10 and 15° before tdc, which is before the exhaust valve closes, while the exhaust valve closes between about 5 and 20° after tdc. As previously explained, this is to take advantage of the depression induced in the cylinder towards the end of the exhaust stroke by the inertia of the outgoing gases. The inlet valve then closes between approximately 40 and 60° after bdc, to take advantage of the inertia effect of the incoming charge.

During the inlet and exhaust valve overlap period around tdc, the direction of motion of the gas depends on the speed of rotation of the engine. At low speeds, when the throttle is closed and the pressure in the induction manifold low, exhaust gas flows back through the inlet valve into the induction port and even into the manifold, only to be reversed as the induction stroke gets properly under way. This reverse pulsation of the flow is virtually unavoidable at idling. At higher speeds and wider throttle openings, when the pressure in the manifold is higher, a different phenomenon tends to occur: some of the fresh charge flows out through the exhaust valve port and may be drawn back into the cylinder as the induction stroke gathers way. In modern engines, because of the regulations regarding exhaust emissions, it must ultimately all flow back into the cylinder.

In general, by opening the exhaust valve early, a good scavenge can be obtained, but potentially at the cost of a reduction in the extraction of useful work from the energy generated by combustion. Closing the inlet valve early, on the other hand, will bring the optimum efficiency of charging down into the lower speed range.

For calculations concerning combustion, we have to take into consideration the following masses of gases involved in the induction, compression and exhaust process:

M_{to} = the total charge drawn into cylinder, some of which may escape during the valve overlap period

M_{af} = the actual fresh charge remaining in the cylinder after the inlet valve is closed

M_{th} = the mass of charge that theoretically can be contained in the piston swept volume

M_r = gas remaining in the combustion chamber when piston is at tdc.

This leads us to another measure of the efficiency of the induction system. Clearly, we want to minimise the loss of unburned charge through the exhaust. Such a loss can be particularly significant in the two-stroke engine and, moreover, cannot be ignored in the four stroke engine. What has been termed the *gas exchange efficiency* $E=M_{to}/M_{th}$, therefore, is an important parameter.

STRATIFICATION

12.15   The stratified charge concept

In the decade or so following the world oil crisis of the early 1970s, a great deal of effort was directed towards the development of stratified charge engines, with the aims of improving fuel economy and reducing emissions of HC and CO. This is, however, by no means a new development. In his patent No. 532, covering the invention of the four-stroke cycle, Otto proposed the admission of only air at the beginning of the induction stroke, to form a layer next to the piston to cushion it from the explosion of the combustible mixture subsequently introduced. The earliest work directed specifically at stratifying the charge, was that of Sir Harry Ricardo, in 1915.

In very recent years, however, interest in stratified charge has waned because it seems unlikely that it can satisfy the very stringent emissions regulations expected to come into force in Europe in 1992, especially as regards NO_x. However, we cannot be sure that someone will not come up with a new development in the technique and thus save the cost of catalytic converters and their controls.

Ideally, a stratified charge engine is one in which the charge in the combustion chamber is a vortex comprising alternate layers of rich mixture and air, with a combustible mixture at the interface. The spark initiates combustion at the interface, along which the flame spreads. Heat generated locally generates turbulence and thus accelerates mixing so the flame quickly becomes thoroughly well established and then, because the overall mixture is very weak, consumes all the fuel present.

Efficiency can be augmented by increasing the compression ratio because, with excess air and rapid spread of combustion throughout the charge, peak combustion temperatures are not so high as with a stoichiometric air:fuel ratio, and therefore the tendency to detonation is reduced. Indeed, to burn such weak mixtures, high compression ratios may in any case be necessary. Regular combustion has been achieved on the test bed with air:fuel ratios as lean as 64:1. However, as has been previously indicated, for best fuel

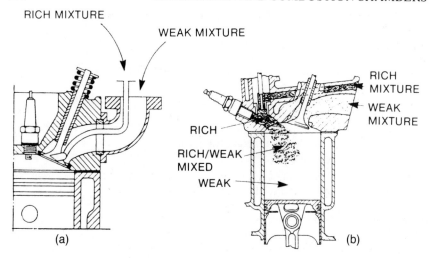

Fig. 12.9   (a) an early experimental stratified charge engine devised by the Société Français de Pétroles; (b) the CVCC engine, a production version based on a similar principle, and designed and manufactured by Honda

economy, lowest emissions and acceptable driveability, ratios of between about 20:1 and 25:1 are considered to be the optimum.

Details of a wide range of stratified charge engines have been given in "The Motor Vehicle" by Newton, Steeds and Garrett, Butterworths. We need concern ourselves now with a few examples of each of the single and dual chamber types, both of which can be designed for either injection or carburation. Where carburettors are employed, the induction systems are usually arranged for supplying a rich mixture through one duct and either a weak mixture or air through the other, Figs. 12.9(a) and (b).

With injection, the possibility arises of locally reducing the velocity of flow within the swirling incoming air, by injecting against the flow at a point ahead of the sparking plug points, so that the flame kernel is not blown out, or quenched, shortly after it is formed. Injection can be either early or late in the induction and compression stroke. Early injection allows plenty of time for mixing and evaporation, while late injection probably leads to more clearly defined stratification. Which is the best is the subject of some controversy.

12.16   Some single chamber systems

The single chamber type is, to a limited extent, analogous to the direct injection diesel engine: it generally has a bowl-in-piston combustion chamber, and the swirl is generated by aligning the induction port tangentially relative to the cylinder bore. Stratification is obtained by injecting the fuel into the swirling gas in a manner such that, instead of penetrating right through the cross section of the gas stream, it is carried round in the layer of air closest to the injector nozzle. Thus a spiral sandwich effect is obtained.

This type is potentially the most efficient. However, as can be easily envisaged, high efficiencies are very difficult to maintain over the whole range of loads and speeds. A successful version is the May Fireball chamber, invented in 1976, and further developed and utilised for the Jaguar V12 HE power unit introduced in 1981. For cruising at steady speeds, an air:fuel ratio of 23:1 is practicable, though enrichment is required for other operating conditions.

Basically, the valve seats are in recesses in the cylinder head, that for the exhaust being deeper than that for the inlet valve. A channel interconnects these recesses. As the piston comes up to tdc, some of the mixture is forced out of the recess under the inlet valve, through the interconnecting channel, which is directed tangentially into the recess beneath the exhaust valve, to generate the necessary swirl. With a rapid flow of gases through a throat, this might be regarded as a compromise between the dual and single chamber systems. However, the gas flowing through the throat is relatively cool because the sparking plug, and therefore point of initiation of ignition, is in the approach to the exhaust valve recess.

Single chamber systems are probably more suitable for industrial applications in which the engine is required to run almost exclusively at constant speed. The Mitsubishi industrial engine, Fig. 12.10, is a good example. Swirl is induced by a tangentially aligned induction port, and the combustion chamber is of the bowl-in-piston type.

MAN has developed experimentally one of its diesel and multi-fuel engines for stratified charge operation. The injector sprays the fuel on to the opposite wall of the bowl-in-piston combustion chamber, some bouncing

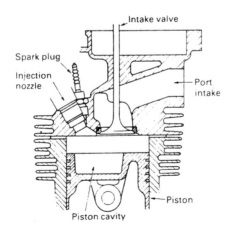

Fig. 12.10   The Mitsubishi industrial engine
A: Injector, B: Spark plug, C: Inlet port

back as an even finer spray and the remainder spreading out over the wall, to be evaporated off by the air swirling past and thus forming the stratified charge. Optimising both the swirl and the proportions of fuel bouncing back and spreading calls for a great deal of painstaking development.

12.17   The dual chamber principle

Dual chamber systems are analogous to the indirect injection diesel engine, in that they have swirl type pre-combustion chambers, usually in the cylinder head. They suffer the same disadvantage, which is the throttling of the gas as it enters and leaves, and the loss of heat by conduction to walls of the throat as the combustion products pass out into the main chamber. Consequently, its thermal efficiency is not potentially so high as that of the single chamber type. On the other hand, management of the swirl, turbulence and fuel-air mixing process is considerably easier.

The first dual chamber system to be put into production for a car was that of the Honda CVCC carburetted engine, Fig. 12.9(b). Later, a great deal of experimental work was done on the Austin Rover 1.85 litre engine, Fig. 12.11. Both engines had separate poppet valves in the tops of their pre-chambers, the latter being thimbles in pockets in their cylinder heads. Such valves can be timed so that the pre-chamber is scavenged before filling it with rich mixture. Another was the Porsche SKS engine which, because it was injected, did not need a separate inlet valve for introducing the rich mixture, Fig. 12.12.

Among the many variables that complicate development are shape and size of the throat of the combustion chamber and the positon of the sparking plug. The combustion chamber on the Honda engine, for example, has a short but large diameter throat. Combustion and consequent expansion of the rich mixture in the chamber forces the burning mixture out, spreading it

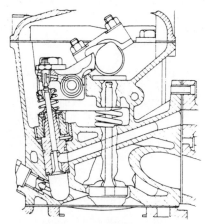

Fig. 12.11   A BMC experimental stratified charge engine

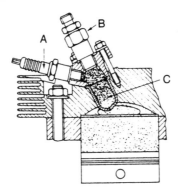

Fig. 12.12   The Porsche SKS stratified charge engine
A: Spark plug, B: Injector, C: Burning mixture

over an ever-broadening front throughout the weak mixture in the main chamber. In the Austin Rover engine, the throat is much longer and of smaller diameter, so the heat loss in it is greater. This quenches much of the flame, so a jet comprising the quenched products, which are mainly chemically active radicals together with some still burning gas, is projected at high velocity right over to the opposite wall of the cylinder. The subsequent scattering of ionised and burning gases leads to a rapid spread of combustion throughout the weak mixture. Cine photographs have shown that the flame does not re-kindle visibly, until the jet has been slowed down on the far side of the cylinder.

In a Daimler Benz stratified charge engine, the throat is also long, but has sharp edges at both ends, which generate macro-turbulence as the gas is forced past them at high velocity. The flame is partially quenched, so the cascade of small eddies of ionised, chemically active gases form a multitude of ignition centres in the weak mixture in the cylinder.

Sparking plug position affects the burning in the following manner. If it is at the end of the pre-combustion chamber remote from the throat, as in the Porsche SKS, the expansion of the burning gas at that end will force most of the rich mixture out in to the cylinder before it has ignited, so the heat loss in the throat will be relatively small. On the other hand, if it is at an intermediate point along the pre-chamber and directly opposite the throat, as in the Austin engine, a high proportion of the rich mixture will have been ignited before it is discharged into the cylinder, so the heat loss will be correspondingly greater. However, combustion overall will probably be more complete.

Chapter 13

Emissions and Their Control

Potentially toxic constituents of the exhaust gas have come to be widely known as exhaust emissions and, as is well known, legislation has been introduced in many countries imposing limits on what levels of such substances are acceptable in exhaust gases. The substances legislated against are: carbon monoxide, CO; unburned hydrocarbons, for which the abbreviation HC is used to denote all the hydrocarbons present; oxides of nitrogen, NO_x; and, principally for diesel engines, particles comprising mostly carbon. Subscript x is used because the exhaust contains two main oxides of nitrogen, NO and NO_2, of which the latter is the most significant as regards toxic and photochemical effects.

Of the HC, only about 30-40% is actually unburned: the remainder comprises products of partial combustion. In the UK, according to a Warren Spring Laboratory report, 85% of all CO in the atmosphere and 28% of HC comes from road transport vehicles, the actual figures being respectively 5624 and 2355 kilotonnes per year.

13.1   The greenhouse effect

Although CO_2 is not among the toxic substances, and moreover, its proportion in the exhaust gas cannot be reduced, there are pressures to improve fuel economy and thus reduce the total quantity produced or, from a few extremists, even to ban the use of internal combustion engines and coal burning power plants except perhaps for certain essential purposes. This is because suspicions have been aroused that it is at least partly responsible for the so called greenhouse effect.

The evidence is mainly the increasing mean ambient temperature throughout the world, which might conceivably be due to the relative transparency to ultraviolet rays of the carbon dioxide that is being released into it. This, is said to be allowing these rays to pass through the atmosphere to earth, where it is converted into heat.

In the early stages of the earth's development, the atmosphere was predominantly carbon dioxide, most of which the evolving plant life subsequently removed, and at the same time released oxygen, until a natural balance was obtained at a low level of carbon dioxide in the atmosphere. During the ensuing millennia, the plant life that originally performed this task became fossilised and, in evolutionary terms much more recently, we

304

have been using it as fuel. This of course entails converting its carbon content back into carbon dioxide, which is then released into the atmosphere.

On the other hand, whereas we have been consuming petroleum fuels for little more than a hundred years and coal at high rates for perhaps rather less than 150 years, we have for centuries also been clearing the forests, which are the principal consumers of carbon dioxide. It is by no means impossible therefore that the answer, if indeed the greenhouse effect is indeed attributable to CO_2, is to replant the trees. However, a great deal more research has to be completed before we can be sure of either precisely what is happening and why, or how to prevent it.

TOXICITY

13.2 The precise nature of the toxicity

The following are the characteristics of the exhaust emissions against which legislation has been introduced. Inhalation of air containing 0.3% by volume of CO, which is a colourless odourless gas, can cause death in half an hour. It is toxic because it is absorbed by the red corpuscles of the blood, inhibiting absorption of the oxygen necessary for sustaining life. Nitric oxide, NO, is also colourless and odourless and, in the presence of oxygen, is rapidly converted into NO_2. This is a reddish brown gas with a sharp odour, and it combines with water to form nitric acid HNO_3, and therefore can progressively destroy lung tissue. Unburned hydrocarbons can, in the presence of sunlight, form oxidants which irritate the mucous membranes and some are believed to be carcinogenic. The chemical processes are outlined in the last paragraph of Section 13.4.

When burned in engine cylinders, alcohol fuels and admixtures of alcohol and gasoline can produce small quantities of other toxic substances. These include principally benzene and 1.3 butadiene. The former is a carcinogen and is the simplest member, C_6H_6, of the aromatics.

Putting the emissions problem into overall perspective, however, one should point out that none of these so called toxic emissions has been shown to be seriously harmful to humans in the concentrations in which they exist in general in the atmosphere in for example the UK. On the other hand, they do at least contribute towards conditions of discomfort experienced in certain areas such as the valley in which Los Angeles is situated, where an inversion layer in the atmosphere traps the contaminants beneath it and brilliant sunlight accelerates certain chemical reactions. However, the automobile is not the only nor necessarily even the main culprit: huge quantities of the same pollutants are emitted also from other sources, such as furnaces for power generation, metal processing etc.

Of relevance is the British Transport and Road Research Laboratory's report RR206/1989, in which the following conclusions were recorded regarding research, with admittedly a limited number of subjects, into the relative proportions of the toxic compounds absorbed by smokers and non-smokers. Even the non-smokers received on average as much as half of their total carbon monoxide intake in their homes and only 25% of that absorbed was traffic related while, for smokers, the traffic related contribution was only 15%. Similarly, to the best of the author's knowledge, no independent research authority of the standing of, for example, the TRRL has come up with any proof that lead compounds in the quantities present in the atmosphere are actually harmful to health. The sort of evidence that is missing is, for instance, that the workers in a factory, or pupils in a school, sited by an exceptionally busy motorway junction have absorbed more lead, to the extent that they have been adversely affected by it, than those in similar establishments some miles away in open countryside. On the other hand, traffic density is rapidly increasing so perhaps governments have been wise to legislate as they have been doing since the middle of the 20th century.

13.3 Products of combustion

Ideally, the exhaust gas would contain only carbon dioxide and water. If, however, the combustion is incomplete, it includes a wide range of hydrocarbons, together with perhaps products of partial combustion, including the previously mentioned carbon monoxide. Present in minute quantities may also be aldehydes such as CHO; ketones, which are molecules containing carbonyl, CO attached to two hydrocarbon radicals; and carboxalic acids, which are COOH attached to a radical.

Thermally cracked products may occur in minute quantities too. These may include acetylene C_2H_2, ethylene C_2H_4 and hydrogen, carbon and polycyclic hydrocarbons, the last mentioned being hydrocarbons containing more than one ring in their molecules. Other products present in small quantities include: nitric oxide and nitrogen dioxide, NO and NO_2; with leaded fuels, lead oxides and lead halogenides; and, from impurities in the fuel, oxides of sulphur.

EMISSION CONTROL

13.4 Historical development of control measures

For a full understanding of the rationale of modern emission control legislation, an appreciation of the forces motivating it and its consequent development historically is essential. Equally necessary is a yardstick against which to measure the advances that have been and still are being made. Such a yardstick may be taken to be the emission levels commonly experienced with cars in 1960: in other words, before the Federal emission regulations came into effect.

Tests carried out by the US Federal Environmental Protection Agency on a range of 1960 American cars indicated that the average output, in g/mile, of undesirable emissions in the exhaust gases of vehicles without any form of emission control that were subjected to the current US Federal emission test procedure was as follows:

HC   10.6
CO   84.0
NO_x 4.1

Further contributions to the hydrocarbon pollution were made by fumes, generated mainly by piston ring blow-by, vented through the crankcase breather at a rate, on average, of 4.1 g/mile and evaporation from the fuel tank and carburettor float chamber vents, at 3.7 g/mile. Incidentally, with the more recent introduction of plastics fuel tanks, hydrocarbons have been found also to permeate in significant quantities through their walls. There are other emissions such as particulates, including lead compounds, but these are produced in quantities so small in gasoline engines as to be insignificant so far as public health is concerned, as also are sulphur dioxide, the ketones and carboxalic acids.

Some idea of what has been achieved can be gained from a comparison between the quantities of emissions quoted in the previous paragraph and those permitted for 1981 and beyond by the 1977 US Federal Clean Air Act Amendment, which are listed in Table 13.1. This comparison shows that HC and CO emissions from the crankcase vent alone have been totally eliminated, while oxides of nitrogen in the exhaust have been reduced by 76%, the overall reduction on the gasoline powered automobile in the USA having been 96%.

Table 13.1   Progressive amendments to the California emissions regulations

1975	HC, CO and NO_x respectively	1.5, 15.0 and 3.1g/mile
1977-9		1.5, 15.0 and 2.0
1980		0.41, 7.0 and 2.0
1981		0.41, 3.4 and 1.0

13.5   The first steps

It all began in Los Angeles where, as early as 1947, the city was declared an "Air Pollution Control District" and the Authorities there began seriously to study the smog and eye irritation problems that were being experienced there. Research published in 1952 by the Dutch-born scientist Dr Arie J. Haagen-Smit suggested that automobiles were the primary cause. The first studies of possible control measures were initiated in California in 1959, leading to local legislation on crankcase ventilation control, to be effective in 1961 and, under US Federal legislation, nationwide in 1963. The Californian legislation of 1959 had also set further emissions limitation standards to become effective for new cars in 1966 while, in the rest of the USA, the 1965 Federal Air Pollution Act set nationwide standards for 1968, ultimately leading to the amended standards for 1978-81 and beyond, which became law on 8 August 1977.

The toxicity of hydrocarbons and oxides of nitrogen is much more complex than has been indicated in Section 13.2. It arises mainly indirectly as a result of photochemical reactions between the two in sunlight, which leads on to the production of other chemicals. As regards the two main oxides of nitrogen, NO and NO_2, the latter is of greatest significance owing to photochemical effects on it in association with hydrocarbons. Incidentally, at high altitudes, where temperatures may be below $-17°C$, NO_2 becomes N_2O_4 and, in the presence of water, both break down into NO and HNO_3. Under the influence of solar radiation, NO_2 breaks down into NO+O, the highly reactive oxygen atom then combining with O_2 to make O_3, which of course is ozone. Normally, this would then rapidly re-combine with the NO and thus be converted back to NO_2, but the presence of hydrocarbons significantly inhibits this reaction and causes the concentration of ozone to increase. The ozone then goes on to combine with other substances to form chemicals which, in combination with moisture in an atmospheric haze, produce what has been described as an obnoxious smoky fog that came to be known as smog. In short, sunlight acting upon constituents of exhaust gas produces ozone, organic peroxides, and peroxy-acetyl-nitrates.

13.6 Early solutions to the problems

Positive crankcase ventilation, PCV, totally eliminated pollution originating from fumes emitted through the crankcase breather, and at what was even at that time a modest cost of $3 per vehicle. It entailed piping the fumes into the air intake, so that they were consumed in the engine. Limitation of exhaust emissions to meet the requirements for the 1968 model year was achieved primarily by weakening the air:fuel ratio to reduce HC emissions, retarding the spark timing to reduce NO_x, and preheating the air passing into the engine intake, to encourage complete evaporation and combustion and thus reduce HC and CO output. On some models, a pump was installed to inject air into the exhaust system to oxidise the HC and CO. These measures reduced the total emissions by about 39-41% in comparison with those of the 1960 cars. Two other developments in 1968 were the demonstration that a carbon canister system could be used for the storage and subsequent combustion of evaporative emissions of fuel, and that catalytic converters could help to control exhaust emissions, but only with unleaded fuel.

By 1968, emissions had been reduced to 6.3 and 5.1 g/mile respectively for HC and CO, but legislative controls on NO_x were not to come until 1973. In 1970, the US Congress adopted regulations requiring by 1975 a reduction of overall emissions of 90% on the figures for the 1970 models and, in November, established the Federal Environmental Protection Agency. The Agency introduced a new method of sampling, FTP 75, described in Chapter 14.

Previously, all the exhaust gas had been collected in one huge bag and then analysed. This had the disadvantage that it gave no indication of how the engine behaved under the different conditions of operation during the test; moreover, in certain circumstances, some of the gases interacted in the bag. Therefore, collection into three bags, one for each main stage of the test, was stipulated by the new regulations. The first stage, termed cold-transient, comprised cycles 1 to 5 of the test, which represented the beginning of a journey starting from cold. Next came 13 cycles, representing the remainder of the journey with the engine warm and including some operation at high temperature. After this, the engine was shut down for 10 minutes to represent a hot soak, before being started up again for a repetition of the first 5 cycles, termed the hot transient stage, and representing a journey started with a warm engine.

By applying weighting factors, to alter the relative effects of the three bag analyses on the totals, it is easy to adjust the test to represent different types of operation. Obviously HC emissions are high for the period following starting from cold, while NO_x emissions are of little significance except under hot running conditions at wide throttle openings. These two facts are important as regards the planning of anti-pollution measures at the design stage. Following the imposition of limits of 3.1 g/mile of NO_x emission, in 1973, the total emissions requirements were progressively amended as shown in Table 13.1.

The 1981 regulations were so tight that, to give time for further development work, some waivers had to be allowed: 4 years on NO_x for diesel engines and innovative technology, and up to 2 years on CO.

Conditions that encourage the generation of NO_x in the combustion chamber are principally high temperature of combustions at high pressures and the length of time during which they dwell at those high temperatures. To reduce gas temperatures, GM had introduced exhaust gas recirculation, EGR, in cars for California in 1972 and nationwide in 1973.

13.7   Lean burn or catalytic conversion?

At this point, some manufacturers, anxious to be able to continue to compete as the years went by and the limits further tightened, were investigating the lean burn concept. Others, coming to the conclusion that further compromises in engine operational parameters to meet the increasingly stringent legal requirements would lead to unacceptable increases in fuel consumption and have adverse effects on the durability of the engines, set catalytic conversion as their aim. The latter led to intensive lobbying, which continued for more than a decade, for legislation to outlaw leaded fuel. GM was in the lead: all their car engines scheduled to come into operation in 1971 were designed for running on 91 Research or 87 Motor Octane fuel. This entailed reducing compression ratios and modifying the valves and their seats.

The primary reason for the use of unleaded fuel is that the lead additives rapidly contaminate the catalytic converters and render them ineffective. However, it brings also several incidental benefits: first, lead oxy-halide salts, the major constituents of particulate emissions from gasoline are eliminated; secondly, there is a consequent reduction in combustion chamber deposits, which tend to quench the flame in the boundary layers of the combustion chambers and thus encourage the formation of HC. Thirdly, an additional reduction in HC emissions is obtained for two reasons: first, further oxidation occurs in the exhaust system more readily owing to the absence of lead additives; and, secondly, if lead salts are deposited on an EGR orifice, they tend to cause deterioration of the flow characteristics through it and thus lead to deterioration of the NO_x control system. Maintenance of spark plugs, exhaust systems, and the frequency of changing lubricating oil were all reduced by both the elimination of the lead salts as also, of course, was the generation of acids by the halide scavengers that have to be used with them. Finally, the use of catalytic converters neatly side-stepped the controversy, so far unresolved, over the alleged toxic effects of lead salts in the environment.

The emissions regulations for the 1975 model year represented reductions of 87% in HC, 82% in CO and 24% in NO_x by comparison with the 1960 levels. To meet these requirements while simultaneously improving both economy and driveability, which had deteriorated severely as a result of the earlier emission controls entailing modification of the engine parameters, the manufacturers in the USA concluded that two-way catalytic converters would be needed. A two-way converter contains only oxidation catalysts, to encourage the burning of the HC and CO in the exhaust to form CO_2 and H_2O. Successful operation, however, implies the presence of oxygen in the exhaust, so the air fuel mixture supplied to the engine must be at least stoichiometric or, better still, lean. Some manufacturers fed air into the exhaust system, primarily for burning the excess hydrocarbons during the first five cycles of the test after a cold start with engines equipped with carburettors. This system, increasing overall costs, is unnecessary with modern computer-controlled injected engines.

With a two-way catalyst, failure of a spark plug would have caused problems: air-fuel mixture would have entered the converter, where it would have burned and thus overheated the unit. Consequently, high energy ignition systems became a necessary adjunct for the 1975 models, and copper-cored spark plugs were subsequently fitted to obviate cold fouling. The overall result of all the measures taken on the GM models was a reduction in fuel consumption of 28% by comparison with that of their 1974 cars. By 1977, this figure had been further improved by 48% and, by 1982, owing to the stimulus of the Corporate Average Fuel Economy (CAFE) legislation, by 103%. Incidentally, under the CAFE legislation, the average fuel consumption of all cars marketed by each corporation in the USA had to improve in stages, from 18 mpg in 1978, by 1 mpg each year to 1980, then 2 mpg annually to 1983 and again by 1 mpg for 1984, and then by 0.5 mpg, to 27.5 mpg, for 1985.

At the time of writing, the latest moves on the ever tightening of emission controls is as follows. In 1989, a US Congress sub-committee unanimously passed a bill stipulating new restrictions beginning for the 1994 model year. Non-methane hydrocarbons emitted are to be limited to 0.25 g/mile for the first five years or 50,000 miles in the life of the vehicle. The NO_x limits are 0.4 g/mile and CO 3.4 g/mile for the first five and 4.2 g/mile for the next five years of the life of the vehicle. From 1994 onwards also, catalytic converters and their closed loop controls will have to remain effective for twice the current 50,000 miles. Some believe that this will so increase the cost of gasoline engines that diesel power will become more economical overall, despite the higher cost of its associated injection equipment and the larger cubic capacity needed for obtaining the same power output.

13.8 Two-way catalytic converters

Two-way catalytic converters comprise a container, usually of chromium stainless steel, the catalysts deposited on a support of some sort, all enclosed in a heat shield, usually of aluminised steel, Fig. 13.1. The catalyst carrier, or support, can be monolithic or in pellet form, Fig. 13.2, and both have been employed though, initially, the alumina pellet type was the most favoured because it had been developed to an advanced stage in other industries. Monolithic supports, Fig. 13.3 did not go into regular production until 1977.

The cost of the noble metal catalysts, Pt or Pa, is of the order of 15 to 20 times that of the stainless steel shell that contains them, so others such as copper and chromium were tried, with some success, but did not come into general use because they are prone to deterioration owing to attack by the sulphuric and other acids formed by combustion of impurities in the fuel. A typical two-way converter for an American car contains 1.6 g of noble metals in the ratio 5 of Pt to 2 of Pl.

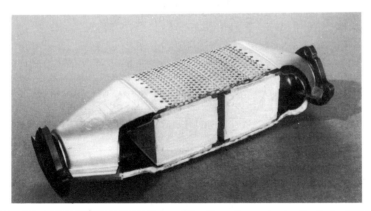

Fig. 13.1   A two-way catalytic converter in a welding jig on the production line in the GM Delco Products factory at Southampton

(a)

(b)

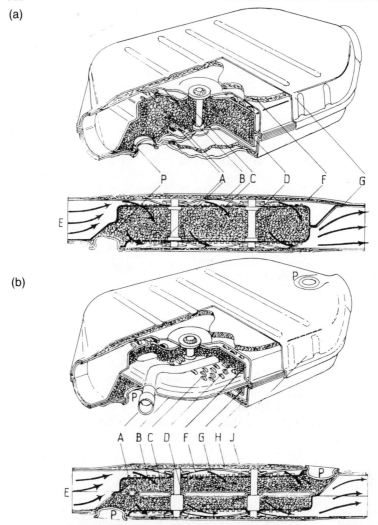

Fig. 13.2   Because of the need to both contain the pellets and deflect the gases uniformly through them, the structure of the pellet type converter (a) and (b) is more complex than that of the monolithic type (c). All three are of GM designs (a) A two-way converter (for oxidising CO and HC) of the pellet type. Its overall dimensions are: Length 429 mm, width 230 mm, Depth 89 mm
A: Louvres, B: Housing for catalytic core assembly, C: Pellet container, D: Refractory pellets coated with catalyst, E: Exhaust gas inflow, F: Insulation, G: Main housing, P: Filler plug for pellets

(b) A three-way (NO$_x$, CO and HC) converter of the pellet type. Its overall depth is the same as that of (a) but its length and width are respectively 475 and 315 mm
A: Air inlet for the second stage of conversion, B: Air plenum chamber, C: Louvres, D: Refractory pellets coated with the first stage (reducing) catalyst, E: Exhaust inflow, F: Housing for catalytic core assembly, G: Refractory pellets coated with the second stage (oxidising) catalyst, H: Insulation, J: Main housing, P: Filler plugs

(c)

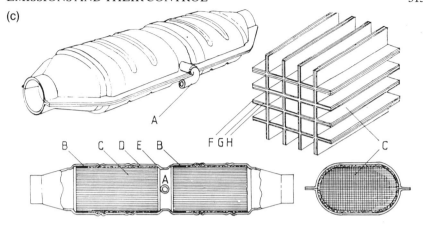

(c) A converter having a ceramic monolithic catalyst carrier with, to a larger scale, a section of the monolith. The overall length of the converter is 619 mm, width 173 mm and depth 89.9

A: Air inlet for the second stage (oxidising) conversion, B: Seals, C: The monolith, D: Metal mesh to accommodate thermal expansion of the monolith, E: Housing, F: Ceramic monolith the elements of which are 12.7 mm square × 1.5 mm wall thickness, G and H: Coating of slurry impregnated with the catalyst

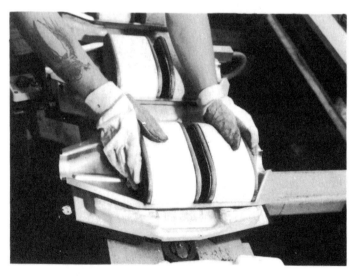

Fig. 13.3   Ceramic monoliths, complete with fibre mat surrounds and end seals, being assembled into the shell of a 2-way converter on the production line at the GM Delco Products factury. Two monoliths are easier to manufacture and both more effective and less difficult to accommodate than one

13.9   Three-way conversion

By 1978 GM Rochester Products Delco Division had developed a 3-way converter. This was needed by 1980 in California and 1981 in the rest of the USA to meet the stringent requirements for the control of NO_x. It involved the addition of another catalytic bed in which Rhodium, Rh, was deposited to reduce the oxides of nitrogen. The total noble metal content accordingly rose to about 3 g. Because the process calls for a reducing atmosphere, the mixture must not be lean. In practice, with a 0.1% rich mixture, about 95% of the NO_x can be removed by such a catalytic converter.

Because it requires a rich mixture, this stage of conversion has to precede the oxidation of the HC and CO. The oxygen released by the conversion of the NO_x is passed on to be used (in addition to that from an extra air supply) in the second stage of the converter. The Pt or Pt-Pl oxidation catalyst is carried either in a separate housing, or downstream of the Rh bed, in what is termed a dual-bed converter, any extra air needed for completing the oxidation being pumped either into the second stage catalyst or, in an integral or dual-bed converter, into a chamber incorporated between the first and second stages. A closed-loop control system has to be incorporated.

CATALYTIC CONVERTER CONSTRUCTION

13.10   Ceramic monoliths

Considerable development effort was devoted to monolithic catalyst supports, in the form of one-piece extruded ceramic honeycomb structures, usually magnesium-aluminium silicate, having large surface areas on to which the noble metal catalysts could be deposited. In practice, a porous wash-coat of aluminium oxide is applied to the honeycomb prior to the catalyst. This greatly increases the potential surface area. Monoliths are simpler than the pellet, or bead, type to assemble and service. Moreover, their gas flow paths are more precisely defined, and they have smaller mass, and therefore warm up more rapidly to their normal working temperature of about 550°C. However, to cater for thermal expansion and manufacturing tolerances, they have to be enshrouded in a fibrous mat, as in Figs. 13.2 and 3, which tends to increase the bulk of the converter.

Pellet systems, on the other hand, continued to be employed in the USA for some trucks, where compactness is not such an overriding requirement and because they can be more durable under adverse conditions. Their packaging is inherently more complex, as regards both design and assembly, particularly for the avoidance of deterioration as a result of vibration and thermal fatigue of the metal components. On the other hand, pellets are relatively insensitive to thermal stress, because they can move to relieve it. Moreover, the hottest part of such a bed is at its centre, whereas that of a ceramic monolith is about 25 mm from its leading edge, accentuating thermal stress problems.

13.11   Catalytic converter control

If rich mixtures were to be supplied to the engine, the oxidation stage would become overheated. Consequently, a closed-loop system has to be incorporated to regulate accurately the supply of fuel in relation to the mass air-flow into the engine. This calls for an oxygen sensor in the exhaust and an on-board microprocessor to exercise that control, both to correct continuously for divergencies from the stoichiometric ratio and to ensure good driveability. Such systems were first marketed in California in 1978, were widely used in the 1979 and 1980 models for nationwide sale, and became universal in all the 1981 GM models.

In practice, the electronic control system has to be more complex than might be assumed from the preceding paragraph. When the engine is being cranked for starting, it has to switch automatically from a closed to an open loop system, to provide a rich mixture. In this condition, the air supply for the second converter bed is diverted into either the exhaust ports or a point in the exhaust manifold close to them, to oxidise the inevitable HC and CO content, without overloading the second stage converter. Under these running conditions, combustion temperatures in the cylinders are low and therefore NO_x production is minimal or even zero.

Then, throughout warm-up, the mixture strength has to be progressively weakened to stoichiometric. Subsequently, to cater for heavy load conditions such as acceleration up hill, the mixture again has to be enriched and, perhaps, exhaust gas recirculation introduced to inhibit the formation of NO_x. The alternative of lowering compression ratio, to reduce the output of NO_x, would of course impair fuel economy. Among the other duties of the on-board microprocessor, are control over idle speed, spark timing, exhaust gas recirculation, purge of hydrocarbons from carbon canister vapour traps, air intake heating to assist evaporation of the fuel, torque converter lock-up, and an in-service fault-diagnosis system.

13.12   Metallic monoliths for catalytic converters

At the time of writing, a proposed EEC standard 1989/458 requires its member countries to bring their regulations into line with those in the USA by 1992. Consequently it appears that, by the end of 1991, all new models over 2 litres swept volume and, by the end of 1992, all new models of all sizes will have to be equipped with two-way catalytic converters. Anticipation of this change has stimulated the application in Europe of considerable effort to the development of monoliths for carrying the catalysts.

In designing matrices as the base on which the catalysts, such as platinum, palladium and rhodium, are to be deposited, the principal aims of compactness, minimum back-pressure in the exhaust system, rapid warm-up to the minimum effective operating temperature which, for this type of monolith, is about 250°C. Another important aim is of course durability at both very high and rapidly changing temperatures. Ceramics do not satisfy all these requirements, hence a search was instituted for ways of producing acceptable metallic matrices.

Previously, the obstacles to progress had been twofold. First came the difficulty of obtaining adequate corrosion resistance with the very thin sections needed for both compactness and acceptably low back-pressure. Secondly, there was the question of how to join these very thin sections while retaining the robustness necessary to withstand the severe thermal loading and fatigue.

By 1989, these problems had been solved by Emitec, a joint GKN-Unicardan subsidiary in Germany. They had developed a special stainless steel alloy, called Emicat, which they used in foil strips only 0.04 mm thick to construct the catalyst carriers in monolithic form. These were employed to make up matrices comprising alternate plain and corrugated strips, wound in an S-form, as shown in Fig. 13.4. They are inserted into steel casings and the whole assembly joined by a patented process, which might be described as high temperature brazing. Spirally wound cylindrical units were tried, but the S-form windings proved to be the more durable.

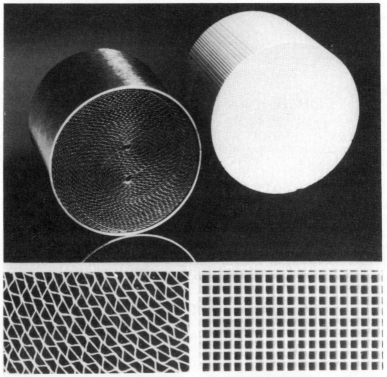

Fig. 13.4   Ceramic and metallic monoliths compared. By winding the alternate plain and cor-rugated metal foils of the Emicat monolith in S-form, the thermally induced stresses are greatly reduced, as compared with those in spirally wound monoliths

Emicat is an Fe, 20% Cr, 5% Al, 0.05 Y alloy. Ytrium, chemical symbol Y and melting point 1250°C, is a metal but with a strong chemical resemblance to rare earths, with which it therefore is usually classified. Its oxide, Y_2O_3, forms on the surface of the foil and protects the substrate from further oxidation. At a content of 0.05%, Ytrium is very effective in enabling the alloy to withstand both the temperatures of up to the 1100°C over long periods and the even higher peaks that can be attained in catalytic converters. Even better protection, however, can be had by increasing it up to 0.3%, though at a higher cost.

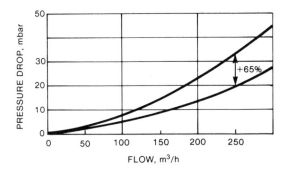

Fig. 13.5 Comparison of back-pressures of metallic (bottom) and ceramic monoliths (top) of identical overall diameters and lengths

The advantages obtained with these metal monoliths include: rapid warm-up and resistance to both thermal shock and rapid cyclical temperature changes up to well over 1300°C (both due to the good thermal conductivity of the material and low heat capacity of the assembly); minimal back-pressure, by virtue of the thin sections of the catalyst carrier foil, Fig. 13.5; compactness due to the absence of the mat needed around a ceramic monolith (to cater for its thermal expansion); large area of the catalyst exposed to the gases flowing through (owing to the large surface:volume ratio of the foil); and avoidance of local overheating, by virtue of both the

Table 13.2   Metal and ceramic monolith materials compared

Property	Metal	Ceramic
Wall thickness, mm	0.04	0.2-0.15
Cell density, cells/in^2	400	400
Clear cross section, %	91.6	67.1
Specific surface area, m^2/l	3.2	2.4
Thermal conductivity, W/mK	14-22	1-1.08
Heat capacity, kJ/kg K	0.5	1.05
Density, g/cm^3	7.4	2.2-2.7
Thermal expansion $\Delta L/L\ 10^{-6}$K	15	1

Note — thicknesses and cross sections are of metals uncoated with catalyst.

good thermal conductivity of the metal as compared with that of ceramic and the compactness of the unit; and, finally, because the complete unit is directly welded into the exhaust system, the costs of assembling ceramic monoliths and their wire mesh or fibre mat elastic supports into their cans are avoided. The properties of the two types of converter are set out in Table 13.2.

13.13 Practical considerations

Because the surface area available for exposing the catalyst to the exhaust gases is larger than that of an equivalent ceramic monolith, the metallic one can be shorter and of smaller diameter. Even so, in the case of at least one large engine of high specific power output, it was found convenient to wind the carrier substrate in two preferred widths of 74.5 and 120 mm, and assemble them into the housing with a gap between them. This decision was taken because the alternative of an overall length of 194 mm would have been difficult to coat satisfactorily. Furthermore, the gap between the two lengths encourages a thorough mixing of the exhaust gas, and the laminar flow in the second section was better than it would have been over the corresponding length in a one-piece monolith, so efficiency of conversion is improved.

For optimum efficiency of flow and therefore minimum back pressure, the inlet and outlet diffusers between the ends of the matrix sub-assembly and its inlet and outlet pipes should be tapered at an included angle of no more than 7°. Even better results are obtained if these parts are bell-mouthed, Fig. 13.6, rather than having straight tapers. With a 127 mm diameter matrix, for instance, bell-mouthed diffusers 180 mm long can be used.

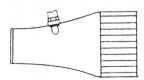

Fig. 13.6   Optimum efficiency is obtained by bell-mouthing the inlet and outlet of the converter

The centres of the two rolls in the S-shape are of course offset from the centre of the cylindrical housing shell, the ends of the foil strips being brazed to the inner face of that shell. Thermal expansion is accommodated by spiral deformation of the individual foils, so the resultant loading throughout the matrix is light. In contrast, a single spiral matrix packed into a cylindrical housing has only extremely limited freedom to deflect, so very the stresses in it due to thermally induced mechanical loading are much higher, Fig. 13.7.

The housing is a cylindrical mantle surrounded by a 0.5 mm thick metal shell, the gap between them being 2.5 mm. This provides a useful degree of insulation, which offers several benefits. First, the internal temperature is

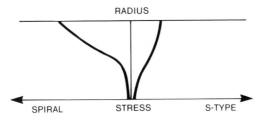

Fig. 13.7   Relative thermal stresses in spiral and s-type metallic monoliths (stress represented along horizontal, radius along vertical axis)

kept high, which increases the efficiency of conversion if the engine is started while still hot. Secondly, the inner shell is well protected from corrosion, since the cooler outer one screens it from water splashed up from the road. Thirdly, the rate of thermal radiation and conduction to adjacent components is low.

CONVERTER CONTROL VALVES

13.14   Air management valves

As was mentioned in Sections 13.6 and 13.8, air may have to be pumped into the exhaust manifold or between the two beds of a 3-way catalytic converter, to burn off CO or hydrocarbons remaining among the combustion products after the exhaust valves have opened. However, the flow of air has to be carefully controlled to prevent explosions in the exhaust system or overheating of the catalyst in the event of an excessively rich mixture's being supplied to the engine. Such over-enrichment is liable to occur when the throttle is closed suddenly.

Air management valves may therefore be used to shut off alternately, as necessary, the supply of air to the exhaust for what is termed *air injection reaction* or (*AIR*) and to the catalyst system, perhaps diverting it to either the induction air cleaner or to atmosphere. These valves may be either manifold depression actuated or electronically controlled. A very simple valve for AIR control is illustrated in Fig. 13.8. In the more complex depression actuated valves, the duration of diversion may be determined by a timing valve in the lower end of the air metering valve stem, as can be seen in Fig. 13.9, which illustrates the Delco Standardised Diverter Valve (SDV). Over a period of a few seconds, this timing valve bleeds away to atmosphere the depression above the diaphragm. The high pressure ducting does not perform any useful function in this valve but is incorporated in the interests of rationalisation, so that the valve body can be utilised also for other valves, to be described later.

One of the several variants of this type of valve is what Delco terms the Low Vacuum Air Control (LAC) valve. It combines the function of preventing explosions in the exhaust system during sudden deceleration, as

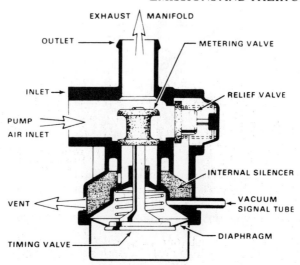

Fig. 13.8   Under normal operating conditions, left, this Rochester AC Delco AIR diverter valve is held open by the diaphragm return spring. On sudden closure of the throttle, right, high manifold depression lifts the diaphragm and opens the valve, to divert the air through the internal silencer to atmosphere

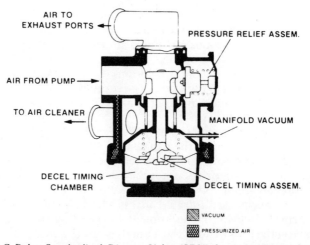

Fig. 13.9   AC Delco Standardised Diverter Valve (SDV) for preventing explosions in air-injected exhaust systems when the throttle is suddenly closed

in Fig. 13.10, with preventing the overheating of the 2-way catalytic converter. As can be seen from the illustration, when the throttle is closed suddenly, the depression in the manifold is high enough to pull down the lower diaphragm, and thus to close the valve that would otherwise let air under pressure into the decel timing chamber and unnecessarily add to the force holding the upper diaphragm in its uppermost position.

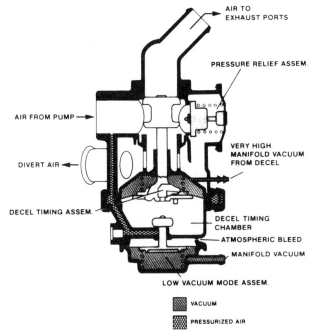

*Fig. 13.10   The Low Vacuum Air Control (LAC) valve prevents both explosions in the exhaust
and overheating of the catalytic converter*

Under heavy load with near wide open throttle, on the other hand, the
depression in the manifold is insufficient to prevent the spring from lifting
the lower diaphragm. Consequently, the valve that releases air at pump
delivery pressure to the decel chamber below the upper diaphragm, will be
open. This time, therefore, it is the pressure that lifts the metering valve, to
divert the air to the air intake air cleaner, to prevent overheating of the
catalytic converter when the mixture is enriched for maximum power
output.

Under normal driving conditions, the depression in the manifold is strong
enough to pull the lower diaphragm down and thus shut off the air supply to
the chamber beneath the upper one, but not high enough to pull the upper
diaphragm up against the influence of its spring. Consequently, the metering
valve is held down on its lower seat, so that air is delivered to the exhaust
ports or manifold.

A so called High Vacuum Air Control (HAC) valve simply combines the
function of preventing explosions in the exhaust system during sudden
deceleration, Fig. 13.11, with diverting air to the air cleaner during normal
road load operating conditions. Its high vacuum sub-assembly is mounted
beneath its base. The aim is at good fuel economy owing to the resultant
reduction in exhaust back-pressure and reduced power consumption for
driving the pump.

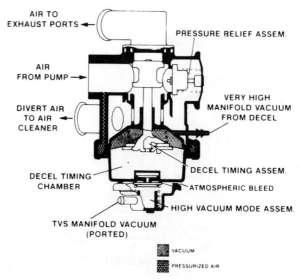

Fig. 13.11   This High Vacuum Air Control (HAC) valve diverts to the air cleaner during normal operation, to avoid high back pressure in the exhaust

During normal road load operation, the high vacuum diaphragm is pulled down, against the influence of its return spring, opening the bleed hole between the deceleration timing chamber and atmosphere. This prevents the pressure above and below the upper diaphragm from being equalised through the decel timing bleed hole in the stem of the metering valve. The upper diaphragm therefore remains in its uppermost position, holding the air management valve open to divert the output from the pump to the air cleaner.

Under heavy load, the increase in pressure in the induction manifold releases the high vacuum diaphragm, allowing it to be pushed upwards by its return spring, to close the bleed hole and thus prevent it from admitting atmospheric pressure to the decel timing chamber. Consequently, the pressures equalise above and below the upper diaphragm, which is pushed down by its return spring, to hold the valve open and thus direct the air to the exhaust ports.

For electric actuation under the control of an on-board computer or engine management system, Fig. 13.12, the arrangements are similar to those just described, but an Electrically Actuated Control (EAC) valve, instead of a low or high vacuum sub-assembly, is installed in the base of the unit. In this valve, a solenoid opens or closes a port through which the delivery pressure of the pump is directed into, or cut off from, the deceleration timing chamber.

Another form of diverter valve is termed the Air Intake Control (AIC) valve, Fig. 13.13. During deceleration, it diverts some air into the induction manifold, instead of to the air cleaner or atmosphere. For normal operation

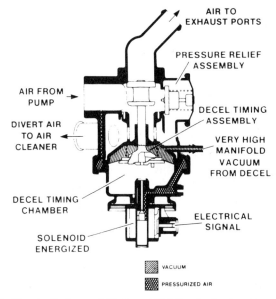

Fig. 13.12   The Electrically Actuated Air Contol (EAC) valve is solenoid-actuated by the engine management system

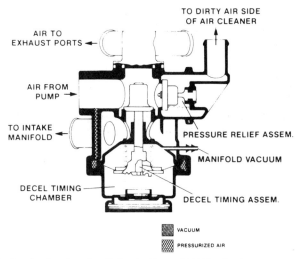

Fig. 13.13   During deceleration, the Air Intake Control (AIC) valve diverts some of the air to the induction manifold, to reduce HC and CO output

of the engine, the metering valve is held down, in the open position, by its return spring. This allows air from the pump to flow through the metering passage to the exhaust ports. With sudden closure of the throttle valve, the low pressure in the manifold is transmitted to the chamber above the diaphragm, pulling it up and thus lifting the metering valve off its lower seat. During this temporary phase, some of the air is directed into the induction manifold, weakening the mixture and consequently reducing the output of HC and CO. At higher speeds, air in excess of what is needed for afterburning in the exhaust manifold is exhausted through the pressure relief valve to the dirty side of the air cleaner.

13.15 Two-valve and integral-valve systems

For exercising both open and closed loop control over a dual bed converter, two of the Delco valves may be installed either independently or as an integrated valve unit. The first in the circuit is the diverter valve, as previously described, while the second performs the air switching function, as in Fig. 13.14. With this particular arrangement, during open loop control for operation when the engine is cold, air is directed into the exhaust ports by the air switching valve. Then, when the engine has become warm and the electronic module calls for closed loop control, air is directed by the air switching valve into the space between the two catalyst beds.

In one electronically controlled two-valve system for open and closed loop operation, the first valve is the normal EAC valve, Fig. 13.12, operating as described before except in that it diverts the air to the second valve instead of the exhaust ports. The second, serving as an AIR switching valve, is the Low Vacuum Air control valve (LACN), Fig. 13.15, the supply of manifold depression to which is controlled by a solenoid in its supply line. When the solenoid is energised, for open loop control, manifold depression is communicated to the lower chamber. This closes the low vacuum valve and thus shuts off the supply of air from the pump to the decel timing chamber, allowing the pressure on both sides of the diaphragm to equalise so that the spring pulls the metering valve down on to its lower seat. Air is therefore supplied to the exhaust ports, helping to bring the converter quickly up to its operating temperature.

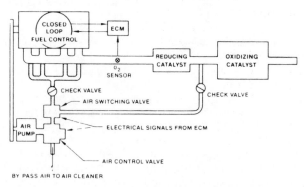

Fig. 13.14   A two-valve AIR system for an electrically controlled dual-bed converter

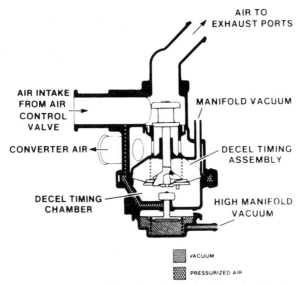

Fig. 13.15   The Low Vacuum Air Control (LACN) valve, shown here in what Delco term its low vacuum mode, serves as a switching valve

For closed loop operation, the solenoid is de-energised and the return spring therefore lifts the lower diaphragm to open the valve that releases air from the pump into the decel timing chamber, thus pushing the metering valve up and closing on to its upper seat. This switches the flow of air to the space between the converter beds to assist oxidation of HC and CO.

An alternative is to mount in series first the low vacuum air control valve (LAC) and, second, an electric air control valve (EACN). Again, the first valve, Fig. 13.10, diverts air to the second, instead of to the exhaust ports. For open loop operation, the solenoid is energised to shut off the flow of air to the decel timing chamber. The depression on both sides of the diaphragm is therefore equalised, through the decel timing assembly, and the spring holds the metering valve open so that air flows to the exhaust ports. During closed loop operation, the solenoid is de-energised, so some of the air from the pump is directed, through a filter, into the decel timing chamber. This lifts the upper diaphragm, causing the metering valve to switch the main air flow to the space between the catalyst beds, Fig. 13.16.

Another option is to use two Low Vacuum Air Control valves (LAC and LACN) Figs. 13.10 and 15). Again the first is used to direct air to the second, which is used as an air switching valve. For open loop operation, manifold depression is communicated to the second valve by energising a solenoid in the supply line. This pulls the lower diaphragm down and shuts off the supply of air to the decel timing chamber so that the pressure on both sides of the upper diaphragm can equalise through the decel timing assembly and the return spring therefore hold the metering valve down, to supply air to the exhaust ports. During closed loop operation, the solenoid is de-energised,

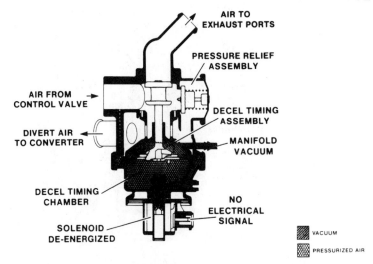

AIR TO
EXHAUST PORTS

PRESSURE RELIEF
ASSEMBLY

AIR FROM
CONTROL VALVE

DECEL TIMING
ASSEMBLY

DIVERT AIR
TO CONVERTER

MANIFOLD
VACUUM

DECEL TIMING
CHAMBER

NO
ELECTRICAL
SIGNAL

SOLENOID
DE-ENERGIZED

VACUUM

PRESSURIZED AIR

Fig. 13.16   The Electric Air Control (EACN) valve in the closed loop condition

so the spring pushes up the low depression diaphragm and valve. Consequently, the decel timing chamber is subjected to the pressure of the air delivery from the pump, which lifts the upper diaphragm and metering valve assembly. Thus the metering valve is closed on to its upper seat, switching the air flow to between the converter beds.

It is also possible to utilise electrically controlled valves (EAC and EAS) for both the air control and air switching functions. The first is like that in Fig. 13.12, but of course diverting air to the second, Fig. 13.17. For open loop operation, the solenoid in the base of the second valve is energised to close the atmospheric bleed on the right, and simultaneously open the valve on the left so that manifold depression is communicated to the chamber below the diaphragm. Thus the metering valve is pulled down to direct air to the exhaust ports. When the solenoid is de-energised, for closed loop operation, the atmospheric bleed is opened and the manifold depression valve on the left closed so that the diaphragm is released and the metering valve lifted by its return spring on to its upper seat, to switch the air flow to the space between the catalyst beds.

Illustrated in Fig. 13.18 is a single assembly combining an EAC and EAS valve, termed the ECES valve. It is provided so that the electronic control can be utilised to divert air under any mode of driving. The lower part is the Electric Air Control, or diverter, valve and the upper part the solenoid-actuated Electric Air Switching valve. When the lower solenoid is energised, all the air is directed to the upper part, except in the event of a sudden deceleration and therefore increase in manifold depression. If is is de-energised, pump delivery air pressure is communicated to the decel timing chamber, to lift the metering valve, regardless of manifold depression, and thus to divert delivery to the intake air cleaner. At high

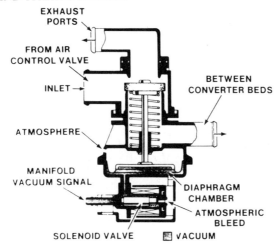

Fig. 13.17   The Electric Air Switching (EAS) valve in the open loop control condition

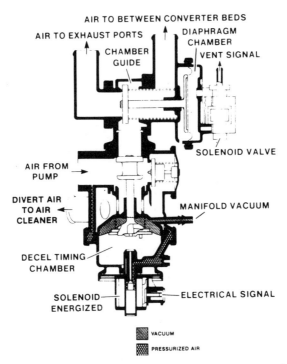

Fig. 13.18   An integrated Electric Air Control (EAC) valve and Electric Air Switching (EAS) valve, termed by AC Delco the ECES valve

engine speeds, air delivery exceeds requirements, so the excess is exhausted through the pressure relief valve to the intake air cleaner.

The upper part of the assembly is a spring-biased two-way valve. For open loop operation when the engine is cold, the upper solenoid is energised, applying manifold depression to the diaphragm chamber, to move the valve to the right, against its bias spring, to direct air to the exhaust ports. When the electronic control calls for closed loop operation, the solenoid is de-energised, to vent the diaphragm chamber to atmosphere so that the bias spring can switch the air supply to the space between the catalyst beds.

A unit comprising an Electric Divert (EDES) and Electric Air Switching (EAS) valve combination, Fig. 13.19, can be used for both converter protection and performing the functions described in the previous two paragraphs. The EDES, or air control section, is in the lower part of the assembly. If the converter becomes too hot, the electronic control signals that air delivery is to be diverted from the EAS to the air cleaner. To perform this function, the lower solenoid is energised to cut manifold depression off from the diaphragm chamber so that the return spring can lift the diaphragm and thus close the metering valve on to its upper seat. At wide open throttle, solenoid operation is however unnecessary, because there is not in any case enough depression to pull the diaphragm down. Again, at high speeds, air is exhausted to the intake air cleaner through the pressure relief valve.

In the second, or air switching, section in the upper part of the assembly,

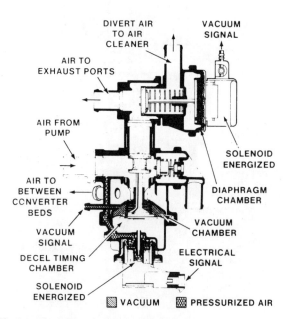

Fig. 13.19   The integrated Electric Divert (EDES) and Electric Air Switching (EAS) valve protects the converter as well as performing the functions of the ECES valve

air is diverted to the exhaust ports for the open, and to the space between the two catalyst beds for the closed loop modes of operation. This section is a spring-biased two-way valve. For cold, open loop, operation its solenoid is energised, introducing depression to the diaphragm chamber and thus pulling the valve to the right, as viewed in the illustration. This switches air to the exhaust ports. If the electronic control calls for closed loop operation, the solenoid is de-energised, venting the diaphragm to atmosphere and allowing the spring to move the valve to the left. This switches the air to the space between the catalyst beds.

There is also an RDES valve. This is identical to the EDES unit previously described except in that the air control solenoid is remotely mounted, in the manifold depression line to the lower section.

Yet another combined air management unit, Fig. 13.20, is the electric air control and electric air switching valve (CSTSE). Its upper portion delivers air to the space between the catalyst beds during both the closed loop and decel modes. The lower, or air control, portion directs air to the exhaust ports for open loop operation and, to protect the catalytic converter, diverts air to the intake air cleaner during both wide open throttle conditions and if the electronic control signals that the converter temperature is too high.

For open loop operation, the solenoid in the lower part is energised to prevent the air pressure from being communicated to the decel timing chamber, so that the spring can push the diaphragm and valve down to direct air to the upper part. During sudden deceleration, however, the manifold

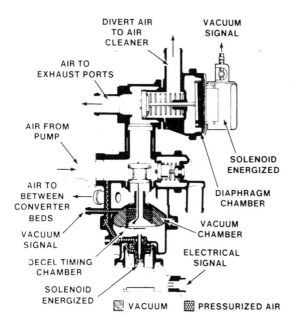

Fig. 13.20   An Electric Air Control (EAC) and Electric Air Switching (EAS) valve, termed the CSTSE valve, in its high manifold vacuum divert condition

depression is strong enough to pull them up, momentarily diverting air to the converter. For closed loop operation, the solenoid is de-energised, allowing air under pump delivery pressure to enter the decel chamber and push the diaphragm and its valve upwards, regardless of manifold depression. This diverts the air to the space between the catalyst beds.

This upper part is a spring-biased two-way valve. During open loop operation its solenoid is energised to introduce manifold depression to the upper diaphragm which pulls the valve to the right and switches air to the exhaust ports. At wide open throttle, the manifold depression acting on the upper diaphragm is so weak that the spring takes over, pushing the valve on to its seat on the left. This switches air to the intake air cleaner. Air can also be switched to the air cleaner under other conditions of operation, by programming the electronic control to de-energise the upper solenoid.

OPERATIONAL AND OTHER CONSIDERATIONS

13.16 Mixture control and driveability

As can be seen from Fig. 13.21, maximum torque and power are generally obtained at a lambda of about 0.9. Unfortunately, however, since the temperature of combustion is highest under these conditions, so also is the output of NO_x. Fuel consumption, HC and CO emissions are all at a minimum at lambda = 1.1, owing to the presence of excess air during combustion. For idling, mixtures of between 0.9 and 1.05 are needed, dependent upon engine temperature: the leaner the mixture, the more likely is misfiring to occur, which of course leads to a marked increase in HC emission.

During overrun with carburettor equipped engines, a rich mixture, even in excess of lambda = 0.9, is needed together with an extra supply of air to the manifold to avoid too great a depression in it. Otherwise misfiring is

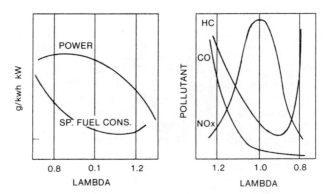

Fig. 13.21   Variation of power, specific fuel consumption and CO, NO_x and HC emissions with lambda at part load and in the middle speed range

liable to occur because the mixture through which the spark is passed may not always be of ignitable quality. A better system is to cut the fuel off completely, but then close control must be exercised to obtain a progressive return to the power-on condition. This is generally more practicable with electronically controlled injection than carburation.

13.17   Heating the incoming air

In cold ambient conditions, evaporation and therefore mixing of the fuel in the induction system is impaired, so emissions of HC in the exhaust inevitably increase. This can be overcome by heating the incoming air. A very simple heating arrangement was devised for the Austin and Rover cars. It was a thermostatically controlled flap valve interposed between two fairly large ports facing inwards towards each other. One was a cold air intake port and the other was ducted to a shroud over the exhaust manifold, the two being relatively close together. As the temperature of the incoming air changed, the flap was swung by a bimetal strip progressively away from one port and towards the other, so that two streams of air, one hot, and the other cold entered and mixed in the appropriate proportions in the intake,

This was adequate for satisfying the emissions regulations at the time. Ideally, however, something more accurate became necessary. A disadvantage of a bimetal strip is that it can sense either only ambient temperature of that of only one part of the air stream, and the flap valve tends to deflect hot air to one side and cold air to the other side of the air intake. The information most needed is the temperature of the air after it has been thoroughly mixed in the induction tract, so that the electronic control can continuously divert the appropriate proportion of hot air into the system. Better control can be accomplished by controlling the mixing valve with the electronic engine management system.

13.18   Engine design factors

A degree of pollution control can be exercised simply by avoiding design features that encourage the formation of the pollutants. As has been mentioned in earlier chapters, distribution of the mixture equally to each cylinder avoids the need to enrich it for the avoidance of detonation in one or two of them. In the combustion chamber, anything that causes stagnation of flow and quenching of flame is to be avoided. For example, top lands of pistons are made as narrow as practicable. In this instance, however, a limit is set by the need for overheating to be avoided, so that it will have adequate strength to support the loads applied to it by the top ring.

For several reasons, a significant degree of quenching occurs in the space between the top land of the piston ring belt and the bore of the cylinder. First, it is not easy for the flame to penetrate into such a small gap. Secondly, when it does, it is moving rapidly over the cooling area of the bore, so there is a greater tendency for it to be quenched. Thirdly, the gas in that space is so turbulent that quenching is even further encouraged; moreover, there is inevitably some blow-by which, although in absolute terms is extremely small, represents nevertheless a significant proportion of the volume of that space. This blowby, by allowing burned gases to enter the clearance space, both contaminates the mixture and increases the velocity of flow, and therefore the quenching effect.

Increasing the compression ratio, up to a limit of 10.5:1, or at the most 11:1, improves fuel economy, without necessarily introducing other problems unconnected with emission control. However, it also tends to increase peak combustion temperature to above the critical level of about 2500°C, at which NO_x is generated. Incidentally, NO_x formation is a function also of the duration of dwell of the gases at the high temperature, so its production will also be reduced by increasing the rate of combustion, or retarding the spark so that more of the burning takes place as the piston is moving down on the power stroke. The latter, however, increases exhaust valve temperatures, reduces torque, lowers thermal efficiency and therefore increases specific fuel consumption.

13.19 Exhaust gas recirculation (EGR)

Generation of NO_x occurs mainly under two conditions. The first is when the engine is hot and operating at or near maximum torque, especially at slow speeds and, secondly, when the mixture is weak: in the latter condition, peak temperatures tend to be higher than with rich or stoichiometric mixtures.

To reduce exhaust contamination with NO_x, the peak temperatures can be lowered by recirculating a proportion of the exhaust gas back into the cylinders to dilute the incoming fresh charge. The simplest, though crudest, method is by adjusting the valve overlap until the required degree of reverse flow into the cylinder takes place before the exhaust valve closes. More effective, however, is an external system for both controlling and accurately metering the interchange in relation to operating conditions.

A diagrammatic illustration of an external exhaust gas recirculation system suitable for use with the Bosch gasoline injection systems is shown in Fig. 11.60. With such a system, the degree of recirculation would be limited, by either a mechanical, pneumatic or an electronic control, preferably to between about 10 and 15% and, at the same time, the ignition timing would be optimised. Significantly higher rates of EGR entail a fuel consumption penalty.

At full load, EGR would inhibit the development of maximum power, but is unnecessary because the associated rich mixture greatly reduces the quantities of NO_x produced. Virtually no NO_x is produced during idling. In both these conditions, therefore, EGR can be, and normally is, switched off.

Emissions of NO_x can be reduced by about 60% by increasing the EGR to higher rates but, as can be seen from Fig. 13.22, HC emissions increase too.

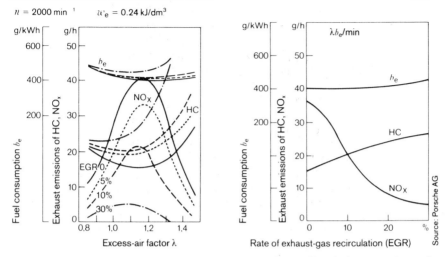

Fig. 13.22   *Curves obtained by Porsche showing how rate of EGR affects fuel consumption, and emissions of HC and NO$_x$*

Moreover, increasing EGR causes rough running and poor driveability. All these effects can be partially offset by precise control over EGR, in relation to throttle position and induction manifold pressure, by the engine management computer. A difficulty that has to be overcome is that deposits from the exhaust gas on the control valves and in the ducts and pipelines tend progressively to impair the accuracy of metering.

For gasoline engine applications, two types of EGR valve are made by the Delco division of GM-Rochester Products. One, is the port-actuated type, Fig. 13.23. This contains a diaphragm, acting on the upper face of which, in

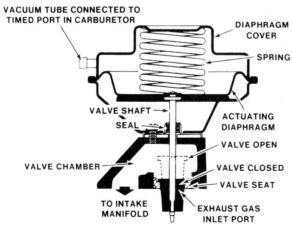

Fig. 13.23   *This Delco EGR valve is actuated by depression taken from a timed port in the induction manifold*

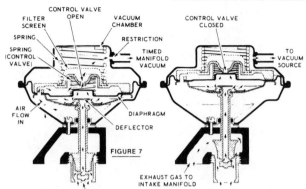

Fig. 13.24   The Delco EGR valve actuated by positive back-pressure in the exhaust manifold

opposition to each other, are a return spring and manifold depression. The exhaust gas recirculation valve below, termed the *pintle*, is lifted off its seat by a tie-rod extending down from the centre of the diaphragm. When it is open, it allows exhaust gas to flow through the larger of the two pipe connections into the induction manifold. The smaller connection, taken from above the diaphragm, is connected to a port downstream of the throttle so that, when the manifold depression is high, the pintle is lifted and EGR is in operation. During idling and at light load with partially closed throttle, there is not enough depression to lift the pintle.

The second EGR valve is the back-pressure type, which is actuated by exhaust back-pressure, Fig. 13.24. In the positive back-pressure version of this unit, the pintle is lifted by a hollow, instead of solid, tie-rod so that the exhaust back-pressure is communicated up through it to a control valve. When this pressure is high enough, it lifts the lower diaphragm, which is fitted around the rim of a central plate; as it lifts, a boss in the centre of this plate closes the control valve port above it, against the resistance of a light return spring. In consequence, the manifold depression now lifts the complete upper and lower diaphragm assembly, to open the pintle valve and release exhaust gas into the induction manifold. Incidentally, hot exhaust gases cannot flow directly on to the lower diaphragm or its central plate, since it is screened by a metal plate interposed between it and the upper end of the hollow tie-rod. Two manifold depression ports can be utilised: one may be just downstream of the throttle valve when it is closed, for actuating the valve only when the mixture is weak, and the second is for communicating wide open throttle depression to the diaphragm chamber.

If the depression above the main diaphragm is light, and there is little back-pressure in the exhaust system, the EGR valve will not open. An increase in the back-pressure, however, will close the control port and, provided the depression above the main diaphragm is adequate, lift the pintle off its seat and thus open the EGR valve. As the pintle rises, the venturi effect of the exhaust gases flowing past the ends of the radial holes

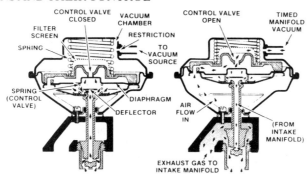

Fig. 13.25   The negative back-pressure version of the Delco EGR valve

communicating with the hollow centre of the tie-rod that lifts it will tend to counteract, or at least significantly reduce, the exhaust back-pressure in that rod. Therefore, the control valve will open again, allowing the depression above the main diaphragm to bleed out to atmosphere and the pintle valve to begin to close. During normal engine operation, the pintle valve alternately opens and partially closes again at a rate of about 40 c/s. Thus, under light throttle conditions, the EGR valve will regulate the quantity of exhaust gas recycled according to the demands made upon the engine. If, on the other hand, the manifold depression is very strong at wide open throttle, the cycling of the pintle valve occurs at a wider mean opening, dependent upon the levels of depression in the manifold and back-pressure in the exhaust.

There is also a negative pressure version of this type of valve. It is the same as the positive pressure type except in that the control valve return spring is below instead of above the diaphragm, and therefore the control valve is normally closed, as shown in Fig. 13.25. The control valve is opened, against its return spring, by a small negative pressure in the hollow shaft. This unit is for installation on engines that have characteristically a low back-pressure.

Again, the valve will not open if the manifold depression is low or zero. However, increasing depression lifts the diaphragm, allowing the pintle valve to be lifted off its seat by its return spring. The resultant flow of exhaust gas past the radial ports in the hollow tie-rod reduces the pressure in it and thus pulls down the smaller diaphragm and opens the control valve. This bleeds off some of the depression above the main diaphragm and allows the pintle to fall again, under the influence of its return spring, towards its seat. Recycling occurs in the manner and rate as has just been described for the positive back pressure type of valve.

13.20   Reduction of emissions during idling

Carburettor or injection control requirements have already been outlined in detail in the chapters on these types of equipment. Among these, the avoidance of intermittent or irregular combustion during idling is important. In overrun conditions, the mixture must be either completely combustible or cut off totally, with subsequently a smooth progression to normal drive. Idling speeds are generally about 750 rev/min for manual transmission, and to avoid both losses and excessive transmission creep, due to torque-converter drag in the drive condition, 550 rev/min for automatic transmission.

To help to avoid irregular firing, the ignition is retarded. This can be done by an electronic control if fitted. If not, the depression in the manifold may be transmitted through a pipe from a point just downstream of the throttle valve to a capsule that actuates a mechanical linkage to rotate the contact breaker assembly, against the influence of its return spring, perhaps about 15° towards the retarded position. To advance the ignition for high speed operation, a centrifugal mechanism rotates it through about 15° in the opposite direction. Retarding the ignition for slow speed running is of course necessary also because combustion would otherwise be completed before tdc, doing negative work on the crankshaft.

Burning off HC and CO in the exhaust by injecting air through nozzles into either the individual exhaust ports or the manifold entails the installation of an engine-driven compressor. With 2-way catalytic conversion, the complexity of an air manifold and multiple nozzles becomes unnecessary, except where control over the air:fuel ratio is inadequate for maintaining under all conditions the weak or chemically correct mixture essential for complete oxidation. In the latter circumstance, air still has to be supplied to the catalytic converter. With 3-way conversion, air had to be injected between the reduction and oxidation stages, as described in Section 13.8. At one time it was thought that the air might be injected directly on to the exhaust valves to perform the additional function of cooling them. However, this was not really practicable since, to avoid rapid oxidation of the valves, they would have had to have been made of extremely costly alloys.

13.21   The gulp valve

When the throttle valve is suddenly closed, the rapid increase in depression due to the pumping effect of the pistons may draw off so much fuel through the slow running system that it cannot be burned completely in the combustion chambers. Therefore, to avoid high levels of HC in the exhaust gas, a gulp valve may be used to admit extra air into the induction manifold in these circumstances, Fig. 13.26. The extra air is taken from the supply for either exhaust manifold injection or the catalytic converter, according to which system is installed. To avoid injection of too much air, the pump delivery pressure is regulated by a relief valve.

In the Delco unit illustrated, a diaphragm type valve actuator is used. The diaphragm is held down by the return spring above it, and lifted by the depression introduced above it through a small diameter pipe from the

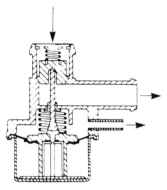

Fig. 13.26 An AC Delco gulp valve of simple design. The pump delivers air into the top and, provided the manifold depression signal to the lowest connection is high enough, it is delivered to the induction manifold through the larger connection on the right

induction manifold. A pushrod extends vertically up from the centre of the diaphragm into a counterbore in the lower end of a check-valve in the delivery connection from the air compressor. When manifold depression lifts the diaphragm, the pushrod unseats the check-valve so that air is delivered into the large diameter outlet pipe to the induction manifold. The chamber below the diaphragm is sealed, except in that there is a bleed orifice in the centre of the diaphragm. Consequently, the diaphragm is first lifted by a sudden increase in manifold depression and then, as the pressures above and below it are equalised through the bleed orifice, it is progressively lowered again. The duration of lift, generally between about 4 and 1 s, is of course determined by the size of the orifice. Slower variations in manifold depression do not move the diaphragm valve, since their effects are nullified by flow through the orifice.

Where air injection into the exhaust system has been used without catalytic conversion, an alternative to the gulp valve has been to cut off the supply of air to the nozzles by venting it to atmosphere, to prevent explosions occurring in the exhaust. This, however, became obsolete with the tightening of the emissions regulations.

EVAPORATIVE EMISSIONS

13.22 Sources of evaporative emissions

Evaporative emissions are mostly hydrocarbons or, with some fuels, alcohol. In general, they come from four sources. These are:
(1) Permeation through the walls of plastics tanks, pipes etc
(2) Vapour issuing through the carburettor float chamber vent
(3) Fumes from the crankcase breather valve, which may include substances additional to unburnt hydrocarbons
(4) From the fuel tank venting system

It is impossible, at this stage in their development, to give anything like realistic figures for plastics tanks, because of the wide variations in their permeability. Items 2 and 3 account for about 25% and item 4 for 20% of the total emissions. The remaining 55% comprises unburned HC in the exhaust. These percentages are based on the use of metal components throughout and they of course vary with ambient temperature.

13.23 Crankcase breather valves

Item (1) has been dealt with in Section 4.8 and 9, and (2) in the last two paragraphs of Section 7.1, and again in several Sections in Chapter 8. Emissions from the crankcase breather can be piped to the air intake, preferably downstream of the filter so that, even over a long period, they will not clog it. An alternative is what is termed a positive crankcase breathing system, in which one branch may be taken from the rocker cover to the point downstream of the filter and another from the crankcase to the induction manifold. Thus, the fumes are drawn by manifold depression out of the crankcase, to be burnt in the cylinders, and are replaced by an inflow of fresh air from the filter to the rocker cover. With the latter system the flow must be restricted to avoid weakening the idling and slow running mixtures. Additionally, some safeguard is needed to prevent blowback in the event of a backfire, and a limit has to be placed on the degree of depression transmitted to the crankcase, otherwise excessive blowby past the piston rings could occur. This safeguard is obtained by placing a crankcase ventilation valve in the line from the crankcase.

Typical of such valves is that produced by Delco, Fig. 13.27. It is a spring-biased plate valve. If the depression is high, it causes the plate to seat on the left-hand port, but a limited flow can still pass through small holes on a pitch circle near to the periphery of the plate. When the pressure in the manifold approaches atmospheric, the coil spring closes the plate on to the smaller diameter port on the right, as illustrated, blanking off the small holes so that no ventilation can occur. With light manifold depression, it floats between both ports.

An alternative is to take the crankcase fumes to the carbon-filled canister, Section 13.23, the main purpose of which is to absorb the HC delivered to it

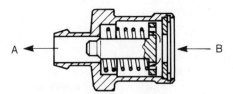

Fig. 13.27   This AC Delco crankcase ventilation valve, by moving on to its right-hand seat, prevents blow-back in the event of a backfire and, by seating on the left, avoids excessive weakening of the idling mixture
A: To manifold, B: From crankcase

from the fuel tank and carburettor float chamber venting systems. This is generally more difficult and costly but, because incoming moist air can cause the oil in the rocker chamber to sludge, it is superior. The carbon granules in the canister trap the hydrocarbon fumes, which are periodically purged from it by drawing air through them into the induction manifold.

Control over the purging function is exercised by a canister purge valve, Fig. 13.29, purge occurring when the engine is idling. Some purge valves are actuated by a timed port in the throttle body, as explained in Section 8.20, while others are actuated by an electronically controlled solenoid. To prevent evaporative emissions from issuing from the air intake when the engine is not running, the carburettor float chamber may be vented through such a purge valve to the canister.

13.24   Carbon canisters

Metal or plastics canisters are employed and filled with activated carbon. This substance is produced by carbonising vegetable matter in a controlled atmosphere such as steam or carbon dioxide. It has the advantage of being capable of absorbing large quantities of gases and vapours, which is why it is used also in gas masks.

Carbon canisters are of either the open- or the closed-bottom type. The open-bottom type is purged by drawing air through a filter in its base, so this filter has to be changed at regular intervals, of perhaps 24 months or 30,000 miles. A major disadvantage is that, in very cold conditions, moisture drawn into the canister with the purge air may freeze and restrict, or even totally block, both the venting and purge actions.

This can happen also with the closed bottom type, but generally only where the purge is drawn directly from the atmosphere through a tube or port and filter on the canister. Mostly, however, closed bottom canisters are purged through a connection the the induction manifold, where excessive moisture is rarely present. Regardless of whether the canister is of the closed- or open-bottom type, two pipes are mostly used for performing the venting and purging functions, one for each. On the other hand, there may be as many as five connections to a closed bottom type.

13.25   Open bottom type

The open bottom type may have three identical connections for the fuel tank vent, float chamber vent, and canister purge. To prevent the float chamber from being vented to the canister while the engine is running, the switching of the venting from induction system to canister is performed by a valve at the float chamber end of the venting system. Alternatively a vapour vent valve may be substituted for the third connection, as in Fig. 13.28. When the engine is off, the coil spring holds this valve open but, when it is running, manifold depression acting on the diaphragm closes it up on to its seat.

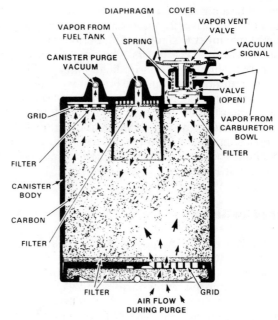

Fig. 13.28   An open bottom canister with vapour vent valve incorporated

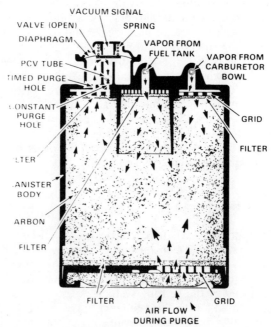

Fig. 13.29   Carbon canister incorporating a purge valve, top left

The function of the central inverted cup, or in some instances a cone, in the canister is to obviate driveability problems, by preventing vapour from the fuel tank from passing directly to the purge connection and on into the induction manifold when the engine throttle is only slightly open. However, this is not necessary in some applications.

In some instances the canister purge operation is timed by a diaphragm valve incorporated in the purge connection to the canister, Fig. 13.29. When the engine is switched off or idling this valve is held closed by a spring. As the throttle is opened, it uncovers a port through which the manifold depression is transmitted to the diaphragm. This lifts the diaphragm valve off its seat, so that purge can take place. Then, when the throttle is opened wider, and the depression therefore falls, the diaphragm valve closes.

13.26   Closed bottom type

A closed bottom canister is illustrated in Fig. 13.30. It has five pipe connections. From left to right in the illustration, the first is the outlet to the timed manifold depression purge port in the induction manifold. Two connections are made to the dome in the centre. Of these, that at the top is the fuel tank vent, which delivers the fumes into the inverted cup, from the mouth of which they spread out into the remainder of the carbon filled canister; the lower one is the inlet for the purge air, normally taken from the clean side of the intake air filter, but in some instances directly from atmosphere. The purge air passes vertically downwards through a tube to

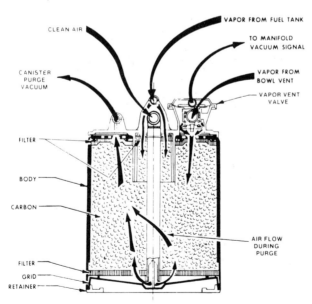

Fig. 13.30   Carbon canister of the closed bottom type

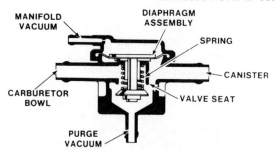

Fig. 13.31   *When the engine is not running, this AC Delco canister control valve vents the carburettor to the canister; when it is running, manifold depression closes the valve*

the base of the canister, whence it turns up again, through a filter and on into the carbon granule bed. Finally, the carburettor vent valve on the right has two connections: that on the right communicates the timed manifold depression signal to the diaphragm chamber, while the other of course is the actual vent connection to the carburettor bowl. All the filters in this unit contain activated carbon, which can absorb any vapour that might otherwise escape.

In some installations, extra canister capacity may be required for special short production run variants of a model in large scale production. In such cases, an auxiliary canister can be installed in series with the main one. This canister has in its base a connection that is piped to the main canister and, on top, the purge air intake port, with an inverted bowl type shroud over it to screen it from contamination. Its carbon granule pack is sandwiched between two filters.

13.27   Canister control valves

For injected engines having electronic control systems, solenoid actuated purge control valves have the advantages of both simplicity and greater

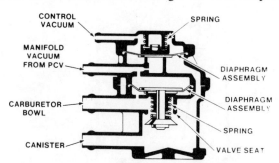

Fig. 13.32   *When the engine is running, manifold depression pulls the lower valve up to shut off the vent from the carburettor float chamber; when it is running above idle speed, control depression pulls the purge control valve (upper diaphram) up to open it*

precision of control. However, manifold depression-actuated control valves are more suitable for carburetted engines but are also used on some injected ones. Delco make two of the depression actuated type, each for mounting separately from the canister. That in Fig. 13.31 functions in a manner similar to the vapour vent valve in Fig. 13.28. When the engine is not running, spring tension holds the valve open to vent the carburettor bowl to the canister, otherwise manifold depression closes the valve down on to seat.

The second type of central valve, Fig. 13.32, performs the functions of both that described in the previous paragraph and the purge valve incorporated in the canister in Fig. 13.29. When the engine is running, the depression from the purge control system pulls the lower diaphragm up to close the vent to the carburettor bowl. As the throttle is opened up from idling, the timed manifold depression signal lifts the upper diaphragm, to purge the canister.

Chapter 14

Sampling and Analysis of Exhaust Emissions

Sampling and analysing exhaust gases for emissions calls for such a huge investment in capital equipment that only the largest among the vehicle manufacturers can contemplate installing it. Furthermore, not only are the engine and vehicle development work involved and the testing for satisfying Type Approval Regulations extremely time-consuming, but also the test equipment is difficult both to calibrate to and maintain at the required degree of accuracy, and therefore can be operated by only experienced and highly qualified engineers. It follows that the considerable on-cost of exhaust emission control per vehicle is more than just the cost of the catalytic converters, injection and electronic and other control equipment that has to be carried in the vehicle.

Furthermore, surprisingly wide discrepancies have been observed in tests undertaken on the same car in different laboratories. For this reason manufacturers may be well advised to have checks made periodically on the results they are getting. If the development work and routine testing, including that for meeting Type Approval Regulations, exceeds the capacity of their own equipment, they may need to sub-contract out some aspects to one of the very few independent companies specialising in such work. Among these, perhaps the best known worldwide is Ricardo Engineering Consultants Ltd, whose roots extend back to 1913 and beyond.

TEST PHILOSOPHIES

14.1   Types of test

As well as existing tests, an additional urban drive cycle, a durability and an evaporative emissions test are proposed in the European Commission Proposal (89) 662-(30.3.90). These may be included in the new regulations for 1992. However, at the time of writing, there are in general only two types of emission test actually in force: the first is a two-cycle (cold start and transient) test for HC, CO and NO_x in the exhaust gas, while the second, which is the SHED test for evaporative emissions, is currently required only in the USA, Japan, Mexico and Australia. The proposed and current European requirements are shown respectively in Tables 14.1 and 14.2 and those for the USA and Japan in Tables 14.3 and 14.4.

The American SHED test has been described in the last four paragraphs of Section 4.9, so there is no need for more on it here, except that the European equivalent is similar but the European driving cycles are used. Since the range of climatic conditions from North to South in Europe does not, in general, differ greatly from that of the USA, it would appear that the politicians ought some how to grasp the opportunity to harmonise internationally at least this part of the evaporative emission regulations when the 1992 regulations are introduced.

For checking exhaust emissions, it is necessary to run the vehicle in conditions reproducing as closely as possible those experienced in normal driving conditions on the road. Unfortunately, such conditions differ widely from country-to-country, so an internationally acceptable standard test will be in this case difficult, and probably even impossible, to achieve. Consequently, each country or group of adjacent countries has specified a test routine specific to its own needs, though the USA, Europe and Japan at least have agreed to use a common method of sampling the exhaust gases. This is the *Constant Volume Sampling* or (CVS) method, and is based on principles demonstrated clearly in Fig. 14.1

In this illustration, air is drawn in through filter at A, and a venturi by the Positive displacement blower BL and exhausted to atmosphere at Y. The potential rate of delivery of BL exceeds the capacity of the venturi, the limit on the flow through which is imposed by the onset of sonic flow conditions in

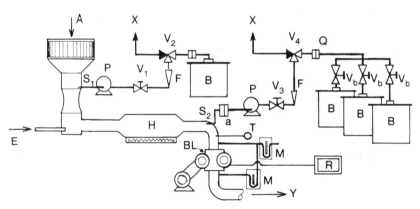

Fig. 14.1   Diagrammatic illustration of the set-up used for exhaust emissions testing by Ricardo Consultant Engineers Ltd. This diagram shows only the part used for testing gasoline engine emissions; an additional circuit enabling the equipment to be used also for diesel engine emissions testing is not shown here

A: Air in through filter, a: Filter for removal of particulates from gas sample, B: Sample bags, BL: Positive displacement blower, E: Exhaust in through tail-pipe probe, F: Flow meters, H: Heat exchanger for controlling temperature of sample gas, Q: Quick release coupling, P: Pumps, M: Manometers, R: Rev. counter, S_1: Air intake sample pick-up, S_2: Diluted exhaust gas sample pick-up, V_1: Air intake sample selector valve, V_2: Air intake sample 3-way valve (to bag, analyser or atmosphere), V_3: Diluted exhaust gas sample selector valve, V_4: Diluted exhaust gas 3-way valve (to bags, analyser or atmosphere), V_b: Bag selector valves, X and Y: Vents to atmosphere the throat. This is termed a *critical flow venturi set up*. With such an arrangement, the through-flow of gas is constant.

The flow of exhaust gas into the system from the tailpipe pick-up at E is known, so also therefore is the dilution ratio of that gas by the air. Dilution at a ratio of at least 5:1 of air to exhaust gas is necessary to prevent condensation of water vapour which, if present, would absorb some of the oxides of nitrogen and lead to underestimates of that pollutant. Furthermore, it inhibits interaction between the products of combustion, which could lead to a low reading for, in particular, the hydrocarbons. The aim is generally a ratio of between about 8:1 and 10:1 of air to exhaust gas, otherwise the measuring instruments must be more accurate.

For the European tests, a heat exchanger H is interposed between the intake filter and positive displacement blower and the temperature of the sample is taken at T, so that both the temperature and pressure in the region from which the sample is taken can be maintained constant by a control system regulating the rates of heating of the gas and its delivery by the pump. A separate pump P maintains, a constant ratio of total flow to sample delivered into the bag. Incidentally, a single bag was used not only in the US FTP 72 test (see Section 14.3) but also in Europe under the ECE Regulations up to and including 15-03. The numeral 15 is the emission control regulation, while 03, 04, etc indicate updates. At the time of writing 04, is in force and 05 is for diesel engines, so the proposal for 1992 presumably will become ECE 15-06.

14.2   General principles of the tests

It is of course important to simulate the driving conditions realistically. Moreover, since measurements of the order of less than 10 parts per million may be involved, extreme accuracy is essential throughout all stages of the testing. The samples are taken from diluted exhaust gas collected in either one or three bags, dependent upon the regulations in the country concerned, and the vehicle is run on a chassis dynamometer. Where the test routine comprises three sections: cold start, stabilised and hot start. Three bags, one for each section of the test, appear to be becoming the general rule.

The method of removing the sample of gas from the tail pipe must be such as not to alter the back-pressure in the exhaust system, so the pressure at the end of the tailpipe must not deviate from atmospheric by more than $\pm$ 0.75 kPa at an equivalent road speed of 50 km/h and $\pm$ 1.25 kPa throughout the whole test. Among the factors that have to be taken into account are the tyre rolling and air resistances. Inclusion of the effects of vehicle inertia is particularly important so that the curve of braking load plotted against speed on the dynamometer is truly representative. Therefore, an adjustable flywheel, is coupled to the dynamometer.

External factors affecting the results include variations in atmospheric temperature, pressure and humidity, as well as the amount of pollution already in the air being ingested into the engine. The former are easy to correct mathematically, while the latter is taken into account by sampling not only the exhaust but also the air ingested by sample pick-up S_1, and subtracting the pollution measured in the latter from that in the former. Both the sizes of the vehicles and the driving styles affect emissions, so the test sequences ultimately drawn up have to represent a realistic average of both. In the current European tests (Reg. 15-04), different limits are set for the engine sizes up to 1.4 litres, from 1.4 to 2 litres and over 2 litres.

Power:weight ratio is another important consideration, but this is not catered for in the setting of different limits. In practice, however, to meet the European requirements, the types of emission control system that will be actually installed on any particular car will reflect its power:weight ratio. Consequently, even vehicles having engines of under 2 litres swept volume with low power:weight ratios may in some instances need three-way catalytic converters and fuel injection systems electronically controlled on the closed loop principle. In general, however, it is still possible that vehicles having smaller engines may be capable of meeting the requirements with systems such as two-way conversion or lean burn.

14.3   Sampling and test sequences

Throughout the test, the flow of diluted exhaust gas is regulated by the flow control valves F, so that the flow of gas passing into the bag or bags is a constant percentage of the total flow through the system, which is itself constant. At the same time, the total flow of the exhaust gas delivered from the engine is measured, so that the total masses of the various pollutants emitted throughout the tests can be calculated from the analyses of the diluted samples.

The test sequences are based on recordings of actual driving on the road.

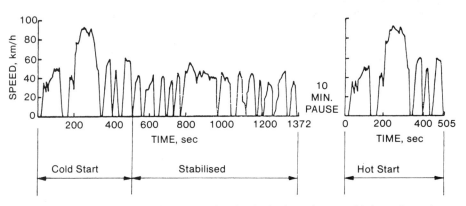

Fig. 14.2   Left, the two-part US FTP 72 and, right, the third part that was added to make up the three-part FTP 75 test sequence. The masses of the pollutants in the samples per unit of distance travelled have to be weighted by using the following factors:
0.43 × cold start + 1.0 × stabilised + 0.57 × hot start

They comprise mainly periods of acceleration, speed and braking, all at constant levels or rates. The earliest cycle to be used officially was that specified in 1966 in California. It was derived from tests made in Los Angeles in the morning peak traffic conditions. Subsequently the 1972 Federal test cycle, Fig. 14.2, evolved from it. The gases were collected in a single bag, and both the cycle and the method of sampling of the gases is still used in Australia, Austria, Brazil, Mexico, Norway and Sweden, South Korea and Switzerland.

For this test, termed the *Federal Test Procedure 72* or (FTP 72), the vehicle has first to stand for 12 h in an ambient temperature of between 20° and 30°C. After the engine has been started, the vehicle is immediately run through whole of the test cycle without any pause. Since both the time and distance represented by the test are known, it is possible to express the mass of pollutants in terms of either gm per test, per unit of time or per unit of distance, the latter being the most widely accepted convention.

THE TEST CYCLES

14.4   The FTP 75 test cycle

The FTP 75 cycle, also illustrated in Fig. 14.2, in which the three bag system came into use in the USA, comprised that of the FTP 72 regulation followed by a *hot transient phase* (duration 505s). However, the first stage was divided into what are termed the *cold transient* (duration 505 s) and *stabilised* (1372 s) phases, each being collected in a separate bag. Of the three phases, the first represents starting out in the morning with the engine cold, the second driving at normal operating temperatures, and the third restarting with a warm engine to continue a journey. Since the gas from each stage is collected in a different bag, anyone wishing to do so can multiply by different factors the proportions of emissions in the gas taken from each bag, to represent the emissions obtain during different types of journey or operation. The factors specified in the emissions regulations for the 49 States of the USA are as follows:

Cold transient	0.43
Stabilised	1.00
Hot transient	0.57

Table 14.1   US FTP 72 and 75 emission limits, gm/mile

	CO	*HC*	*NO$_x$*
FTP 72	2.1	0.25	0.62
FTP 75	3.4	0.41	1.0
California	7	0.41	0.4

Note — The following countries have adopted the US FTP 75 test cycle, but a few with different emissions limits; Australia, Austria, Brazil, Canada, Finland, Norway, South Korea, Sweden. Norway, Finland, Sweden, Mexico and Switzeland apply the the FTP 72 limits with the FTP 75 cycle.

Table 14.2   ECE Regulation 15-04 emisions limits (type approval) gm/test

Mass (kg)	CO	HC + NO$_x$
Up to 1020	58	19.0
1020-1250	67	20.5
1250-1470	76	22.0
1470-1700	84	23.5
1700-1930	93	25.0
1930-2150	101	26.5
Over 2150	110	28.0

The limits specified in Table 14.1 have to be maintained from the time when the vehicle is new until it has covered 50,000 miles. Indeed, because of the difficulty of monitoring emissions from each vehicle on a regular basis throughout its life, in Californa encouragement to manufacturers to ensure that standards are maintained is offered by allowing higher pollution levels provided proof can be given they will be maintained for 100,000 miles.

14.5   The ECE and EC test cycle

In Europe, the test cycle was originally formulated to represent typical inner-city driving conditions, and it did not include hot transient phase. However, a hot transient test, or urban driving cycle, is recommended in the European Commission Proposal (89) 662-(30.3.90), Fig. 14.3. The current routine, following a cold start, comprises three cycles as follows: 3 s at 15 km/h, 24 s at 32 km/h and 12 s at 50 km/h, including acceleration and deceleration up to and down from these speeds, and preceded and followed in each instance respectively by a dwell of 21s at idling. These three cycles are repeated four times without pause, the gas being collected by the CVS method in one or more bags, according to which test is being run. It should be noted that whereas the Americans express their results in terms of g/mile, the Europeans specify g/test. Furthermore, in Europe, the limits on HC and NO$_x$ are not specified separately, but apply to only the total of these two gases present, and all limits are related to engine size.

Table 14.3   Limits in European Commission Proposed (89) 662, in gm/km

Category	CO	HC+NO$_x$	Particulates
Type approval	2.72	0.97	0.19
Production, tolerance	3.16	1.13	0.24

Note — Originally, it was proposed to have different limits for up to 1.4, 1.4-2.0, and over 2.0 litre engines, and a limit for NO$_x$ as well as for HC+NO$_x$ but the latest proposal is to have only the two categories above for all cars, as above.

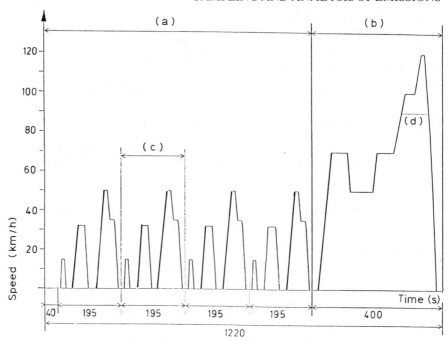

Fig. 14.3   The left-hand part of the cycle (a) is the test cycle valid under the ECE Regulations up to 15.04, while the section on the right (b) is the hot start addition recommended for 1992 in Proposal (89) 662-(30.3.90). Section (c) is the basic cycle which as can be seen from the diagram, is repeated four times, while (d) is a concession for vehicles incapable of attaining the normal specified maximum speed. Sampling begins after 40 s and continues to the end of either the fourth 105 s cycle or the 1220 s, according to which regulation is in force

14.6 Japanese test cycle

Under Japanese law, a more complex cycle is specified, Fig. 14.4, but only one bag is used, though, at the time of writing, this is being changed. As in Europe, the components of the cycle are synthetically generated and the CVS system of sampling is employed, but there are two phases. The first is an 11-mode cold cycle which, after starting from cold, is run through four times. Next there is a hot start test, prior to which the engine is first run up to normal temperature for approximately 15 m at the equivalent of 40 km/h, after which the concentrations of HC, CO and CO_2 are measured while the engine is idling. Next, after a further warm up period of 15 m at 40 km/h, the 10 mode hot test begins, the cycle being run through six times. Throughout the whole of first the cold and then the hot test, the diluted gas samples are analysed. On the other hand, while for the former, the results are expressed in g/test, for the latter they are expressed in terms of g/km. This regulation, however, has already been updated but those of us in the rest of the world are still having difficulties in interpreting the precise requirements and implications.

10 mode driving cycle (hot test)

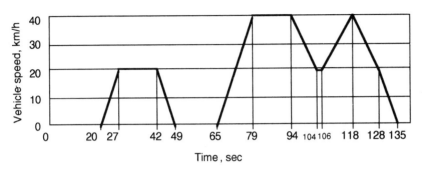

11 mode driving cycle (cold test)

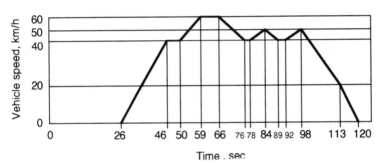

Fig. 14.4 The Japanese test procedure: left, the cycle to be run 11 times as the cold start, and right, that which has to be run 10 times as the hot start test

Table 14.4 Japanese emissions limits, gm/km

Cycle	CO	HC	NO_x
10-mode	2.1	0.25	0.25
11-mode	60.0	7.0	4.4

METHODS OF ANALYSIS

14.7 Some equipment used

For analysis of NO_x, CO and, where required, CO_2 content, the non-dispersive infra-red process is used while, for HC, the simplest method is flame ionisation detection. Basically, the flame ionisation method involves burning the sample in a jet of hydrocarbon gas and air mixed thoroughly in proportions such that both constituents are completely consumed. The degree of ionisation within the flame is then an indication of the proportions of hydrocarbon present in the sample, additional to the requirements for complete combustion of the jet.

For the non-dispersive infra-red method, a wide range of instruments is available, among which the Bosch equipment illustrated diagrammatically, in Fig. 14.5, is fairly representative. Basically the infra-red lamp at a temperature of about 700°C radiates upwards through transparent partitions separating successively the three cells. Since air and CO are heated differentially by infra-red radiation, if all three cells contain identical mixtures of this gas and air, the temperatures in the cell closest to the lamp will be the highest and that most remote the lowest.

From the diagram, it can be seen that the two uppermost cells are sealed except in that they are interconnected by a small passage with a restriction in it. Consequently, any differences in their temperatures will cause the gases in them to expand differentially and therefore flow to occur from the hottest into the coolest (from the intermediate to the uppermost cell). For measuring the flow, a hot wire type sensor is mounted in the restriction and connected into a Wheatstone bridge circuit.

The instrument is calibrated by first passing pure filtered air through the lower chamber and measuring the rate of flow. Then a mixture of air and CO in precisely known proportions, usually about 25% higher than the maximum likely to be experienced during the tests, is passed through, so that the range can be set on the scale. Finally, readings of CO content of samples of the diluted exhaust gas as they pass through the lower chamber are taken, the whole procedure being microprocessor-controlled.

Item E in the diagram is a rotating plate with apertures in it, to serve as a chopper alternately exposing and screening the gas cells from the infra-red radiation. This causes pulsations to occur in pressures of the gases in the sealed chambers, and therefore in the flow through the restriction in their interconnecting duct. It follows that samples from the diluted exhaust can be passed through the lower chamber and their CO content determined simply by recording electronically the magnitudes of the fluctuations of the rates of flow. The same procedure can be used for each of the three gaseous pollutants, and CO_2, or mixtures of any or all of them. As is well known, however, the only control that can be exercised over the CO_2 content is to increase thermal efficiency and thus reduce fuel consumption.

The gas flow system is illustrated diagrammatically in Fig. 14.6. From the pick-up A, which is inserted to a depth of at least 30 cm into the exhaust tailpipe, the gas sample is drawn by a diaphragm type pump H, through a coarse filter B into a water trap C. This sequence removes the coarse particulates, by filtration, and the water content by condensation. The next stage is further removal of particulates by the coarse and fine filters, D and E respectively, in tandem. Cleanliness is essential not only for preventing particulates from interfering with the infra-red light transmission and thus giving rise to inaccurate readings of the CO content, but also to prevent the transparent panels in the sensor from becoming fouled unacceptably rapidly.

Leaving the filtration system, the gas passes through a solenoid actuated

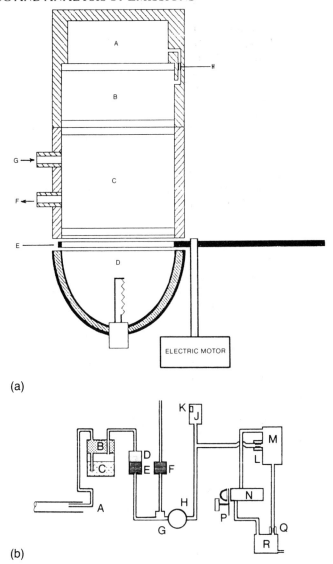

(a)

(b)

Fig. 14.5   (a) a diagram illustrating the principle of the Bosch infra-red test for CO. (b) the gas flow system

(a) A and B: Chambers containing compensating volumes, C: Test chamber, D: Infra-red lamp, E: Motor-driven chopper disc with circular aperture in it, F: Exhaust sample outlet, G: Exhaust sample inlet, H: Flow sensor
(b) A: Sample pick-up in exhaust tailpipe, B: Coarse filter, C: Water trap, D: Coarse filter, E and F: Fine filters, G: Solenoid-actuated 3-way valve, H: Diaphragm type pump, J: Plenum chamber, K: Pressure switch, L: Restrictor, M: Safety reservoir, N: Measuring chamber, P: motor driven chopper, Q: Restrictor, R: Water collection tank

3-way cock to the pump. The third connection to the cock is a pipe from atmosphere, for the initial calibration. Air for calibration is passed through the fine filter F. Actuation of the 3-way cock in the appropriate sequence is effected automatically by the electronic system.

From the pump, the clean gas passes up to a plenum chamber J containing a pressure switch K. Should the flow of gas be obstructed, the pressure switch opens and a warming lamp is illuminated. Next, the gas passes through a restrictor L into the safety reservoir M. The function of the restrictor L is to cause a back-pressure in the plenum chamber, for actuating the pressure switch. There are two outlets from reservoir M. Some of the gas goes through a fine restrictor Q into tank R, whence it is discharged to atmosphere; the remainder is delivered directly into the measuring chamber N, through which passes the alternating beam of infra-red radiation. The motor-driven chopper is shown at P. In the event of the operator failing to empty the water trap at the appropriate intervals, any water passing into the reservoir M will fall down into the tank R and pass out to atmosphere, leaving only relatively dry air to be fed into the measuring chamber.

Throughout the test, the system is controlled electronically as follows. The system is switched on and there follows a 3 m warm-up period during which an automatic checking sequence is run through. Next, the 3-way switch is opened to allow air to pass through for 10 s, for flushing out the system. Then, after a further 10s, a zero reading is automatically recorded by the microprocessor. Finally, the 3-way switch is moved to select exhaust gas, measurements are taken and corrections made for temperature in the measuring chamber, barometric pressure and power supply frequency.

INDEX

355